Math **Diagnosis** and **Intervention** System

Booklet A

Numbers, Place Value, Money, and Patterns in Grades K–3

Overview of Math Diagnosis and Intervention System

The system can be used in a variety of situations:

- **During School** Use the system for intervention on prerequisite skills at the beginning of the year, the beginning of a topic, or the beginning of a lesson. Use for intervention during the Topic when more is needed beyond the resources already provide for the lesson.
- **After-school, Saturday school, summer-school (intersession) programs** Use the system for intervention offered in special programs.

The system provides resources for:

- **Assessment** Diagnostic Tests are provided. Each Diagnostic Test assesses the content for a grade. Use a test at the start of the year for entry-level assessment or anytime during the year as a summative evaluation.
- **Diagnosis** An item analysis identifies areas where intervention is needed.
- **Intervention** Booklets A–E in Part 1 and Booklets F–J in Part 2 identify specific concepts and assign a number to each concept, for example, A12 or E10. For each concept, there is a two-page Intervention Lesson that provides an instructional activity followed by practice. References for the Intervention Lessons are provided in teacher materials for *en**Vision**MATH.*
- **Monitoring** The Teacher's Guide provides both Individual Record Forms and Class Record Forms to monitor student progress.

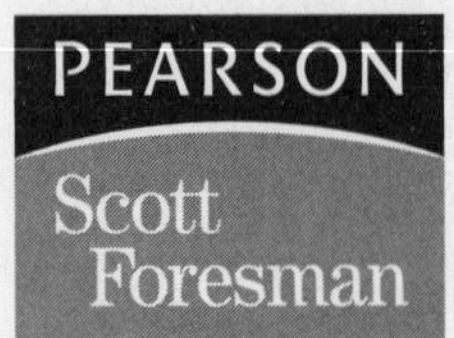

Editorial Offices: Glenview, Illinois • Parsippany, New Jersey • New York, New York

Sales Offices: Boston, Massachusetts • Duluth, Georgia • Glenview, Illinois
Coppell, Texas • Sacramento, California • Mesa, Arizona

ISBN-13: 978-0-328-31128-6
ISBN-10: 0-328-31128-6

16 V069 12 11

Table of Contents

Booklet A: Numbers, Place Value, Money, and Patterns in Grades K-3

Table of Contents continued

Booklet A: Numbers, Place Value, Money, and Patterns in Grades K-3

Zero to Five

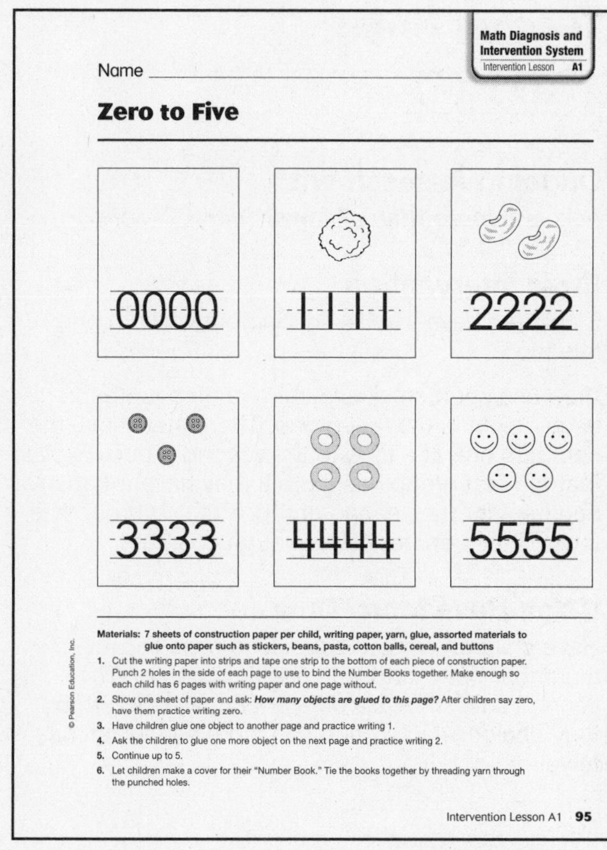

Math Diagnosis and Intervention System
Intervention Lesson A1

Name ______________________

Zero to Five

0000 1111 2222

3333 4444 5555

Materials: 7 sheets of construction paper per child, writing paper, yarn, glue, assorted materials to glue onto paper such as stickers, beans, pasta, cotton balls, cereal, and buttons

1. Cut the writing paper into strips and tape one strip to the bottom of each piece of construction paper. Punch 2 holes in the side of each page to use to bind the Number Books together. Make enough so each child has 6 pages with writing paper and one page without.
2. Show one sheet of paper and ask: ***How many objects are glued to this page?*** After children say zero, have them practice writing zero.
3. Have children glue one object to another page and practice writing 1.
4. Ask the children to glue one more object on the next page and practice writing 2.
5. Continue up to 5.
6. Let children make a cover for their "Number Book." Tie the books together by threading yarn through the punched holes.

Intervention Lesson A1 **95**

Math Diagnosis and Intervention System
Intervention Lesson A1

Name ______________________

Zero to Five (continued)

How many?

1. 2 2 2 2
2. 5 5 5 5
3. 0 0 0 0
4. 4 4 4 4

96 Intervention Lesson A1

Teacher Notes

Ongoing Assessment

Make sure children can rote count to 5, that is, say the numbers in order without using objects.

Error Intervention

If children count some of the circles twice,

then have them cross out each counter as they say a number.

If You Have More Time

Have children make a summary page for their number book with pictures they draw to represent each number next to the symbols.

More and Fewer

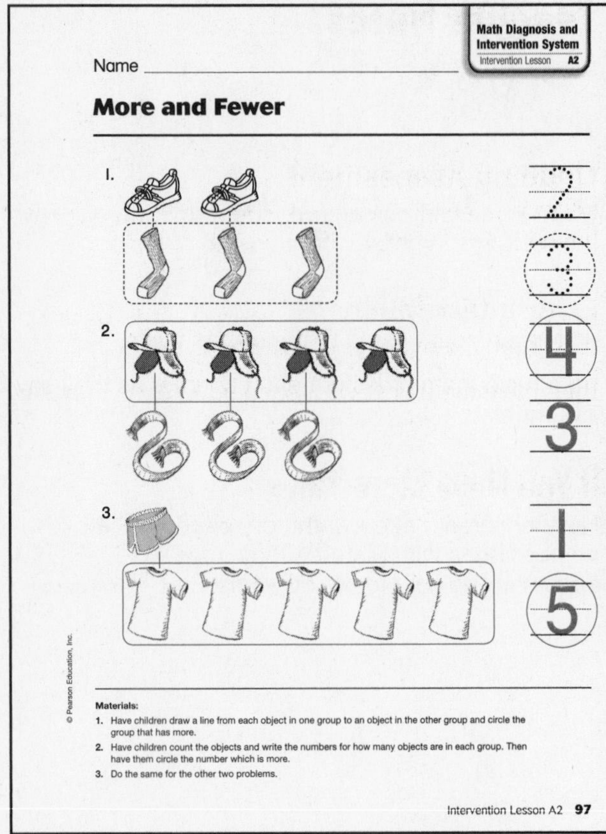

Math Diagnosis and Intervention System
Intervention Lesson A2

Name ______________________

More and Fewer

1. 2 3

2. 4 3

3. 1 5

Materials:

1. Have children draw a line from each object in one group to an object in the other group and circle the group that has more.
2. Have children count the objects and write the numbers for how many objects are in each group. Then have them circle the number which is more.
3. Do the same for the other two problems.

© Pearson Education, Inc.

Intervention Lesson A2 **97**

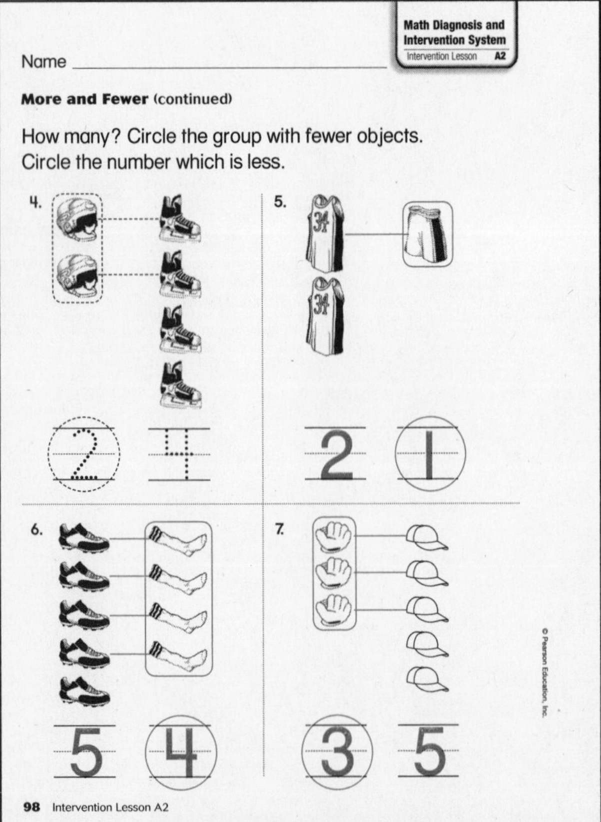

Math Diagnosis and Intervention System
Intervention Lesson A2

Name ______________________

More and Fewer (continued)

How many? Circle the group with fewer objects.
Circle the number which is less.

4. 2 4

5. 2 1

6. 5 4

7. 3 5

© Pearson Education, Inc.

98 Intervention Lesson A2

Teacher Notes

Ongoing Assessment

Ask: ***Is 5 more than or fewer than 0?*** More

Error Intervention

If children have trouble figuring out which group has more,

then use counters. Have them put a counter on each object in the first group. Then, they move the counters one at a time to the second group. Explain that the first group has more if they have too many counters for the second group. The first group has fewer if they do not have enough counters.

If You Have More Time

Have children work in pairs. One child shows a number between 1 and 5 with counters. The second child shows a different number. Together they decide which group has more and which has fewer.

Six to Ten

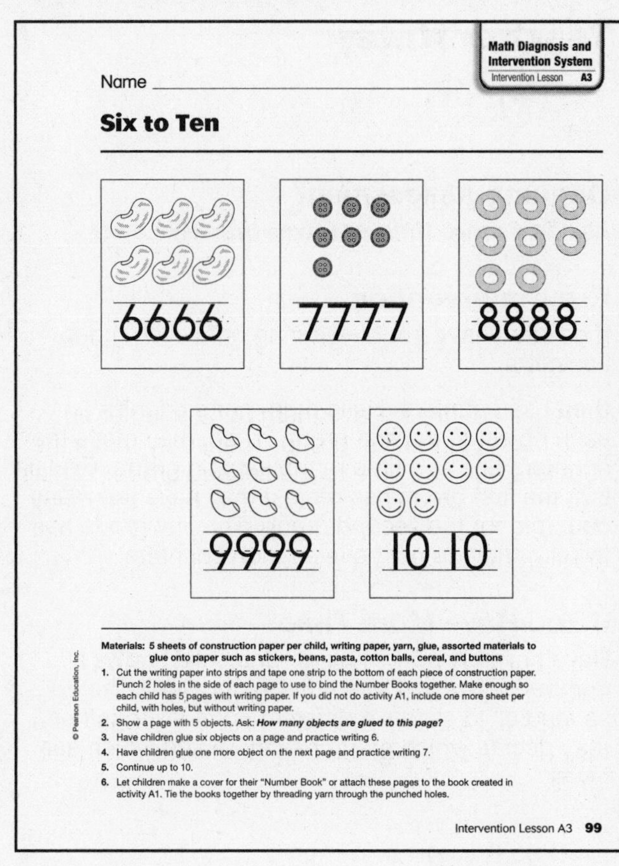

Math Diagnosis and Intervention System
Intervention Lesson A3

Name ______________________

Six to Ten

6666 7777 8888

9999 10 10

Materials: 5 sheets of construction paper per child, writing paper, yarn, glue, assorted materials to glue onto paper such as stickers, beans, pasta, cotton balls, cereal, and buttons

1. Cut the writing paper into strips and tape one strip to the bottom of each piece of construction paper. Punch 2 holes in the side of each page to use to bind the Number Books together. Make enough so each child has 5 pages with writing paper. If you did not do activity A1, include one more sheet per child, with holes, but without writing paper.
2. Show a page with 5 objects. Ask: ***How many objects are glued to this page?***
3. Have children glue six objects on a page and practice writing 6.
4. Have children glue one more object on the next page and practice writing 7.
5. Continue up to 10.
6. Let children make a cover for their "Number Book" or attach these pages to the book created in activity A1. Tie the books together by threading yarn through the punched holes.

Intervention Lesson A3 **99**

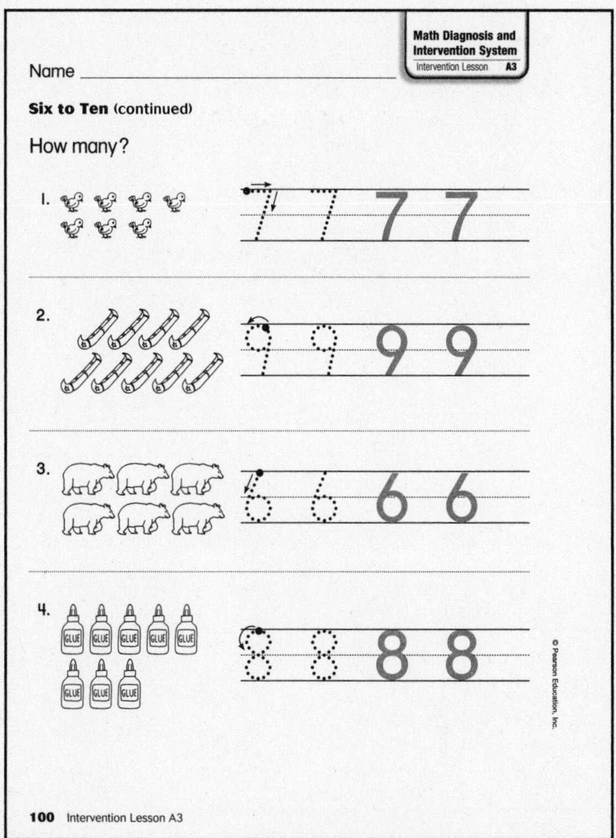

Math Diagnosis and Intervention System
Intervention Lesson A3

Name ______________________

Six to Ten (continued)

How many?

1. 7 7 7 7
2. 9 9 9 9
3. 6 6 6 6
4. 8 8 8 8

100 Intervention Lesson A3

Teacher Notes

Ongoing Assessment

Make sure children can rote count to 10, that is, say the numbers in order without using objects.

Error Intervention

If children count some of the circles twice,

then have them cross out each counter as they say a number.

If You Have More Time

Have children make a summary page for their number book with pictures they draw to represent each number next to the symbols for 6 to 10.

Comparing Numbers

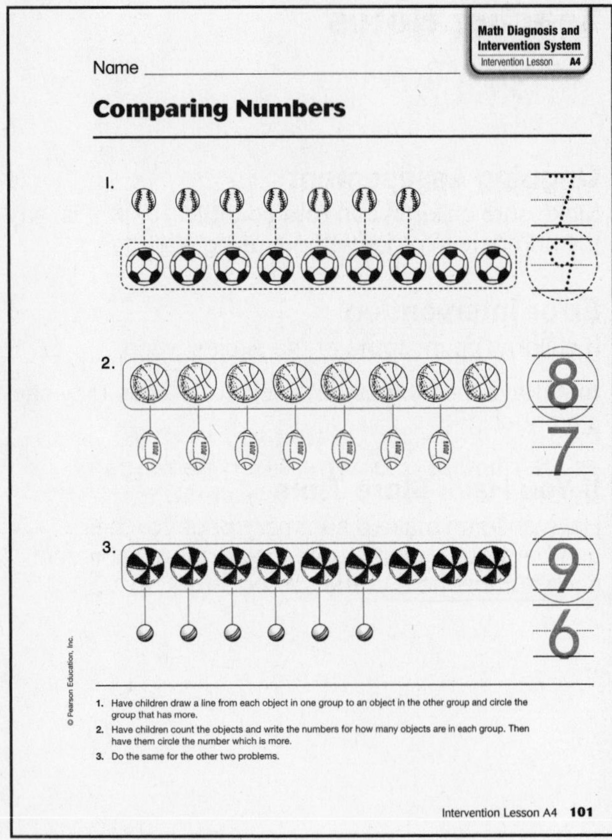
Math Diagnosis and Intervention System
Intervention Lesson A4

Name ______________________

Comparing Numbers

1. 7 9

2. 8 7

3. 9 6

1. Have children draw a line from each object in one group to an object in the other group and circle the group that has more.
2. Have children count the objects and write the numbers for how many objects are in each group. Then have them circle the number which is more.
3. Do the same for the other two problems.

© Pearson Education, Inc.

Intervention Lesson A4 **101**

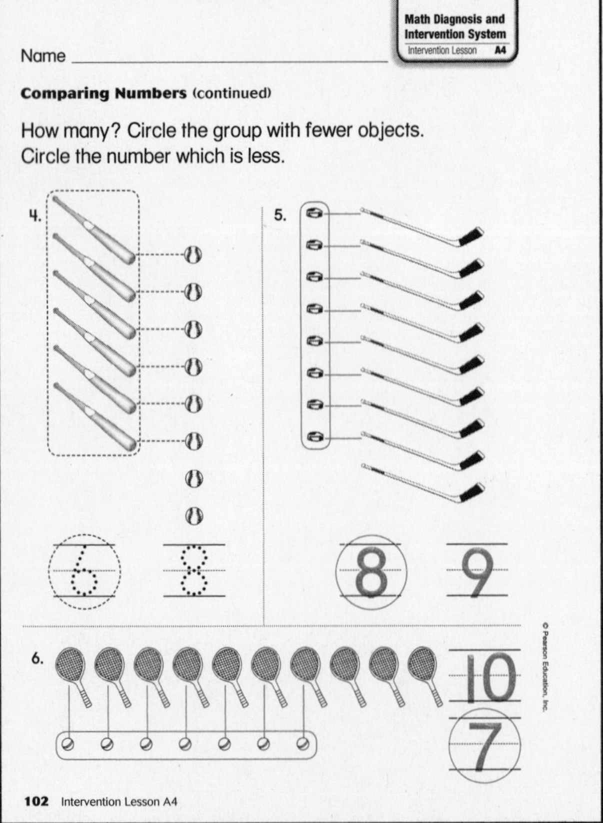
Math Diagnosis and Intervention System
Intervention Lesson A4

Name ______________________

Comparing Numbers (continued)

How many? Circle the group with fewer objects.
Circle the number which is less.

4. 6 8

5. 8 9

6. 10 7

© Pearson Education, Inc.

102 Intervention Lesson A4

Teacher Notes

Ongoing Assessment

Ask: ***Is 4 more than or fewer than 9?*** Fewer

Error Intervention

If children have trouble figuring out which group has more,

then use counters. Have them put a counter on each object in the first group. Then, they move the counters one at a time to the second group. Explain that the first group has more if they have too many counters for the second group. The first group has fewer if they do not have enough counters.

If You Have More Time

Have children work in pairs. One child shows a number between 1 and 10 with counters. The second child shows a different number. Together they decide which group has more and which has fewer.

11 to 19

Math Diagnosis and Intervention System
Intervention Lesson A5

Name ______________________

11 to 19

11 12 13 14 15
16 17 18 19

Materials: Two-color counters, 19 per child

1. Have children fill the tens grid with counters and count as they place the counters. Ask: ***How many?*** 10
2. Have children place one more counter on the page and say eleven. Have them write 11.
3. Have children place one more counter on the page and say twelve. Have them write 12.
4. Continue to 19.

Intervention Lesson A5 **103**

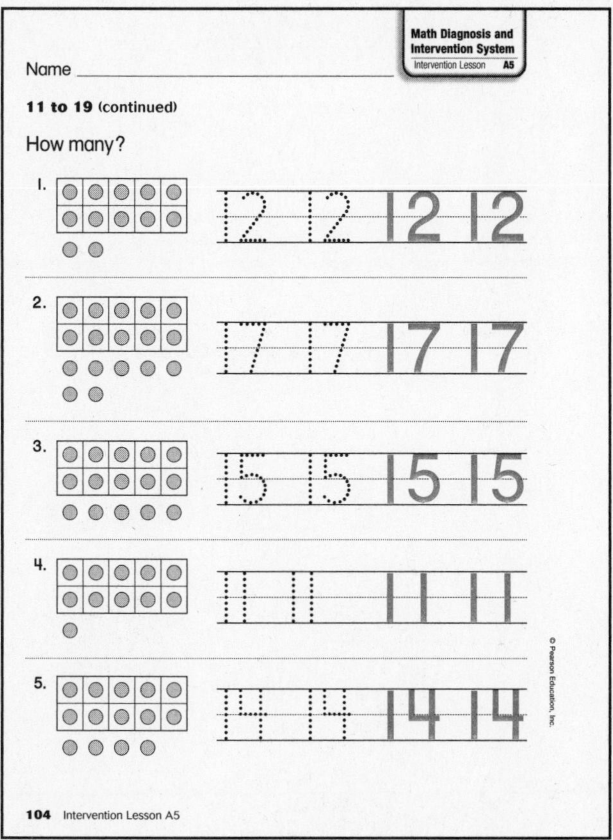

Math Diagnosis and Intervention System
Intervention Lesson A5

Name ______________________

11 to 19 (continued)

How many?

1. 12 12 12 12
2. 17 17 17 17
3. 15 15 15 15
4. 11 11 11 11
5. 14 14 14 14

© Pearson Education, Inc.

104 Intervention Lesson A5

Teacher Notes

Ongoing Assessment

Make sure children can rote count to 19, that is, say the numbers in order without using objects.

Error Intervention

If children have difficulty writing numbers from 11 to 19,

then Ask: ***Is the digit after the 1 in 12 the same as the number of counters outside the tens frame when you show 12 counters?*** Yes; ***Is this true for all the numbers between 11 and 19?*** Yes

If You Have More Time

Write a number between 11 and 19 on the board and have children show the number on their activity page.

Numbers to 30

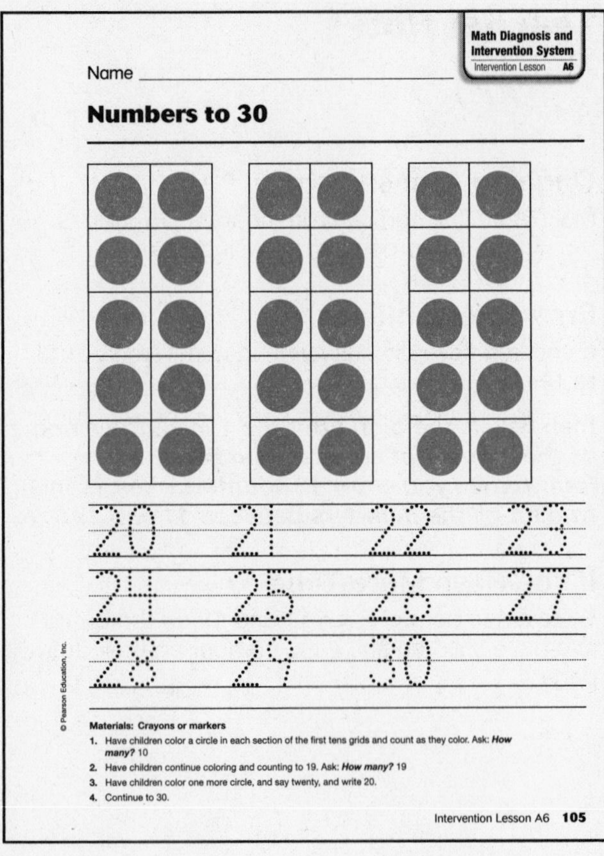
Math Diagnosis and Intervention System
Intervention Lesson A6

Name ________________

Numbers to 30

20 21 22 23
24 25 26 27
28 29 30

Materials: Crayons or markers

1. Have children color a circle in each section of the first tens grids and count as they color. Ask: *How many?* 10
2. Have children continue coloring and counting to 19. Ask: *How many?* 19
3. Have children color one more circle, and say twenty, and write 20.
4. Continue to 30.

© Pearson Education, Inc.

Intervention Lesson A6 **105**

Teacher Notes

Ongoing Assessment

Make sure children can rote count to 30, that is, say the numbers without using objects.

Error Intervention

If children have trouble counting up to 19,

then use A5: 11 to 19.

If children have trouble counting from 21 to 29,

then have them say twenty and one, twenty and two, and so on.

If You Have More Time

Let children extend their number books from lessons A1 and A3 by adding some larger numbers. If children did not do that activity, let them create a number book as described in those lessons, but for larger numbers.

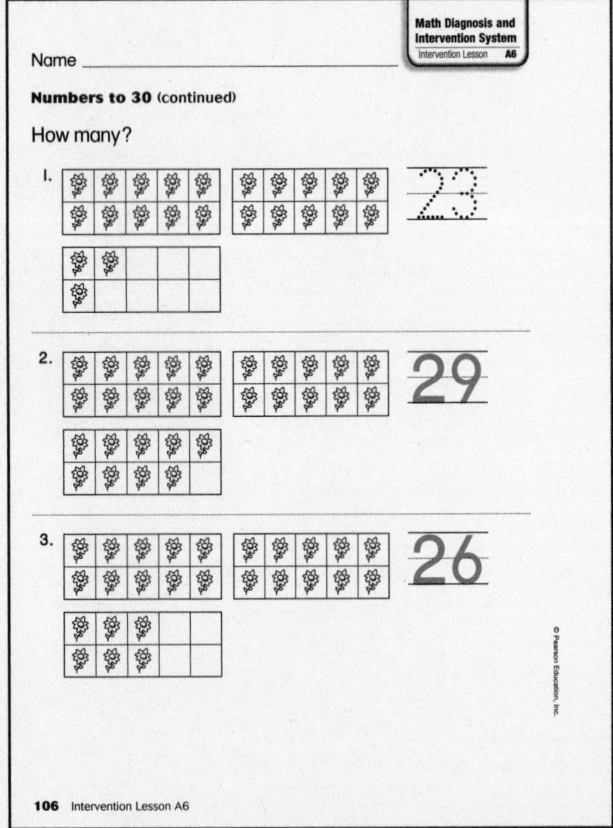
Math Diagnosis and Intervention System
Intervention Lesson A6

Name ________________

Numbers to 30 (continued)

How many?

1. 23
2. 29
3. 26

© Pearson Education, Inc.

106 Intervention Lesson A6

Counting by 10s to 100

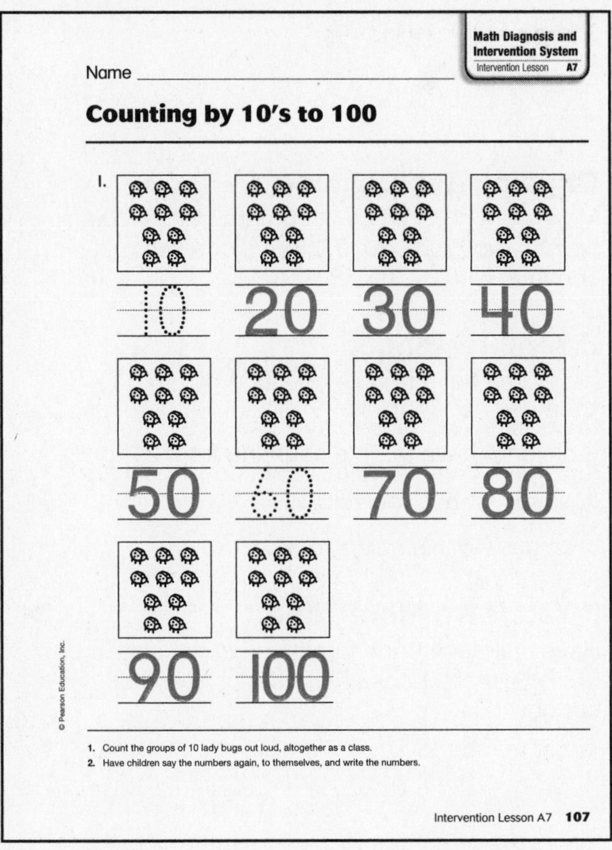

Math Diagnosis and Intervention System
Intervention Lesson A7

Name ____________________

Counting by 10's to 100

1.

10 20 30 40

50 60 70 80

90 100

1. Count the groups of 10 lady bugs out loud, altogether as a class.
2. Have children say the numbers again, to themselves, and write the numbers.

© Pearson Education, Inc.

Intervention Lesson A7 **107**

Teacher Notes

Ongoing Assessment

Have children count out loud by 10s to 100.

Error Intervention

If children have trouble deciding which multiple of ten, to write,

then tell them the first digit tells how many groups of ten. So if there are 4 groups of ten, the number is a 4 and a 0.

If You Have More Time

Have children make tens out of snap cubes for a partner to count.

Math Diagnosis and Intervention System
Intervention Lesson A7

Name ____________________

Counting by 10's to 100 (continued)

How many?

2. 40

3. 60

4. 30

© Pearson Education, Inc.

108 Intervention Lesson A7

Counting to 100

Math Diagnosis and Intervention System
Intervention Lesson A8

Name ____________________

Counting to 100

1	2	3	4	5	6	7	8	9	10
11	12	13	14	15	16	17	18	19	20
21	22	23	24	25	26	27	28	29	30
31	32	33	34	35	36	37	38	39	40
41	42	43	44	45	46	47	48	49	50
51	52	53	54	55	56	57	58	59	60
61	62	63	64	65	66	67	68	69	70
71	72	73	74	75	76	77	78	79	80
81	82	83	84	85	86	87	88	89	90
91	92	93	94	95	96	97	98	99	100

1. Count to 100 as a class. Have children put a finger on each number as it is said.
2. Have children count to themselves and write the missing numbers.
3. Have children find 52. Have them count to 52 by saying 10, 20, 30, 40, 50, 51, 52.

Intervention Lesson A8 109

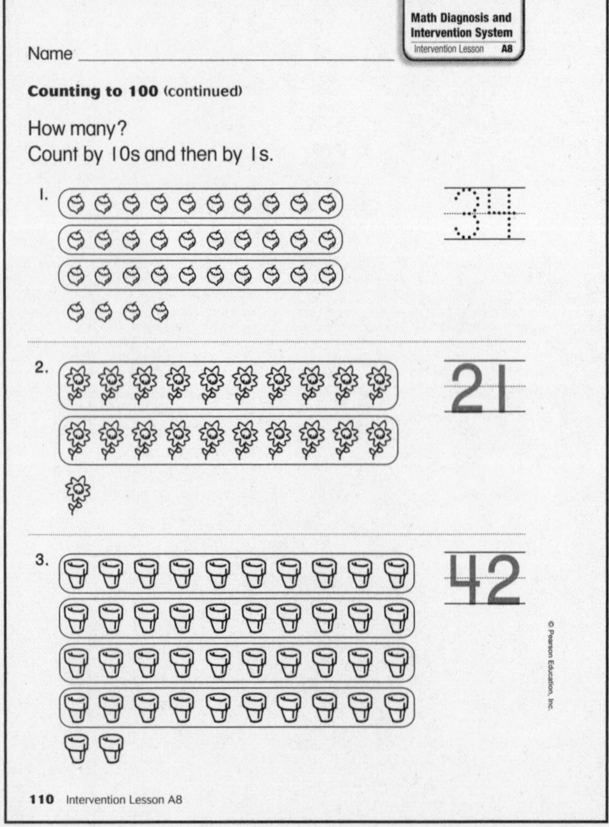
Math Diagnosis and Intervention System
Intervention Lesson A8

Name ____________________

Counting to 100 (continued)

How many?
Count by 10s and then by 1s.

1. 34
2. 21
3. 42

110 Intervention Lesson A8

Teacher Notes

Ongoing Assessment

Make sure children can count on. Ask: ***What comes next? 29, 30, 31.*** See if children can continue with 32, 33, and so on.

Error Intervention

If children have trouble counting by tens,

then use A7: Counting by 10's to 100.

If children have trouble finding how many for the question with 21 objects,

then use A6: Numbers to 30.

If You Have More Time

Have children count something in the classroom like how many books there are or how many milk cartons.

Numbers to 12

Math Diagnosis and Intervention System
Intervention Lesson **A9**

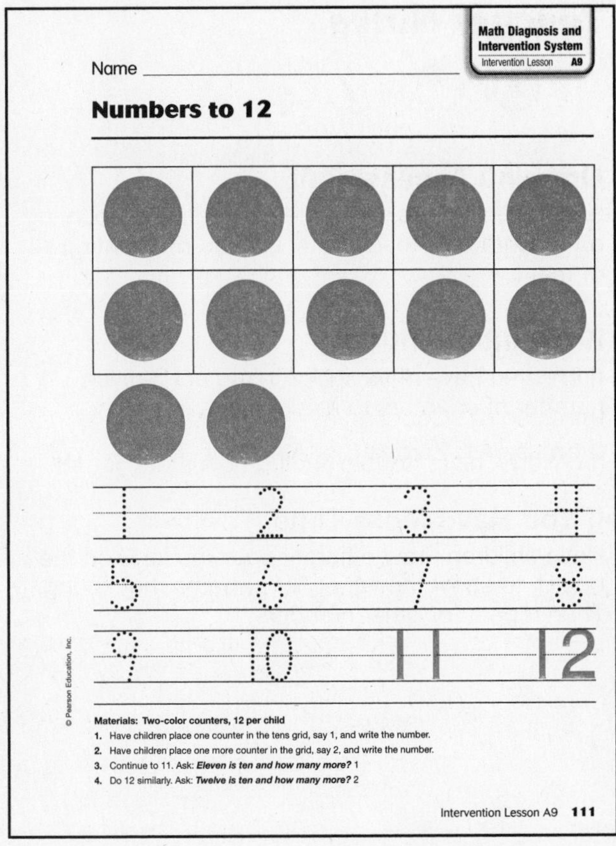
Name

Numbers to 12

1 2 3 4
5 6 7 8
9 10 11 12

Materials: Two-color counters, 12 per child
1. Have children place one counter in the tens grid, say 1, and write the number.
2. Have children place one more counter in the grid, say 2, and write the number.
3. Continue to 11. Ask: *Eleven is ten and how many more?* 1
4. Do 12 similarly. Ask: *Twelve is ten and how many more?* 2

Intervention Lesson A9 **111**

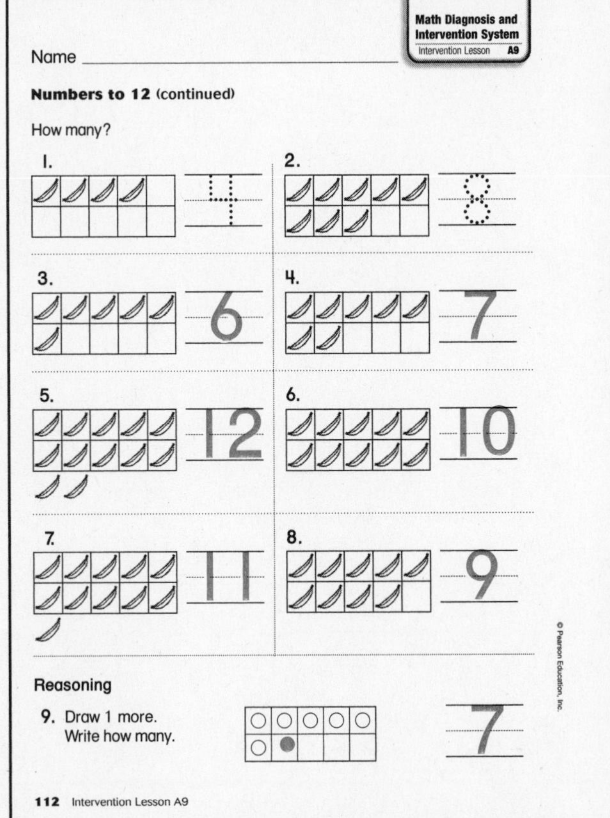
Name

Numbers to 12 (continued)

How many?

1. 4
2. 8
3. 6
4. 7
5. 12
6. 10
7. 11
8. 9

Reasoning

9. Draw 1 more. Write how many. 7

112 Intervention Lesson A9

Teacher Notes

Ongoing Assessment

Ask: ***How did you show 12?*** Ten and two more

Error Intervention

If children have difficulty finding how many,

then use A1: Zero to 5, A3: Six to Ten, and A5: 11 to 19.

If You Have More Time

Have children play I Spy with a partner. One child says, I spy 8 things together. The partner guesses what the first child sees. Then, they change roles and repeat.

Spatial Patterns for Numbers to 10

Math Diagnosis and Intervention System
Intervention Lesson **A10**

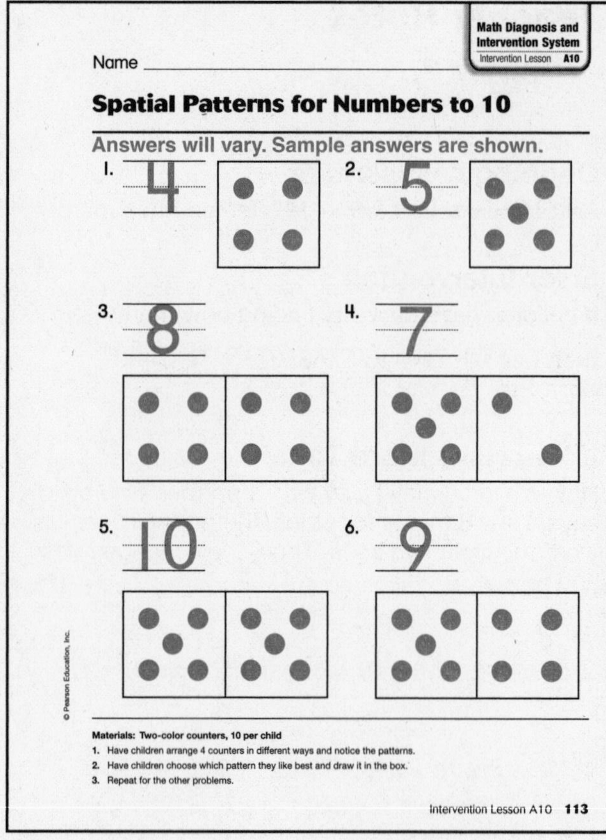

Teacher Notes

Ongoing Assessment

See if children are using the patterns and counting on to write how many dots, instead of counting all of them.

Error Intervention

If children have difficulty counting out a given number of counters to use to make patterns,

then use A1: Zero to 5 or A3: Six to Ten.

If You Have More Time

Have children draw different patterns for 8 on the board, to show the variety of patterns they found. Then repeat for other numbers.

Comparing Numbers to 10

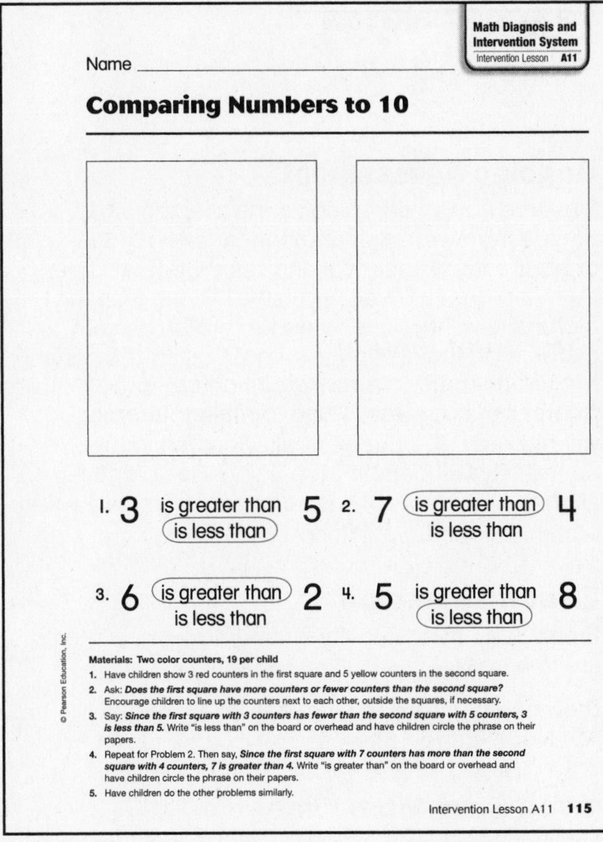

Math Diagnosis and Intervention System
Intervention Lesson A11

Name ____________________

Comparing Numbers to 10

1. 3 is greater than / (is less than) 5
2. 7 (is greater than) / is less than 4
3. 6 (is greater than) / is less than 2
4. 5 is greater than / (is less than) 8

Materials: Two color counters, 19 per child

1. Have children show 3 red counters in the first square and 5 yellow counters in the second square.
2. Ask: ***Does the first square have more counters or fewer counters than the second square?*** Encourage children to line up the counters next to each other, outside the squares, if necessary.
3. Say: ***Since the first square with 3 counters has fewer than the second square with 5 counters, 3 is less than 5.*** Write "is less than" on the board or overhead and have children circle the phrase on their papers.
4. Repeat for Problem 2. Then say, ***Since the first square with 7 counters has more than the second square with 4 counters, 7 is greater than 4.*** Write "is greater than" on the board or overhead and have children circle the phrase on their papers.
5. Have children do the other problems similarly.

Intervention Lesson A11 115

Math Diagnosis and Intervention System
Intervention Lesson A11

Name ____________________

Comparing Numbers to 10 (continued)

Circle the number that is **less** than the other number.

5. 4 or (3)
6. (2) or 5
7. 8 or (6)
8. (7) or 10

Circle the answer.

9. 6 (is greater than) / is less than 5
10. 1 is greater than / (is less than) 4
11. 7 (is greater than) / is less than 3
12. 2 is greater than / (is less than) 5
13. 5 is greater than / (is less than) 7
14. 9 (is greater than) / is less than 8
15. 8 is greater than / (is less than) 10
16. 4 is greater than / (is less than) 6

116 Intervention Lesson A11

Teacher Notes

Ongoing Assessment

Make sure children have mastered the pre-number concepts of one-to-one correspondence and comparing. Give children two groups of counters, for example 4 yellow and 6 red. Ask them to match the yellow and red as much as possible. Children who understand one-to-one-correspondence should be able to match each yellow counter with a red counter. Then ask: ***Which group has more?*** The child should point to the red counters. Omit any reference to the number of counters in each group.

Error Intervention

If children cannot decide which number is more or fewer,

then use A2: More and Fewer and A4: Comparing Numbers.

If You Have More Time

Have children work in pairs. Each child shows a group of counters. Then the partners write how many are in each group. Finally, they decide which number is greater than the other and which number is less than the other.

Ordering Numbers to 12

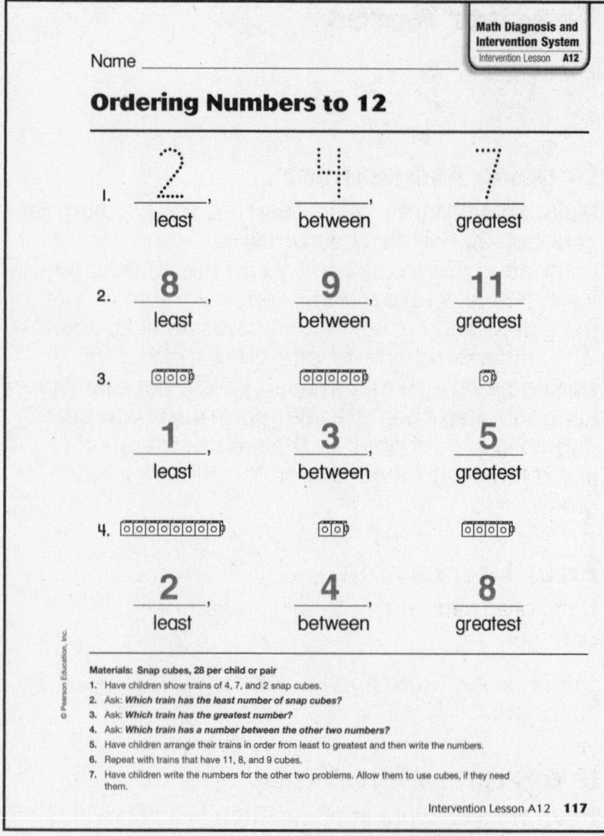

Math Diagnosis and Intervention System
Intervention Lesson A12

Name ______

Ordering Numbers to 12

1. 2, 4, 7
least, between, greatest

2. 8, 9, 11
least, between, greatest

3. 1, 3, 5
least, between, greatest

4. 2, 4, 8
least, between, greatest

Materials: Snap cubes, 28 per child or pair

1. Have children show trains of 4, 7, and 2 snap cubes.
2. Ask: ***Which train has the least number of snap cubes?***
3. Ask: ***Which train has the greatest number?***
4. Ask: ***Which train has a number between the other two numbers?***
5. Have children arrange their trains in order from least to greatest and then write the numbers.
6. Repeat with trains that have 11, 8, and 9 cubes.
7. Have children write the numbers for the other two problems. Allow them to use cubes, if they need them.

© Pearson Education, Inc.

Intervention Lesson A12 **117**

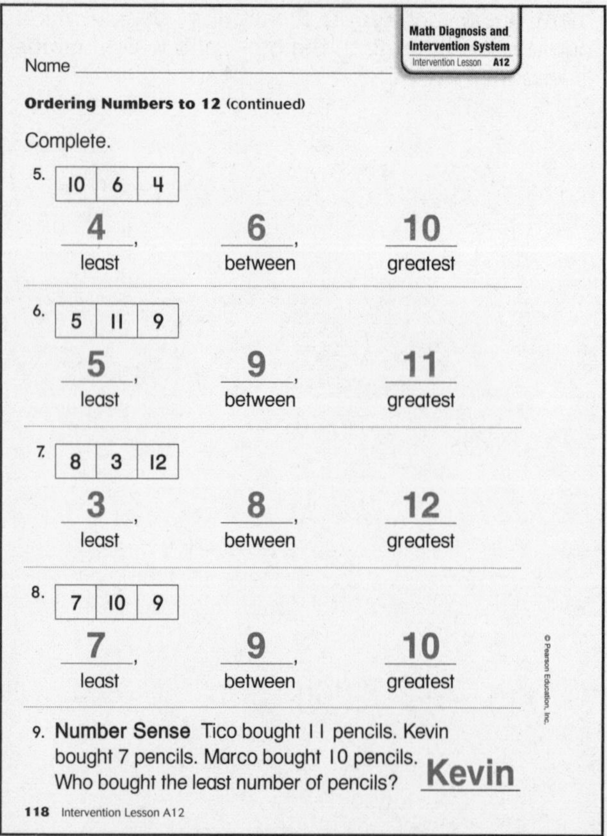

Math Diagnosis and Intervention System
Intervention Lesson A12

Name ______

Ordering Numbers to 12 (continued)

Complete.

5. | 10 | 6 | 4 |
4, 6, 10
least, between, greatest

6. | 5 | 11 | 9 |
5, 9, 11
least, between, greatest

7. | 8 | 3 | 12 |
3, 8, 12
least, between, greatest

8. | 7 | 10 | 9 |
7, 9, 10
least, between, greatest

9. **Number Sense** Tico bought 11 pencils. Kevin bought 7 pencils. Marco bought 10 pencils. Who bought the least number of pencils? **Kevin**

© Pearson Education, Inc.

118 Intervention Lesson A12

Teacher Notes

Ongoing Assessment

Observe how children solve the problems to decide if they are working concretely, pictorially, or abstractly. Those working concretely will use the snap cubes on all problems. Those working pictorially will be able to do the problems with pictures on the first page without using the cubes, but will need the cubes or will need to draw pictures for the second page. Those working abstractly will not need the cubes at all. Children working concretely will benefit from using manipulatives on all their math work. Those working pictorially will benefit from manipulatives or pictures.

Error Intervention

If children have difficulty writing how many cubes are in a train,

then use A1: Zero to Five, A3: Six to Ten, and A9: Numbers to 12.

If You Have More Time

Have children order numbers using individual cubes instead of trains. With the trains, have children compare length and, with the individual cubes, have them compare sets of objects.

Ordering Numbers to 12 with a Number Line

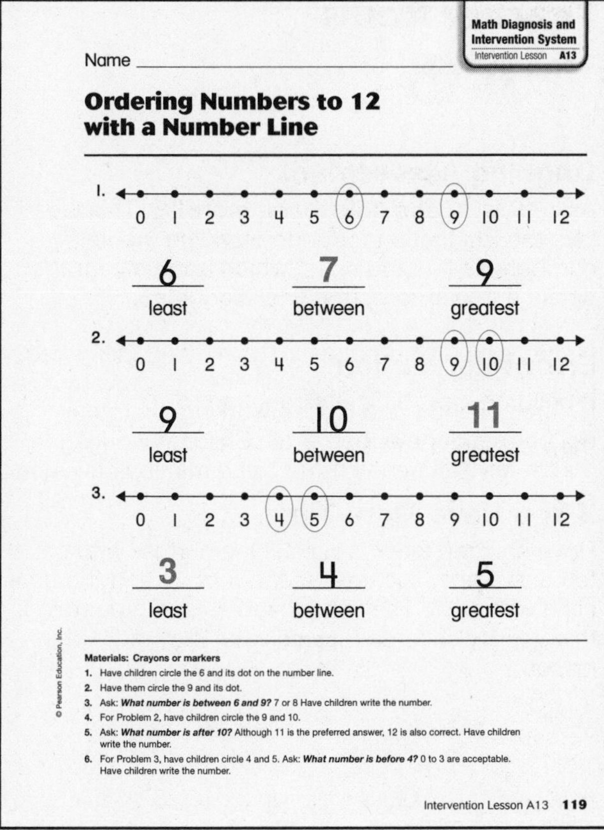

Math Diagnosis and Intervention System
Intervention Lesson A13

Name ______________________

Ordering Numbers to 12 with a Number Line

1. 0 1 2 3 4 5 6 7 8 9 10 11 12

6 least | 7 between | 9 greatest

2. 0 1 2 3 4 5 6 7 8 9 10 11 12

9 least | 10 between | 11 greatest

3. 0 1 2 3 4 5 6 7 8 9 10 11 12

3 least | 4 between | 5 greatest

Materials: Crayons or markers

1. Have children circle the 6 and its dot on the number line.
2. Have them circle the 9 and its dot.
3. Ask: ***What number is between 6 and 9?*** 7 or 8 Have children write the number.
4. For Problem 2, have children circle the 9 and 10.
5. Ask: ***What number is after 10?*** Although 11 is the preferred answer, 12 is also correct. Have children write the number.
6. For Problem 3, have children circle 4 and 5. Ask: ***What number is before 4?*** 0 to 3 are acceptable. Have children write the number.

Intervention Lesson A13 **119**

Teacher Notes

Ongoing Assessment

Ask: ***Are the numbers on the number line in the same order that you count?*** Yes

Error Intervention

If children confuse the terms before and after,

then make sure they know their right from left. The number before is to the left and the number after is to the right.

If You Have More Time

Ask children how many pets they have and write the numbers from least to greatest using the number line.

Math Diagnosis and Intervention System
Intervention Lesson A13

Name ______________________

Ordering Numbers to 12 with a Number Line (continued)

Use the number line.
Write the missing number.

0 1 2 3 4 5 6 7 8 9 10 11 12

4. 5 least | 6 between | 7 greatest
5. 9 least | 10 between | 11 greatest
6. 2 least | 3 between | 4 greatest
7. 6 least | 7 between | 8 greatest
8. 8 least | 9 between | 10 greatest
9. 7 least | 8 between | 9 greatest
10. 3 least | 4 between | 5 greatest
11. 10 least | 11 between | 12 greatest

12. **Reasoning** Find the two numbers between 3 and 6.

3 least | 4 between | 5 between | 6 greatest

120 Intervention Lesson A13

Making Numbers 11 to 20

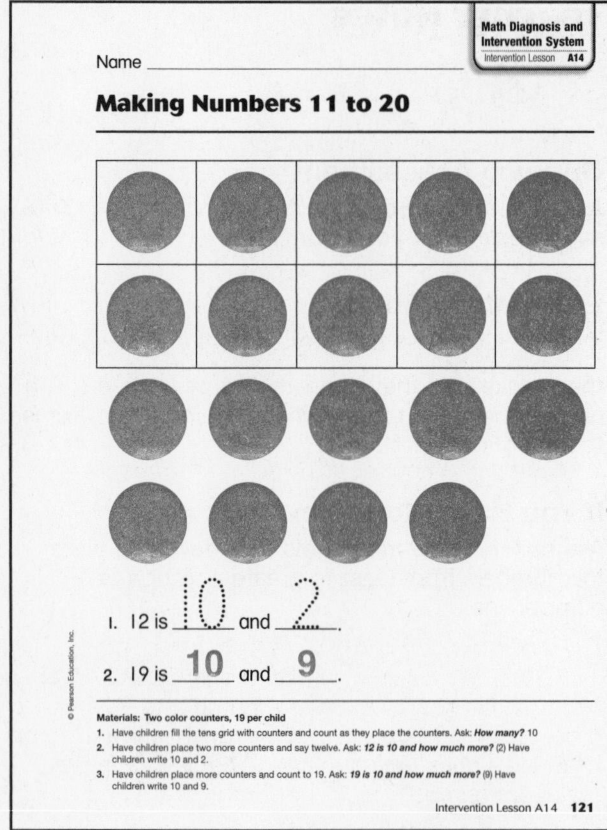

Math Diagnosis and Intervention System
Intervention Lesson A14

Name ______________________

Making Numbers 11 to 20

1. 12 is 10 and 2.
2. 19 is 10 and 9.

Materials: Two color counters, 19 per child

1. Have children fill the tens grid with counters and count as they place the counters. Ask: ***How many?*** 10
2. Have children place two more counters and say twelve. Ask: ***12 is 10 and how much more?*** (2) Have children write 10 and 2.
3. Have children place more counters and count to 19. Ask: ***19 is 10 and how much more?*** (9) Have children write 10 and 9.

© Pearson Education, Inc.

Intervention Lesson A14 **121**

Math Diagnosis and Intervention System
Intervention Lesson A14

Name ______________________

Making Numbers 11 to 20 (continued)

Write each number as 10 and some left over.

3. fourteen — 14 is 10 and 4.

4. seventeen — 17 is 10 and 7.

5. fifteen — 15 is 10 and 5.

6. **Reasoning** twenty — 20 is 10 and 10.

© Pearson Education, Inc.

122 Intervention Lesson A14

Teacher Notes

Ongoing Assessment

Ask: ***19 is 10 and how much more?*** 9; This idea lays the foundation for understanding greater numbers as ten and ones, which is critical for the whole number computational algorithms.

Error Intervention

If children have difficulty counting to 19,

then use A5: 11 to 19.

If You Have More Time

Have children work in pairs. One partner writes a ten and a one, such as *10 and 6 more* and the other child writes 16. They change roles and repeat. In this activity children reverse what they did in the lesson.

Using Numbers 11 to 20

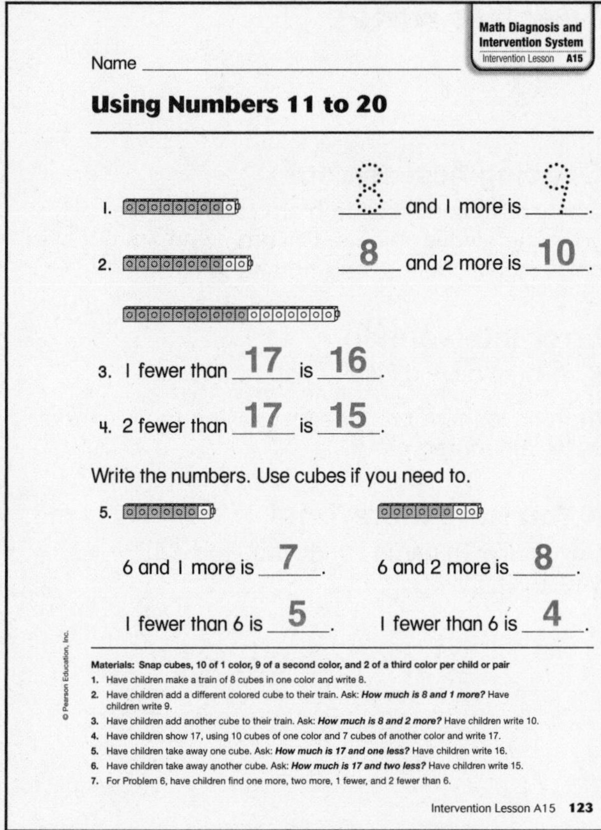

Math Diagnosis and Intervention System
Intervention Lesson A15

Name ____________

Using Numbers 11 to 20

1. 8 and 1 more is 9.
2. 8 and 2 more is 10.
3. 1 fewer than 17 is 16.
4. 2 fewer than 17 is 15.

Write the numbers. Use cubes if you need to.

5. 6 and 1 more is 7. 6 and 2 more is 8.

1 fewer than 6 is 5. 1 fewer than 6 is 4.

Materials: Snap cubes, 10 of 1 color, 9 of a second color, and 2 of a third color per child or pair

1. Have children make a train of 8 cubes in one color and write 8.
2. Have children add a different colored cube to their train. Ask: ***How much is 8 and 1 more?*** Have children write 9.
3. Have children add another cube to their train. Ask: ***How much is 8 and 2 more?*** Have children write 10.
4. Have children show 17, using 10 cubes of one color and 7 cubes of another color and write 17.
5. Have children take away one cube. Ask: ***How much is 17 and one less?*** Have children write 16.
6. Have children take away another cube. Ask: ***How much is 17 and two less?*** Have children write 15.
7. For Problem 6, have children find one more, two more, 1 fewer, and 2 fewer than 6.

Intervention Lesson A15 **123**

Math Diagnosis and Intervention System
Intervention Lesson A15

Name ____________

Using Numbers 11 to 20 (continued)

Write the numbers.
Use cubes if you need to.

6. 18 and 1 more is 19. 18 and 2 more is 20.

7. 1 fewer than 16 is 15. 2 fewer than 16 is 14.

8. 9 and 1 more is 10. 9 and 2 more is 11.

9. 1 fewer than 7 is 6. 2 fewer than 7 is 5.

10. 10 and 1 more is 11. 10 and 2 more is 12.

11. **Reasoning** 6 and 1 more is 7. Is 6 and 2 more the same as 7 and 1 more?

(yes) no

124 Intervention Lesson A15

Teacher Notes

Ongoing Assessment

Make sure children can count on. Have a stack of 10 counters and two other ones. Count 10, 11, 12. Then show the stack and 5 other counters. Ask the child to count the same way you did. Children who need to break down the stack and count from one, can not count on.

Error Intervention

If children need cubes to do all the problems,

then let them use cubes, but then ask the same question right after they write the answer while you cover up what they wrote.

If You Have More Time

Have children work in pairs and play Guess My Number. One partner writes a number to 20 and the other partner tries to guess the number. The second child asks questions such as, *What is one fewer than your number?*

Using Skip Counting

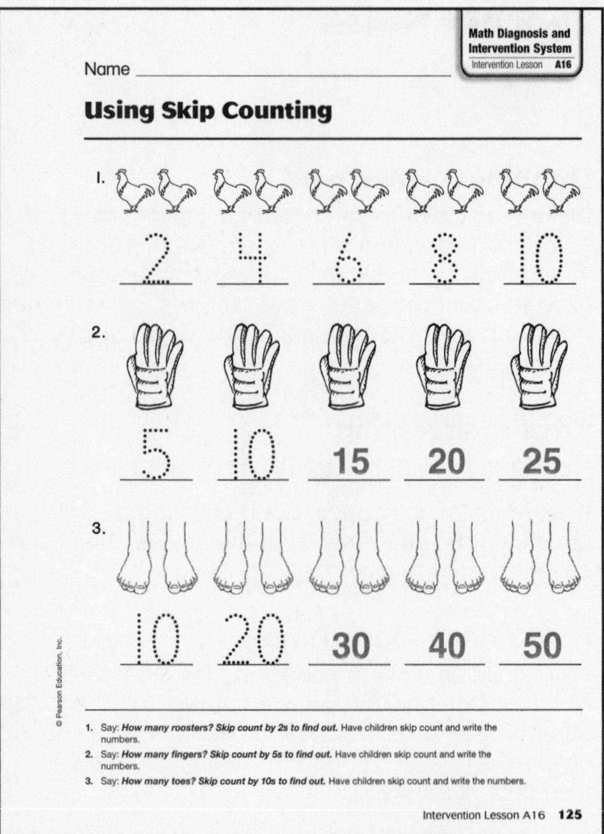

Math Diagnosis and Intervention System
Intervention Lesson A16

Name ____________________

Using Skip Counting

1. 2 4 6 8 10

2. 5 10 15 20 25

3. 10 20 30 40 50

© Pearson Education, Inc.

1. Say: *How many roosters? Skip count by 2s to find out.* Have children skip count and write the numbers.
2. Say: *How many fingers? Skip count by 5s to find out.* Have children skip count and write the numbers.
3. Say: *How many toes? Skip count by 10s to find out.* Have children skip count and write the numbers.

Intervention Lesson A16 **125**

Teacher Notes

Ongoing Assessment

Observe to see if children are skip counting or counting all the objects. Children who are not skip counting will take a long time to finish.

Error Intervention

If children have difficulty skip counting,

then have them practice just saying the numbers, using a hundred chart.

If You Have More Time

Have children name things that come in 2s, 5s, and 10s.

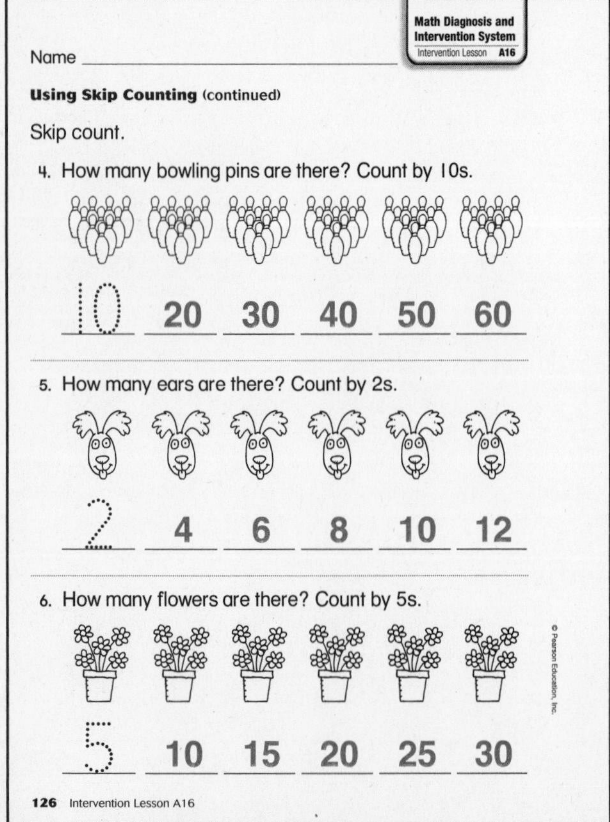

Math Diagnosis and Intervention System
Intervention Lesson A16

Name ____________________

Using Skip Counting (continued)

Skip count.

4. How many bowling pins are there? Count by 10s.

10 20 30 40 50 60

5. How many ears are there? Count by 2s.

2 4 6 8 10 12

6. How many flowers are there? Count by 5s.

5 10 15 20 25 30

© Pearson Education, Inc.

126 Intervention Lesson A16

Odd and Even

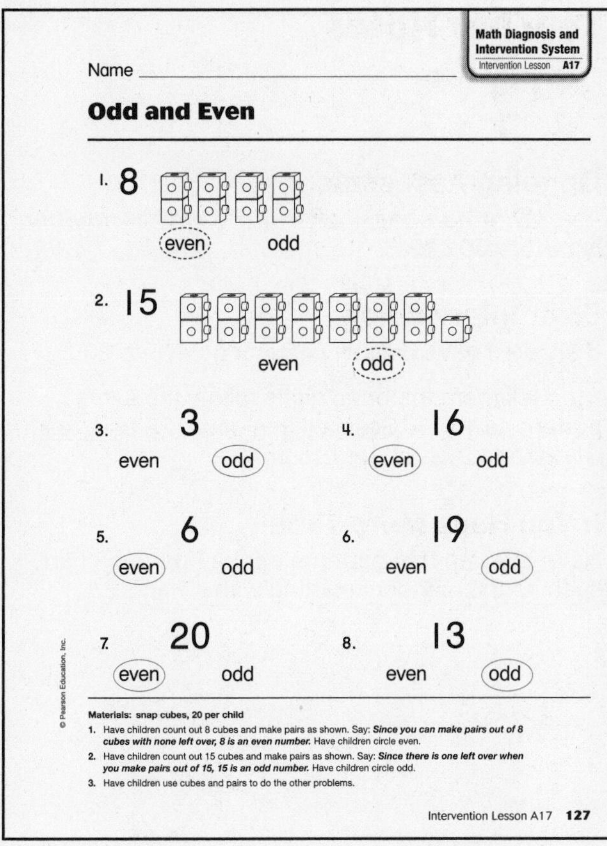

Math Diagnosis and Intervention System
Intervention Lesson A17

Name ____________________

Odd and Even

1. 8 — **even** odd

2. 15 — even **odd**

3. 3 — even **odd**

4. 16 — **even** odd

5. 6 — **even** odd

6. 19 — even **odd**

7. 20 — **even** odd

8. 13 — even **odd**

Materials: snap cubes, 20 per child

1. Have children count out 8 cubes and make pairs as shown. Say: ***Since you can make pairs out of 8 cubes with none left over, 8 is an even number.*** Have children circle even.
2. Have children count out 15 cubes and make pairs as shown. Say: ***Since there is one left over when you make pairs out of 15, 15 is an odd number.*** Have children circle odd.
3. Have children use cubes and pairs to do the other problems.

© Pearson Education, Inc.

Intervention Lesson A17 **127**

Math Diagnosis and Intervention System
Intervention Lesson A17

Name ____________________

Odd and Even (continued)

Circle **even** or **odd**.
Use cubes if you like.

9. 9 — even **odd**

10. 14 — **even** odd

11. 18 — **even** odd

12. 17 — even **odd**

13. 12 — **even** odd

14. 11 — even **odd**

15. 5 — even **odd**

16. 4 — **even** odd

Look at the pattern
What comes next?

17. 5, 7, 9, 11

18. 4, 6, 8, 10

19. 10, 12, 14, 16

20. 9, 11, 13, 15

© Pearson Education, Inc.

128 Intervention Lesson A17

Teacher Notes

Ongoing Assessment

Ask: ***4 is an even number. Is 14 even or odd?*** even
7 is an odd number. Is 17 even or odd? odd

Error Intervention

If children have trouble writing number patterns of even numbers,

then encourage them to skip count by 2s.

If You Have More Time

Give children 30 snap cubes and have them classify 21 to 30 as even or odd.

Counting from Any Number

Name ______________________

Counting from Any Number

1	2	3	4	5	6	7	8	9	10
11	12	13	14	15	16	17	18	19	20
21	22	23	24	25	26	27	28	29	30
31	32	33	34	35	36	37	38	39	40
41	42	43	44	45	46	47	48	49	50
51	52	53	54	55	56	57	58	59	60
61	62	63	64	65	66	67	68	69	70
71	72	73	74	75	76	77	78	79	80
81	82	83	84	85	86	87	88	89	90
91	92	93	94	95	96	97	98	99	100

1. 48, 49, 50, 51, 52
2. 63, 62, 61, 60, 59

1. Have children point to the number 48 on the hundred chart. Ask: ***What number comes after 48?*** 49 ***What number comes after 49?*** 50; Continue to 52. Have children write the numbers.
2. Have children point to the number 63 on the hundred chart. Ask: ***What number comes before 63?*** 62 ***What number comes before 62?*** 61; Continue to 59. Have children write the numbers.

Name ______________________

Counting from Any Number (continued)

Count by 1s.
Write the numbers.

3. 23, 24, 25, 26, 27
4. 74, 75, 76, 77, 78
5. 37, 38, 39, 40, 41
6. 19, 20, 21, 22, 23
7. 88, 89, 90, 91, 92
8. 94, 95, 96, 97, 98

Count back by 1s.
Write the numbers.

9. 43, 42, 41, 40, 39
10. 9, 8, 7, 6, 5
11. 80, 79, 78, 77, 76
12. 52, 51, 50, 49, 48
13. 60, 59, 58, 57, 56
14. 100, 99, 98, 97, 96

Reasoning Skip count by 2s.
Write the numbers.

15. 72, 74, 76, 78, 80
16. 30, 28, 26, 24, 22

Teacher Notes

Ongoing Assessment

Ask: ***What number is after 30?*** 31 ***What number is before 30?*** 29

Error Intervention

If children have difficulty counting beyond 20,

then tell them the ones digits follow the same pattern as 1 to 9. So, they can count 20 and 1 or 21, 20 and 2 or 22, and so on.

If You Have More Time

Have children find patterns on the hundred chart, such as the diagonal starting with 11 and 22.

Before, After, and Between

Math Diagnosis and Intervention System
Intervention Lesson A19

Name ____________________

Before, After, and Between

1. 52, 53, 54
2. 38, 39, 40
3. 97, 98, 99
4. 19, 20, 21
5. 13, 14, 15
6. 71, 72, 73

Materials: Snap cubes, 100 per pair or group

1. Have children show 52 with snap cubes, making five 10-trains and one 2-train. Have them add one more cube. Ask: ***What number comes after 52?*** Have them add one more cube and tell what number comes after 53. Have them write 54.
2. Repeat, starting with 38.
3. Have children show 99 with snap cubes. Have them take away one cube. Ask: ***What number comes before 99?*** Have them take away one more cube and tell what number comes before 98. Have them write 97.
4. Repeat, starting with 21.
5. Have children show 13 with snap cubes. Have them add one more cube. Ask: ***What number comes after 13? Does 15 come after 14?*** Say: ***So, 14 is between 13 and 15.***
6. Repeat, starting with 71.

Intervention Lesson A19 **131**

Math Diagnosis and Intervention System
Intervention Lesson A19

Name ____________________

Before, After, and Between (continued)

Write the number that comes just after.

7. 21, 22, 23
8. 43, 44, 45
9. 52, 53, 54
10. 28, 29, 30

Write the number that comes just before.

11. 16, 17, 18
12. 83, 84, 85

Write the number that comes between.

13. 26, 27, 28
14. 98, 99, 100
15. 48, 49, 50
16. 65, 66, 67

Reasoning Write the numbers that come just before and just after.

17. 85, 86, 87
18. 30, 31, 32
19. 78, 79, 80
20. 59, 60, 61

132 Intervention Lesson A19

Teacher Notes

Ongoing Assessment

Make sure children can rote count to 100, that is, say the number in order without objects.

Error Intervention

If children have trouble counting from any number,

then use A8: Counting to 100 and A18: Counting from Any Number.

If You Have More Time

Have pairs play Guess My Number. One child writes down a two-digit number. The other child asks questions like, *What is the number before your number?* or, *What two numbers is your number between?* After the first child answers, the second child says the number. Then, they change roles and repeat.

Counting with Tens and Ones

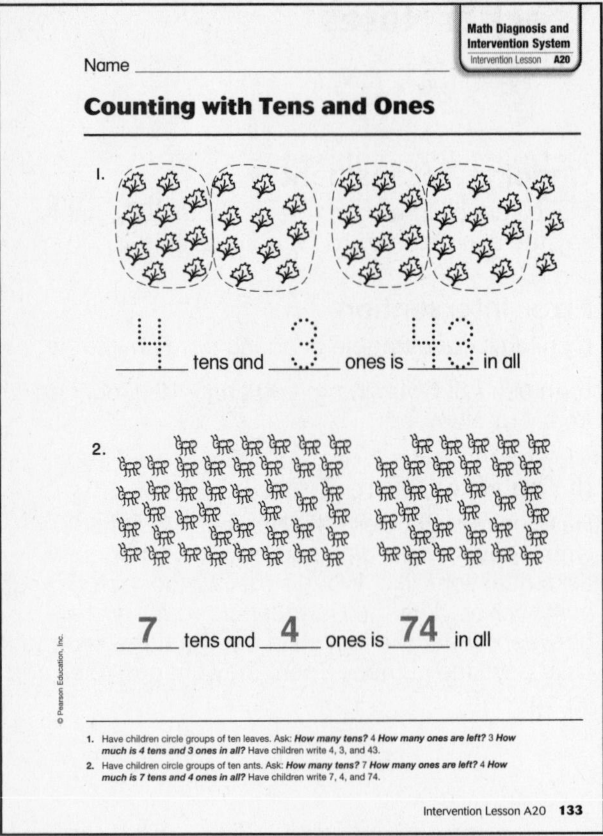

Math Diagnosis and Intervention System
Intervention Lesson A20

Name ______________________

Counting with Tens and Ones

1\. 4 tens and 3 ones is 43 in all

2\. 7 tens and 4 ones is 74 in all

1. Have children circle groups of ten leaves. Ask: *How many tens?* 4 *How many ones are left?* 3 *How much is 4 tens and 3 ones in all?* Have children write 4, 3, and 43.
2. Have children circle groups of ten ants. Ask: *How many tens?* 7 *How many ones are left?* 4 *How much is 7 tens and 4 ones in all?* Have children write 7, 4, and 74.

Intervention Lesson A20 **133**

Math Diagnosis and Intervention System
Intervention Lesson A20

Name ______________________

Counting with Tens and Ones (continued)

Circle groups of ten. Count the tens and ones. Write the numbers.

3\. 1 tens and 7 ones is 17 in all

4\. 5 tens and 5 ones is 55 in all

5\. 3 tens and 5 ones is 35 in all

6\. **Reasoning** Alberto has trading cards in groups of 10. He has 4 groups of 10 and 8 left over. Write the numbers that tell how many in all.
4 tens and 8 ones is 8 in all

134 Intervention Lesson A20

Teacher Notes

Ongoing Assessment

Make sure children circle 10 objects each time.

Error Intervention

If children have trouble counting by tens and ones, like 10, 20, 30, 40, 41, 42, 43,

then use A8: Counting to 100.

If You Have More Time

Have children count something in the room, such as buckets of crayons or counters or children.

Estimating with Groups of 10

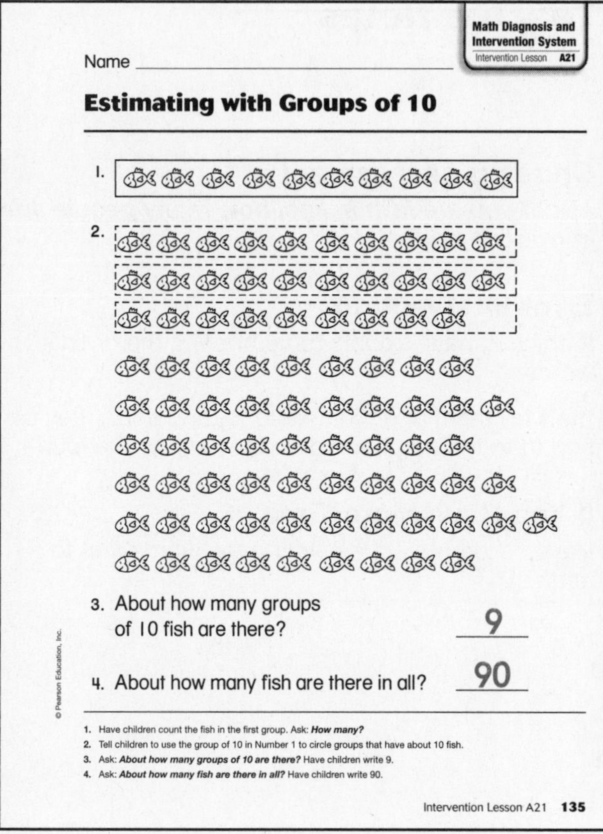

Math Diagnosis and Intervention System
Intervention Lesson A21

Name ____________________

Estimating with Groups of 10

1.

2.

3. About how many groups of 10 fish are there? 9

4. About how many fish are there in all? 90

1. Have children count the fish in the first group. Ask: ***How many?***
2. Tell children to use the group of 10 in Number 1 to circle groups that have about 10 fish.
3. Ask: ***About how many groups of 10 are there?*** Have children write 9.
4. Ask: ***About how many fish are there in all?*** Have children write 90.

© Pearson Education, Inc.

Intervention Lesson A21 **135**

Math Diagnosis and Intervention System
Intervention Lesson A21

Name ____________________

Estimating with Groups of 10 (continued)

Use groups of 10 to estimate the total number of objects.

5. About how many groups of 10 are there? 2

There are about 10 / (20) / 30 stars.

6. About how many groups of 10 are there? 4

There are about 20 / 30 / (40) seahorses.

Circle a group of 10.
Then circle the best estimate for how many objects there are in all.

7. There are about 40 / (50) / 60.

8. There are about (30) / 40 / 50.

9. **Reasoning** If you estimate that there are about 10 frogs in a pond, what could the actual number of frogs be? Circle the **best** answer.

2 4 (9)

© Pearson Education, Inc.

136 Intervention Lesson A21

Teacher Notes

Ongoing Assessment

The purpose of the lesson is to teach children to estimate, not count. As students work through the lesson, make sure they are not simply counting all the objects.

Error Intervention

If children circle only 5 or 6 objects instead of 9 to 11,

then encourage them to use the length of the group of 10 to estimate. They can mark the length on the edge of a piece of scrap paper and use that length to estimate.

If You Have More Time

Have students estimate the number of cars in the parking lot, if they can see them from an upstairs window.

Ordinal Numbers Through Tenth

Math Diagnosis and Intervention System
Intervention Lesson A22

Name ______________________

Ordinal Numbers through Tenth

Answers will vary.

____	____	____	
1st first	2nd second	3rd third	
4th fourth	5th fifth	6th sixth	
7th seventh	8th eighth	9th ninth	10th tenth

1. Choose 10 children with 10 different first initials and have them line up in the front of the class, facing the rest of the class.
2. Say: ***Some numbers help us tell the order in which people or things are arranged. These numbers are called ordinal numbers.*** Go to the first child and say the child's name and then, ***is first in line.*** Write *first* and *1st* on the board or overhead.
3. Have children who are seated write the child's initial on the first line of their worksheet.
4. Continue to tenth.
5. Have children who were standing write initials after they take a seat, as the class reviews the order.

Intervention Lesson A22 **137**

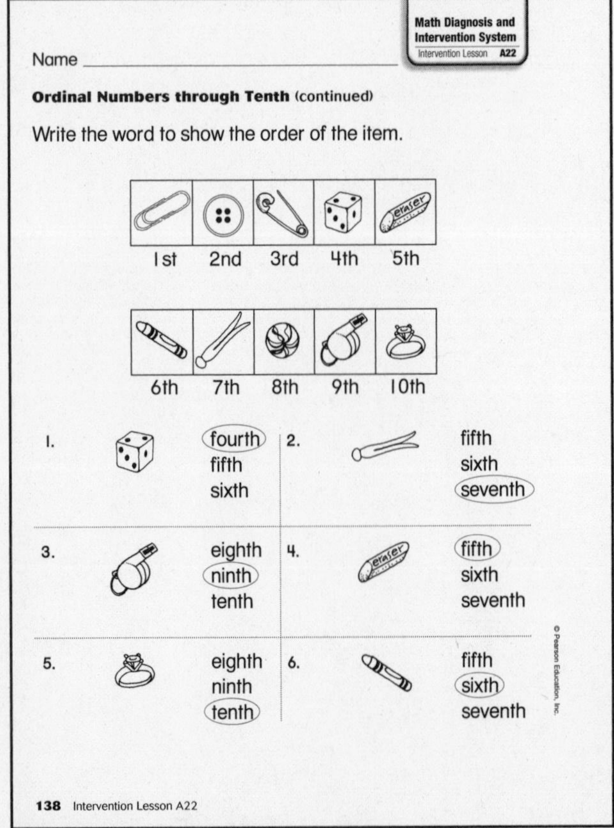

Math Diagnosis and Intervention System
Intervention Lesson A22

Name ______________________

Ordinal Numbers through Tenth (continued)

Write the word to show the order of the item.

1st 2nd 3rd 4th 5th

6th 7th 8th 9th 10th

1. fourth (circled), fifth, sixth
2. fifth, sixth, seventh (circled)
3. eighth, ninth (circled), tenth
4. fifth (circled), sixth, seventh
5. eighth, ninth, tenth (circled)
6. fifth, sixth (circled), seventh

138 Intervention Lesson A22

Teacher Notes

Ongoing Assessment

Ask: ***If you are fifth in line, how many people are in front of you?*** 4

Error Intervention

If children have trouble remembering the ordinal words,

then tell them after first, second, and third, they can add *th* to the number words they know, like four*th*.

If You Have More Time

Have children practice writing the words *first* to *tenth*.

Tens

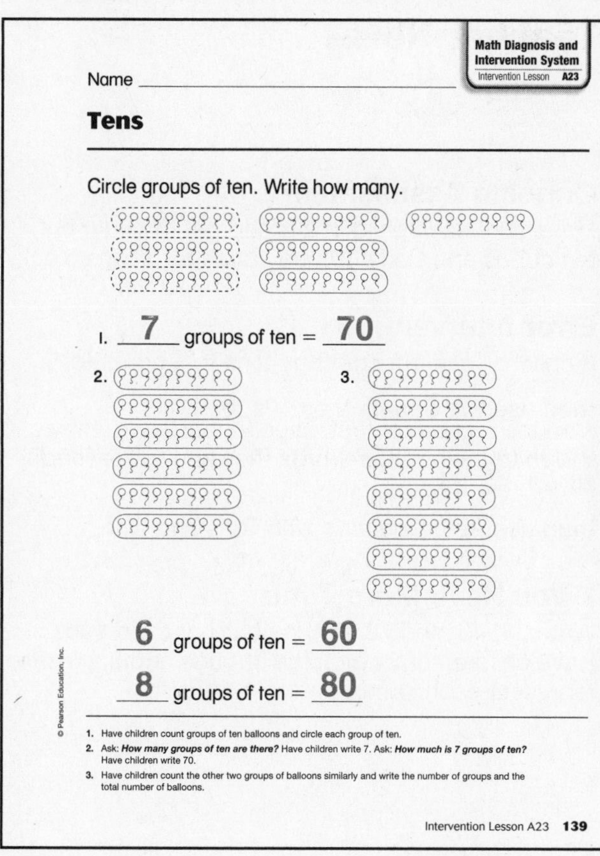

Math Diagnosis and Intervention System
Intervention Lesson A23

Name ____________________

Tens

Circle groups of ten. Write how many.

1. 7 groups of ten = 70

2. 3.

6 groups of ten = 60

8 groups of ten = 80

© Pearson Education, Inc.

1. Have children count groups of ten balloons and circle each group of ten.
2. Ask: ***How many groups of ten are there?*** Have children write 7. Ask: ***How much is 7 groups of ten?*** Have children write 70.
3. Have children count the other two groups of balloons similarly and write the number of groups and the total number of balloons.

Intervention Lesson A23 **139**

Math Diagnosis and Intervention System
Intervention Lesson A23

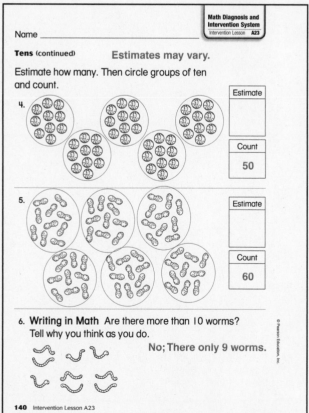

Name ____________________

Tens (continued) **Estimates may vary.**

Estimate how many. Then circle groups of ten and count.

4.

Estimate

Count
50

5.

Estimate

Count
60

6. **Writing in Math** Are there more than 10 worms? Tell why you think as you do.

No; There only 9 worms.

© Pearson Education, Inc.

140 Intervention Lesson A23

Teacher Notes

Ongoing Assessment

Although the rows and groups are arranged in tens, make sure children still count each group. Also, make sure they count one to ten each time. The purpose of the lesson is to help them think in tens to get ready for place value concepts.

Error Intervention

If children have trouble deciding how much, e.g. 4 tens are,

then use A7: Counting by 10s to 100.

If You Have More Time

Ask children to name things which come in tens. Then ask how much 5 groups would be. For example: ***How many fingers do 5 people have in all?***

Tens and Ones

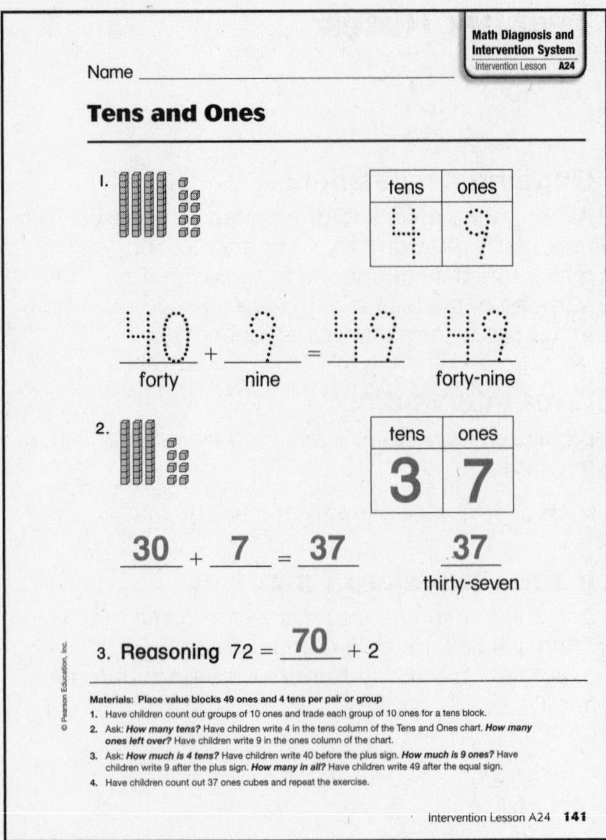

Math Diagnosis and Intervention System
Intervention Lesson A24

Name ______________

Tens and Ones

1.

tens	ones
4	9

40 + 9 = 49 49
forty nine forty-nine

2.

tens	ones
3	7

30 + 7 = 37 37
thirty-seven

3. **Reasoning** 72 = 70 + 2

Materials: Place value blocks 49 ones and 4 tens per pair or group

1. Have children count out groups of 10 ones and trade each group of 10 ones for a tens block.
2. Ask: ***How many tens?*** Have children write 4 in the tens column of the Tens and Ones chart. ***How many ones left over?*** Have children write 9 in the ones column of the chart.
3. Ask: ***How much is 4 tens?*** Have children write 40 before the plus sign. ***How much is 9 ones?*** Have children write 9 after the plus sign. ***How many in all?*** Have children write 49 after the equal sign.
4. Have children count out 37 ones cubes and repeat the exercise.

© Pearson Education, Inc.

Intervention Lesson A24 **141**

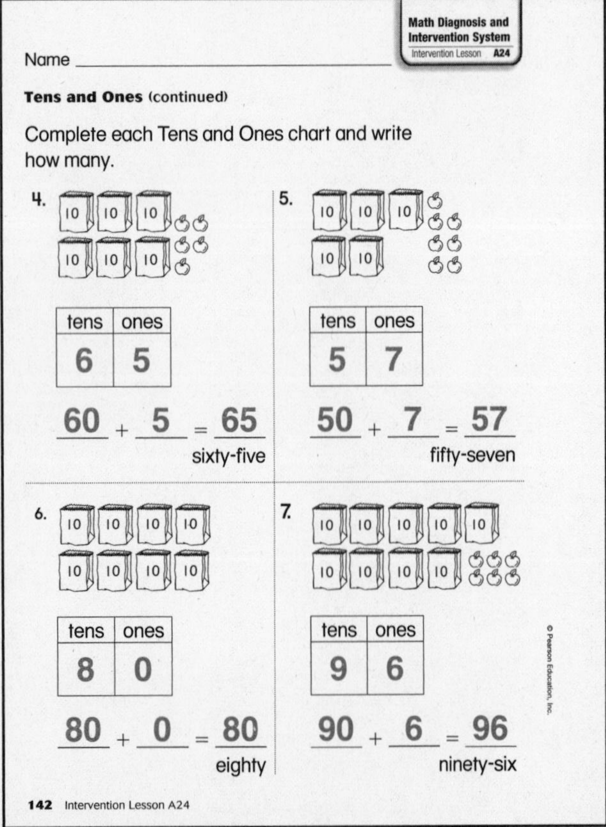

Math Diagnosis and Intervention System
Intervention Lesson A24

Name ______________

Tens and Ones (continued)

Complete each Tens and Ones chart and write how many.

4.

tens	ones
6	5

60 + 5 = 65
sixty-five

5.

tens	ones
5	7

50 + 7 = 57
fifty-seven

6.

tens	ones
8	0

80 + 0 = 80
eighty

7.

tens	ones
9	6

90 + 6 = 96
ninety-six

© Pearson Education, Inc.

142 Intervention Lesson A24

Teacher Notes

Ongoing Assessment

Make sure each child in a group get to count out ten cubes and trade 10 one cubes for 1 tens block.

Error Intervention

If children can not count by tens to a hundred,

then use A7: Counting by 10s to 100.

If children can not count by tens and ones, like 10, 20, 21, 22, 23,

then use A20: Counting with Tens and Ones.

If You Have More Time

Write 34, 45, and 78 on the board or overhead. Have children draw pictures of bags and apples to represent each number.

Number Patterns to 100

Name ______________________________

Number Patterns to 100

1	2 green	3	4	5	6	7 red	8	9	10
11	12 green	13	14	15	16	17 red	18	19	20
21	22 green	23	24	25	26	27 red	28	29	30
31	32 green	33	34	35	36	37 red	38	39	40
41	42 green	43	44	45	46	47 red	48	49	yellow 50
yellow 51	yellow 52 green	yellow 53	yellow 54	yellow 55	yellow 56	yellow 57 red	yellow 58	yellow 59	60
61	62 green	63	64	65	66	67 red	68	69	70
71	72 green	73	74	75	76	77 red	78	79	80
81	82 green	83	84	85	86	87 red	88	89	blue 90
blue 91	blue 92 green	blue 93	blue 94	blue 95	blue 96	blue 97 red	blue 98	blue 99	100

Materials: Crayons or markers

1. Have children circle the numbers with 7 ones in red.
2. Have children circle the numbers with 9 tens in blue.
3. Ask: ***What number has 7 ones and 9 tens?*** 97
4. Repeat with numbers with 2 ones in green and numbers with 5 tens in yellow.
5. Ask: ***What number has 2 ones and 5 tens?*** 52

Name ______________________________

Number Patterns to 100 (continued)

Use the hundred chart to fill in the blanks.

1. List the numbers with 8 tens.

80, 81, 82, 83, 84,
85, 86, 87, 88, 89

2. List the numbers with 4 ones.

4, 14, 24, 34, 44,
54, 64, 74, 84, 94

3. What number has 8 tens and 4 ones? 84

4. Write the missing numbers in the chart below.

41	42	43	44	45	46	47	48	49	50
51	52	53	54	55	56	57	58	59	60
61	62	63	64	65	66	67	68	69	70
71	72	73	74	75	76	77	78	79	80
81	82	83	84	85	86	87	88	89	90
91	92	93	94	95	96	97	98	99	100

Teacher Notes

Ongoing Assessment

Ask: ***How many tens are in 36?*** 3

Error Intervention

If children have trouble filling in the missing numbers,

then use A18: Counting from Any Number.

If You Have More Time

Have children play "Guess My Number" with a partner. One child writes down a number from the hundred chart. The other child tries to guess by asking yes-or-no questions, such as: *Does it have 6 tens? Is it 28?*

1 More or 1 Less, 10 More or Less

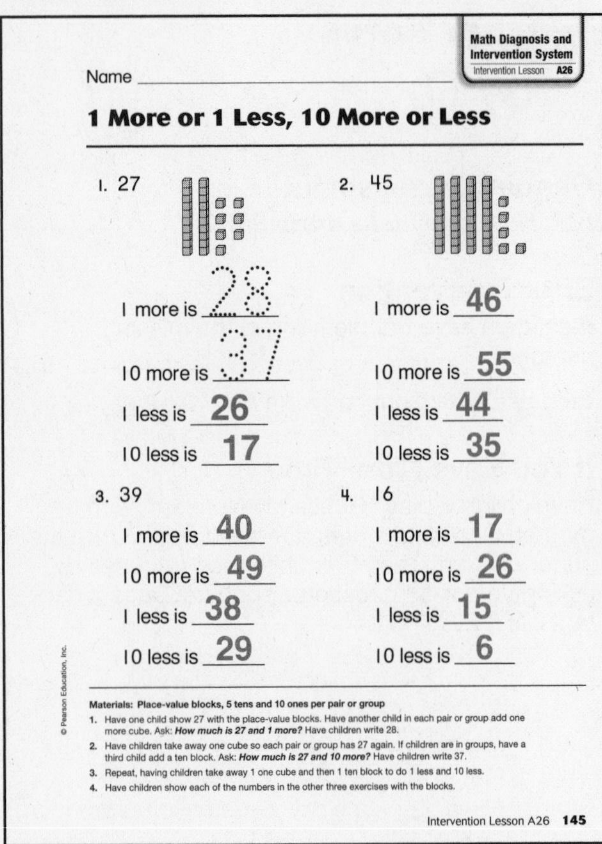

Math Diagnosis and Intervention System
Intervention Lesson A26

Name ______________________

1 More or 1 Less, 10 More or Less

1. 27

1 more is 28
10 more is 37
1 less is 26
10 less is 17

2. 45

1 more is 46
10 more is 55
1 less is 44
10 less is 35

3. 39

1 more is 40
10 more is 49
1 less is 38
10 less is 29

4. 16

1 more is 17
10 more is 26
1 less is 15
10 less is 6

© Pearson Education, Inc.

Materials: Place-value blocks, 5 tens and 10 ones per pair or group

1. Have one child show 27 with the place-value blocks. Have another child in each pair or group add one more cube. Ask: ***How much is 27 and 1 more?*** Have children write 28.
2. Have children take away one cube so each pair or group has 27 again. If children are in groups, have a third child add a ten block. Ask: ***How much is 27 and 10 more?*** Have children write 37.
3. Repeat, having children take away 1 one cube and then 1 ten block to do 1 less and 10 less.
4. Have children show each of the numbers in the other three exercises with the blocks.

Intervention Lesson A26 **145**

Teacher Notes

Ongoing Assessment

Observe to see which children figure out that they can add or subtract one from the correct digit and which ones need to use the blocks.

Error Intervention

If children have difficulty showing the numbers as tens and ones,

then use A14: Making Numbers 11 to 20 and A20: Counting with Tens and Ones.

If You Have More Time

Have children play "I'm Thinking of a Number" with a partner. One child writes down a number and says: *I'm thinking of a number. Ten more than my number is 28. What is my number?* The other partner says the number. Then, they change roles and repeat.

Math Diagnosis and Intervention System
Intervention Lesson A26

Name ______________________

1 More or 1 Less, 10 More or Less (continued)

Write how many.
Use tens and ones if you like.

5. 36 1 more is 37	6. 56 1 less is 55
7. 29 10 more is 39	8. 60 10 less is 50
9. 73 10 more is 83	10. 41 1 less is 40
11. 24 1 less is 23 1 more is 25 10 less is 14 10 more is 34	12. 63 1 less is 62 1 more is 64 10 less is 53 10 more is 73

13. **Reasoning** Which digit in 75 changes when you find 10 more or 10 less? Why?
7; It tells how many tens.

14. **Reasoning** Which digit in 32 changes when you find 1 more or 1 less? Why?
2; It tells how many ones.

146 Intervention Lesson A26

Using $>$, $<$, and $=$ to Compare Numbers

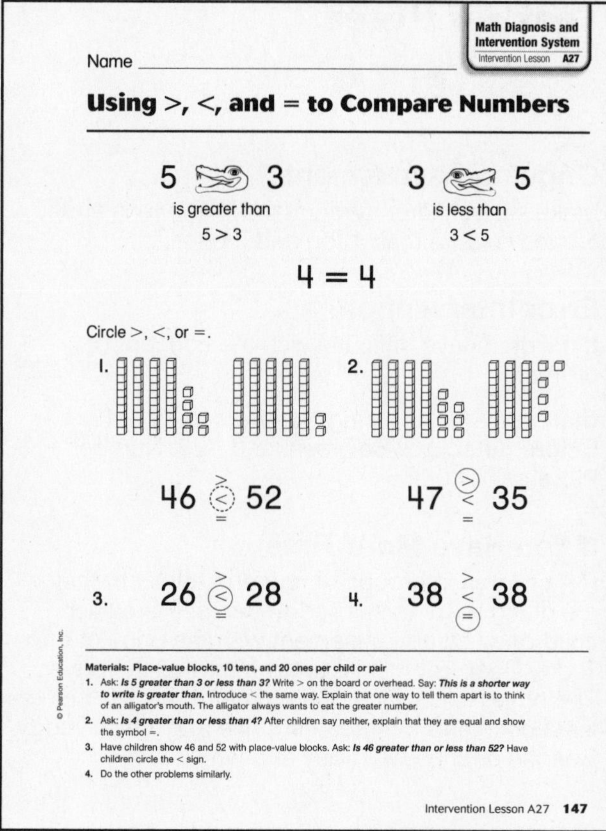

Math Diagnosis and Intervention System
Intervention Lesson A27

Name ____________________

Using $>$, $<$, and $=$ to Compare Numbers

5 [alligator] 3
is greater than
$5 > 3$

3 [alligator] 5
is less than
$3 < 5$

$4 = 4$

Circle $>$, $<$, or $=$.

1. 46 (circle $<$) 52
2. 47 (circle $>$) 35
3. 26 (circle $<$) 28
4. 38 (circle $=$) 38

Materials: Place-value blocks, 10 tens, and 20 ones per child or pair

1. Ask: ***Is 5 greater than 3 or less than 3?*** Write $>$ on the board or overhead. Say: ***This is a shorter way to write is greater than.*** Introduce $<$ the same way. Explain that one way to tell them apart is to think of an alligator's mouth. The alligator always wants to eat the greater number.
2. Ask: ***Is 4 greater than or less than 4?*** After children say neither, explain that they are equal and show the symbol $=$.
3. Have children show 46 and 52 with place-value blocks. Ask: ***Is 46 greater than or less than 52?*** Have children circle the $<$ sign.
4. Do the other problems similarly.

Intervention Lesson A27 **147**

Math Diagnosis and Intervention System
Intervention Lesson A27

Name ____________________

Using $>$, $<$, and $=$ to Compare Numbers (continued)

Write $>$, $<$, or $=$.

5. 74 $>$ 56	6. 43 $=$ 43
7. 57 $>$ 49	8. 62 $>$ 26
9. 23 $<$ 32	10. 86 $<$ 89
11. 47 $=$ 47	12. 51 $>$ 15
13. 63 $>$ 57	14. 19 $=$ 19
15. 72 $<$ 78	16. 31 $>$ 21
17. 40 $<$ 50	18. 95 $>$ 85

148 Intervention Lesson A27

Teacher Notes

Ongoing Assessment

Make sure children can translate simple number sentences like $7 < 8$, $4 > 2$, and $6 = 6$ into words.

Error Intervention

If children think 46 is greater than 52 because 46 has 10 blocks and 52 has 7 blocks,

then have them compare the blocks by lining up 46 vertically and 52 next to it. The 4 tens in each are the same. The 6 ones in 46 should be next to a ten in 52, showing that 46 is less. Explain that 46 has fewer tens than 52, so it is less.

If children have difficulty with the concepts of greater than and less than,

then use A11: Comparing Numbers to 10.

If You Have More Time

Write the number of children in your class and in another class on the board. Have children compare the numbers using $>$, $<$, or $=$.

Ordering Three Numbers

Math Diagnosis and Intervention System
Intervention Lesson **A28**

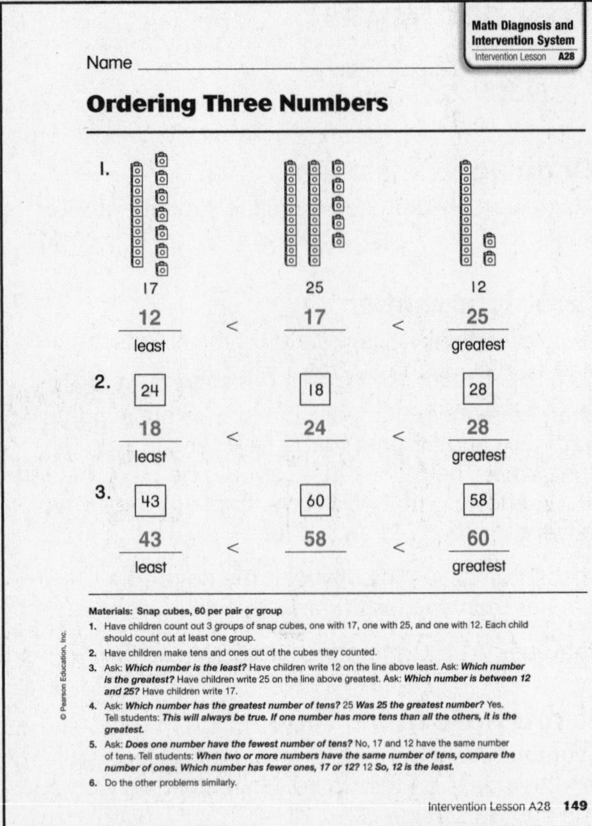

Math Diagnosis and Intervention System
Intervention Lesson A28

Name ______________________

Ordering Three Numbers

1. 17 25 12

12 < 17 < 25
least greatest

2. 24 18 28

18 < 24 < 28
least greatest

3. 43 60 58

43 < 58 < 60
least greatest

Materials: Snap cubes, 60 per pair or group

1. Have children count out 3 groups of snap cubes, one with 17, one with 25, and one with 12. Each child should count out at least one group.
2. Have children make tens and ones out of the cubes they counted.
3. Ask: ***Which number is the least?*** Have children write 12 on the line above least. Ask: ***Which number is the greatest?*** Have children write 25 on the line above greatest. Ask: ***Which number is between 12 and 25?*** Have children write 17.
4. Ask: ***Which number has the greatest number of tens?*** 25 ***Was 25 the greatest number?*** Yes. Tell students: ***This will always be true. If one number has more tens than all the others, it is the greatest.***
5. Ask: ***Does one number have the fewest number of tens?*** No, 17 and 12 have the same number of tens. Tell students: ***When two or more numbers have the same number of tens, compare the number of ones. Which number has fewer ones, 17 or 12?*** 12 ***So, 12 is the least.***
6. Do the other problems similarly.

Intervention Lesson A28 **149**

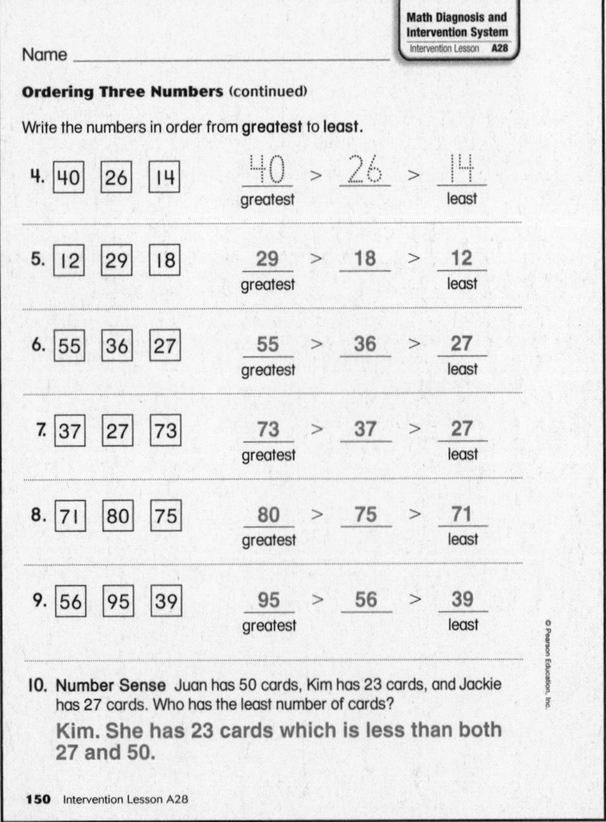

Math Diagnosis and Intervention System
Intervention Lesson A28

Name ______________________

Ordering Three Numbers (continued)

Write the numbers in order from **greatest** to **least**.

4. 40 26 14 — 40 > 26 > 14 (greatest … least)
5. 12 29 18 — 29 > 18 > 12 (greatest … least)
6. 55 36 27 — 55 > 36 > 27 (greatest … least)
7. 37 27 73 — 73 > 37 > 27 (greatest … least)
8. 71 80 75 — 80 > 75 > 71 (greatest … least)
9. 56 95 39 — 95 > 56 > 39 (greatest … least)

10. **Number Sense** Juan has 50 cards, Kim has 23 cards, and Jackie has 27 cards. Who has the least number of cards?
Kim. She has 23 cards which is less than both 27 and 50.

150 Intervention Lesson A28

Teacher Notes

Ongoing Assessment

Make sure children understand that 2 tens and 5 ones is more than 1 ten and 7 ones.

Error Intervention

If children have difficulty with the concept of ordering,

then use A12: Ordering Numbers to 12, A19: Before, After, and Between, and A25: Number Patterns to 100.

If You Have More Time

Put children in groups of four and tell them they are going to try to sell Teddy Bears. Have each child draw an advertisement with the price of their Teddy Bear. Each child takes a turn as the buyer. The buyer tells which of the other three ads has the least price and the greatest price and which Teddy Bear he or she would buy and why.

Number Words to Twenty

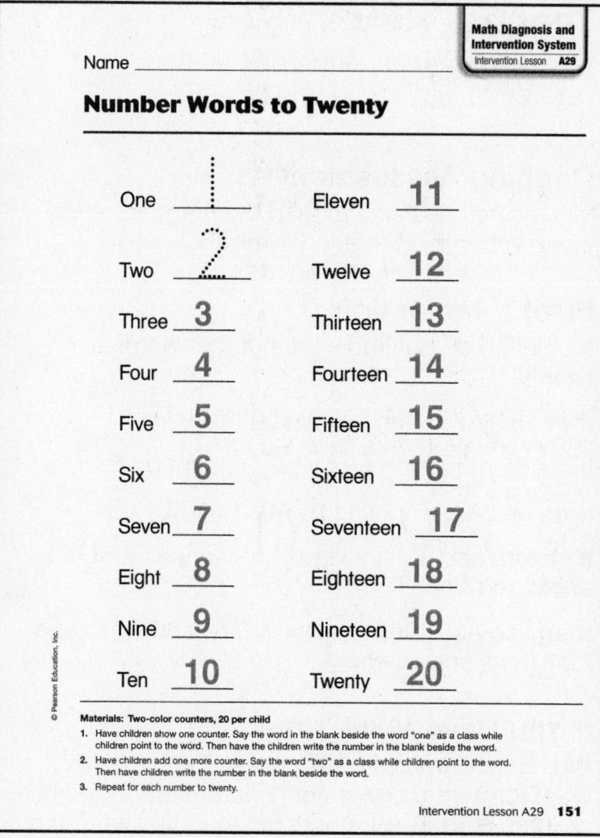

Math Diagnosis and Intervention System
Intervention Lesson A29

Name ____________________

Number Words to Twenty

One	1	Eleven	11
Two	2	Twelve	12
Three	3	Thirteen	13
Four	4	Fourteen	14
Five	5	Fifteen	15
Six	6	Sixteen	16
Seven	7	Seventeen	17
Eight	8	Eighteen	18
Nine	9	Nineteen	19
Ten	10	Twenty	20

Materials: Two-color counters, 20 per child

1. Have children show one counter. Say the word in the blank beside the word "one" as a class while children point to the word. Then have the children write the number in the blank beside the word.
2. Have children add one more counter. Say the word "two" as a class while children point to the word. Then have children write the number in the blank beside the word.
3. Repeat for each number to twenty.

Intervention Lesson A29 **151**

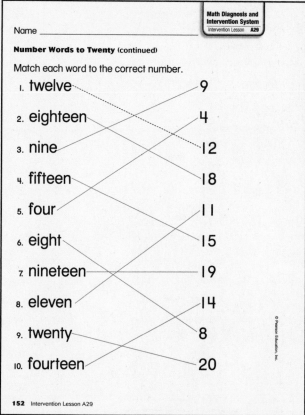

Math Diagnosis and Intervention System
Intervention Lesson A29

Name ____________________

Number Words to Twenty (continued)

Match each word to the correct number.

1. twelve	9
2. eighteen	4
3. nine	12
4. fifteen	18
5. four	11
6. eight	15
7. nineteen	19
8. eleven	14
9. twenty	8
10. fourteen	20

152 Intervention Lesson A29

Teacher Notes

Ongoing Assessment

Make sure children can rote count to 20. Encourage them to count and point to each number word and symbol as they say the number.

Error Intervention

If children keep looking at the first page in order to do the matching,

then help them read the number words using phonics.

If You Have More Time

Have pairs of students write the words and the symbols on index cards and then shuffle the deck. Each child takes 7 cards from the deck and makes as many pairs as possible with those cards. Then the children take turns drawing a card from the deck, trying to make a pair, and throwing one card away. The other child may pick up the discarded card or may draw a card from the deck. The game is over when one child pairs up all his or her cards.

Number Words

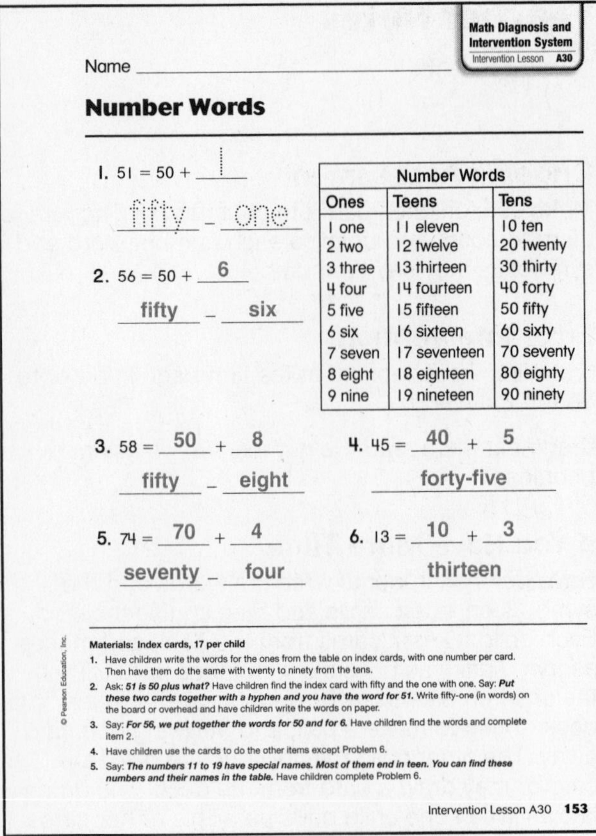

Math Diagnosis and Intervention System
Intervention Lesson A30

Name ______________________

Number Words

1. 51 = 50 + 1
fifty - one

2. 56 = 50 + 6
fifty - six

Number Words		
Ones	Teens	Tens
1 one	11 eleven	10 ten
2 two	12 twelve	20 twenty
3 three	13 thirteen	30 thirty
4 four	14 fourteen	40 forty
5 five	15 fifteen	50 fifty
6 six	16 sixteen	60 sixty
7 seven	17 seventeen	70 seventy
8 eight	18 eighteen	80 eighty
9 nine	19 nineteen	90 ninety

3. 58 = 50 + 8
fifty - eight

4. 45 = 40 + 5
forty-five

5. 74 = 70 + 4
seventy - four

6. 13 = 10 + 3
thirteen

Materials: Index cards, 17 per child

1. Have children write the words for the ones from the table on index cards, with one number per card. Then have them do the same with twenty to ninety from the tens.
2. Ask: ***51 is 50 plus what?*** Have children find the index card with fifty and the one with one. Say: ***Put these two cards together with a hyphen and you have the word for 51.*** Write fifty-one (in words) on the board or overhead and have children write the words on paper.
3. Say: ***For 56, we put together the words for 50 and for 6.*** Have children find the words and complete item 2.
4. Have children use the cards to do the other items except Problem 6.
5. Say: ***The numbers 11 to 19 have special names. Most of them end in teen. You can find these numbers and their names in the table.*** Have children complete Problem 6.

Intervention Lesson A30 **153**

Math Diagnosis and Intervention System
Intervention Lesson A30

Name ______________________

Number Words (continued)

Write the number for each word.

7. two 2
8. thirty-six 36
9. sixteen 16
10. twenty-eight 28
11. seventy 70
12. eighty-one 81
13. eight 8
14. twelve 12
15. fifty-seven 57
16. fourteen 14

Write the word for each number.

17. 62 sixty-two
18. 30 thirty
19. 7 seven
20. 11 eleven
21. 49 forty-nine
22. 23 twenty-three

Write the word for each number of objects.

23. thirty

24. twenty-two

154 Intervention Lesson A30

Teacher Notes

Ongoing Assessment

Make sure children can read the numbers in the table written next to each symbol.

Error Intervention

If children do not know the number words to twenty,

then use A29: Number Words to Twenty.

If children do not know how to count by tens,

then use A7: Counting by 10s to 100.

If children do not know how to write a number in expanded form,

then use A20: Counting with Tens and Ones and A24: Tens and Ones.

If You Have More Time

Provide children with examples of numbers in word form from newspapers and magazines. Have children read the numbers out loud and write them in symbol form.

Ordinal Numbers

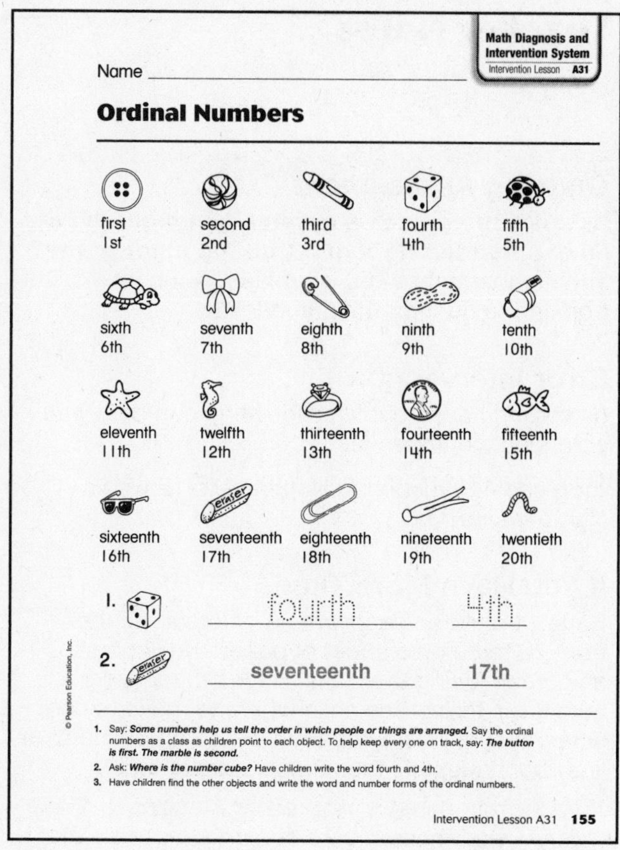

Name ______________________

Ordinal Numbers

first 1st	second 2nd	third 3rd	fourth 4th	fifth 5th
sixth 6th	seventh 7th	eighth 8th	ninth 9th	tenth 10th
eleventh 11th	twelfth 12th	thirteenth 13th	fourteenth 14th	fifteenth 15th
sixteenth 16th	seventeenth 17th	eighteenth 18th	nineteenth 19th	twentieth 20th

1. fourth 4th
2. seventeenth 17th

1. Say: *Some numbers help us tell the order in which people or things are arranged.* Say the ordinal numbers as a class as children point to each object. To help keep every one on track, say: *The button is first. The marble is second.*
2. Ask: *Where is the number cube?* Have children write the word fourth and 4th.
3. Have children find the other objects and write the word and number forms of the ordinal numbers.

© Pearson Education, Inc.

Intervention Lesson A31 **155**

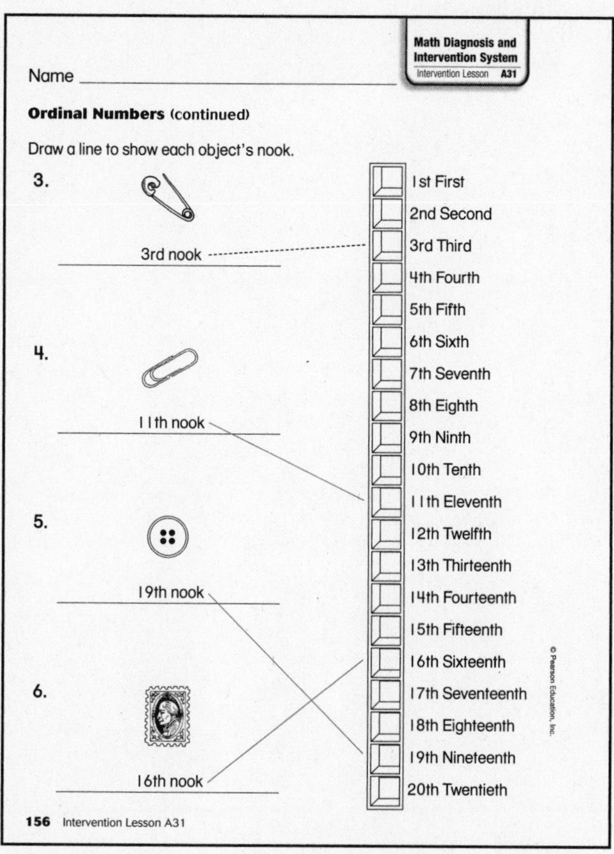

Name ______________________

Ordinal Numbers (continued)

Draw a line to show each object's nook.

3. 3rd nook
4. 11th nook
5. 19th nook
6. 16th nook

1st First
2nd Second
3rd Third
4th Fourth
5th Fifth
6th Sixth
7th Seventh
8th Eighth
9th Ninth
10th Tenth
11th Eleventh
12th Twelfth
13th Thirteenth
14th Fourteenth
15th Fifteenth
16th Sixteenth
17th Seventeenth
18th Eighteenth
19th Nineteenth
20th Twentieth

© Pearson Education, Inc.

156 Intervention Lesson A31

Teacher Notes

Ongoing Assessment

While waiting in line, ask the ninth child to raise his or her hand. Then ask the fourteenth child, and so on.

Error Intervention

If children have difficulty with the small ordinal numbers,

then use A22: Ordinal Numbers through Tenth.

If You Have More Time

Have children practice writing the words first to twentieth.

Numbers to 100 on the Number Line

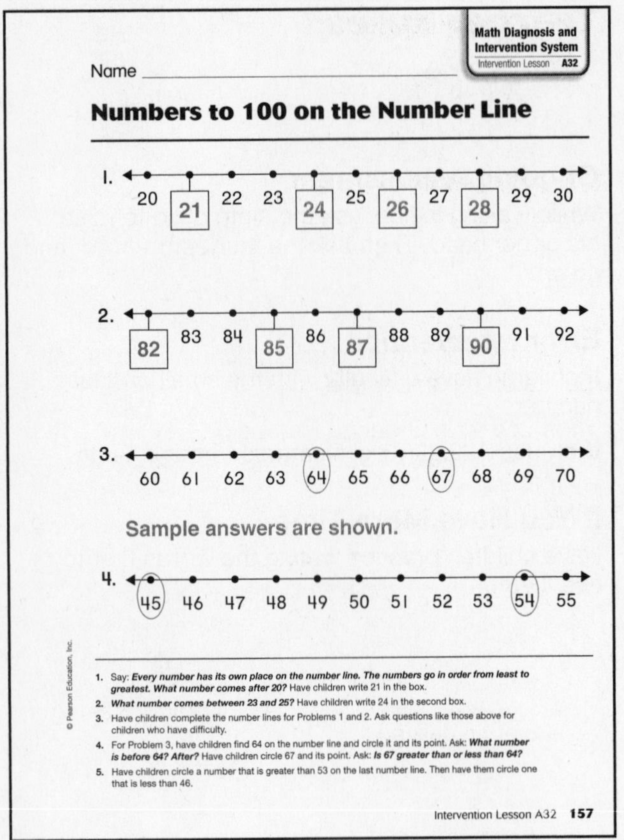

Math Diagnosis and Intervention System
Intervention Lesson A32

Name ______________________

Numbers to 100 on the Number Line

1. 20 [21] 22 23 [24] 25 [26] 27 [28] 29 30

2. [82] 83 84 [85] 86 [87] 88 89 [90] 91 92

3. 60 61 62 63 (64) 65 66 (67) 68 69 70

Sample answers are shown.

4. (45) 46 47 48 49 50 51 52 53 (54) 55

1. Say: ***Every number has its own place on the number line. The numbers go in order from least to greatest. What number comes after 20?*** Have children write 21 in the box.
2. ***What number comes between 23 and 25?*** Have children write 24 in the second box.
3. Have children complete the number lines for Problems 1 and 2. Ask questions like those above for children who have difficulty.
4. For Problem 3, have children find 64 on the number line and circle it and its point. Ask: ***What number is before 64? After?*** Have children circle 67 and its point. Ask: ***Is 67 greater than or less than 64?***
5. Have children circle a number that is greater than 53 on the last number line. Then have them circle one that is less than 46.

© Pearson Education, Inc.

Intervention Lesson A32 **157**

Teacher Notes

Ongoing Assessment

Ask: ***Which number is greater, a number left of 50 or a number right of 50, on the number line?*** The number right of 50 is greater. Numbers increase from left to right on the number line.

Error Intervention

If children have trouble associating numbers with points on a number line,

then use A13: Ordering Numbers to 12 with a Number Line.

If You Have More Time

Have 11 children each write a different number from 70 to 80 on a sheet of paper and line up in any order, facing the class. Have other children take turns telling one child where to move to show where that child's number would go on the number line. Continue until the numbers are in order.

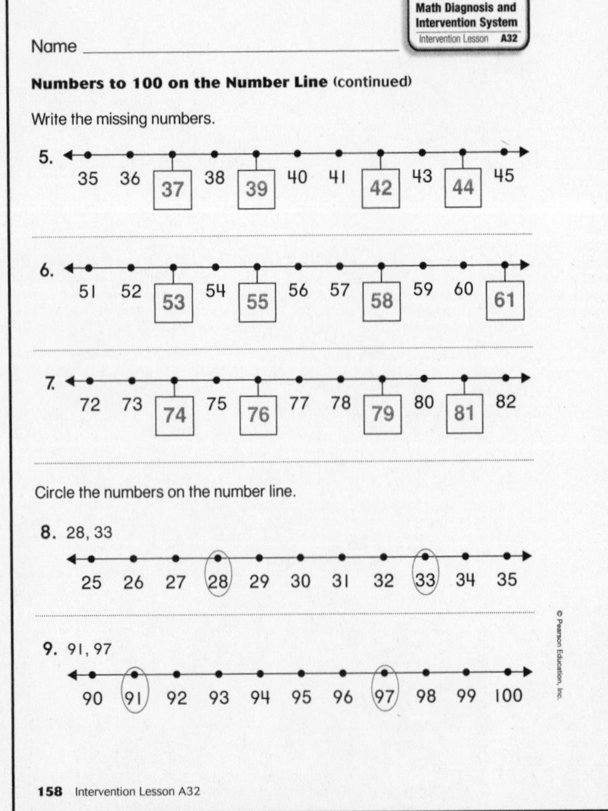

Math Diagnosis and Intervention System
Intervention Lesson A32

Name ______________________

Numbers to 100 on the Number Line (continued)

Write the missing numbers.

5. 35 36 [37] 38 [39] 40 41 [42] 43 [44] 45

6. 51 52 [53] 54 [55] 56 57 [58] 59 60 [61]

7. 72 73 [74] 75 [76] 77 78 [79] 80 [81] 82

Circle the numbers on the number line.

8. 28, 33
25 26 27 (28) 29 30 31 32 (33) 34 35

9. 91, 97
90 (91) 92 93 94 95 96 (97) 98 99 100

© Pearson Education, Inc.

158 Intervention Lesson A32

Number Line Estimation

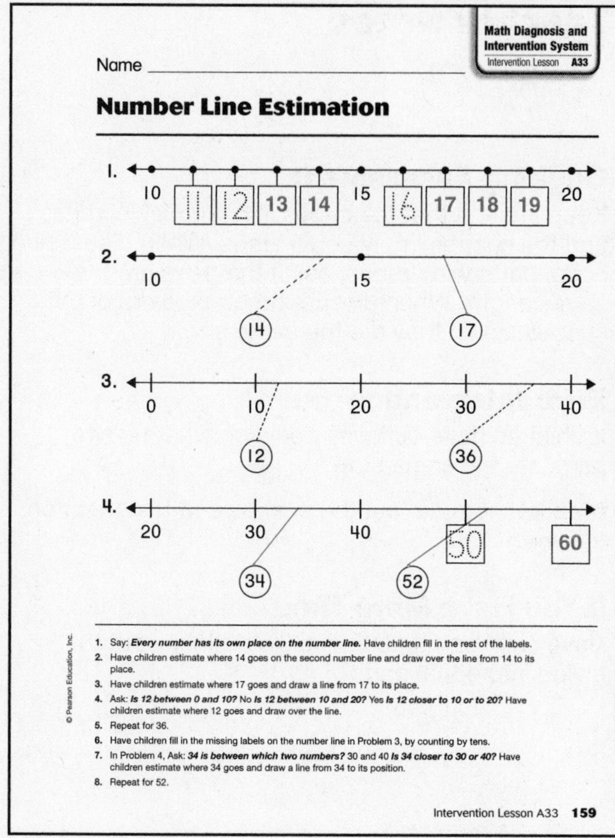

Name ______________________

Math Diagnosis and Intervention System
Intervention Lesson A33

Number Line Estimation

1. 10 11 12 13 14 15 16 17 18 19 20
2. 10 15 20
(14) (17)
3. 0 10 20 30 40
(12) (36)
4. 20 30 40 50 60
(34) (52)

1. Say: ***Every number has its own place on the number line.*** Have children fill in the rest of the labels.
2. Have children estimate where 14 goes on the second number line and draw over the line from 14 to its place.
3. Have children estimate where 17 goes and draw a line from 17 to its place.
4. Ask: ***Is 12 between 0 and 10?*** No ***Is 12 between 10 and 20?*** Yes ***Is 12 closer to 10 or to 20?*** Have children estimate where 12 goes and draw over the line.
5. Repeat for 36.
6. Have children fill in the missing labels on the number line in Problem 3, by counting by tens.
7. In Problem 4, Ask: ***34 is between which two numbers?*** 30 and 40 ***Is 34 closer to 30 or 40?*** Have children estimate where 34 goes and draw a line from 34 to its position.
8. Repeat for 52.

© Pearson Education, Inc.

Intervention Lesson A33 **159**

Name ______________________

Math Diagnosis and Intervention System
Intervention Lesson A33

Number Line Estimation (continued)

Complete the number line.
Then draw lines to show where the numbers go.

5. 0 10 20 30 40
(26) (11) (36)

6. 20 30 40 50 60
(35) (22) (46)

7. 30 40 50 60 70
(41) (65) (53)

8. 60 70 80 90 100
(61) (85) (70)

9. **Number Sense** Is the number 5 tens and 8 ones closer to 50 or 60? Explain.
5 tens and 8 ones is 58, so it is closer to 60.

160 Intervention Lesson A33

Teacher Notes

Ongoing Assessment

Make sure children know, for example, 34 is between 30 and 40.

Error Intervention

If children have trouble associating numbers with points on a number line,

then use A13: Ordering Numbers to 12 with a Number Line and A32: Numbers to 100 on the Number Line.

If You Have More Time

Have children draw two houses on paper, one on the left side of the paper and the other on the right side. Have them write 40 on the first house and 50 on the other house. Finally, have them draw a house with 48, where they think it would belong between 40 and 50.

Halves

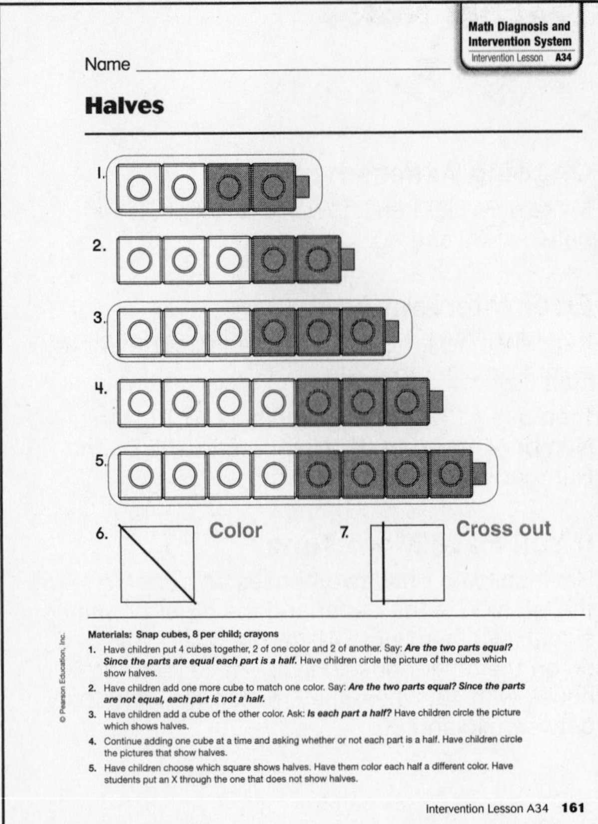
Math Diagnosis and Intervention System
Intervention Lesson A34

Name

Halves

1.
2.
3.
4.
5.
6. Color
7. Cross out

Materials: Snap cubes, 8 per child; crayons

1. Have children put 4 cubes together, 2 of one color and 2 of another. Say: ***Are the two parts equal? Since the parts are equal each part is a half.*** Have children circle the picture of the cubes which show halves.
2. Have children add one more cube to match one color. Say: ***Are the two parts equal? Since the parts are not equal, each part is not a half.***
3. Have children add a cube of the other color. Ask: ***Is each part a half?*** Have children circle the picture which shows halves.
4. Continue adding one cube at a time and asking whether or not each part is a half. Have children circle the pictures that show halves.
5. Have children choose which square shows halves. Have them color each half a different color. Have students put an X through the one that does not show halves.

© Pearson Education, Inc.

Intervention Lesson A34 **161**

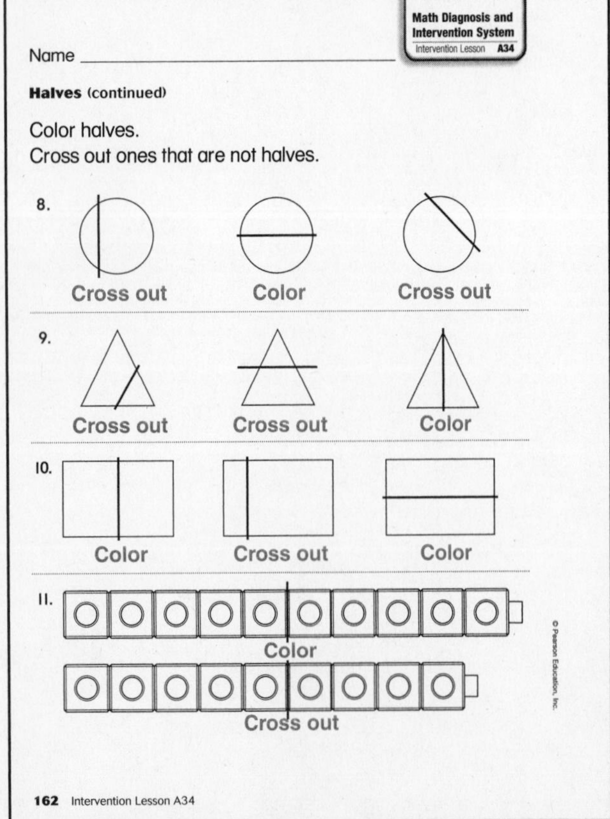
Math Diagnosis and Intervention System
Intervention Lesson A34

Name

Halves (continued)

Color halves.
Cross out ones that are not halves.

8. Cross out | Color | Cross out
9. Cross out | Cross out | Color
10. Color | Cross out | Color
11. Color
Cross out

© Pearson Education, Inc.

162 Intervention Lesson A34

Teacher Notes

Ongoing Assessment

Keep in mind that the cubes imply equal lengths and the shapes imply equal areas. When discussing equal parts with cubes, ask if the parts are the same length. When discussing equal parts of the shapes, ask if they are the same size.

Error Intervention

If children have difficulty deciding whether two parts are the same size,

then let them cut out the shapes and fold them on the line.

If You Have More Time

Have children name things they might want to divide into equal parts.

Equal Parts

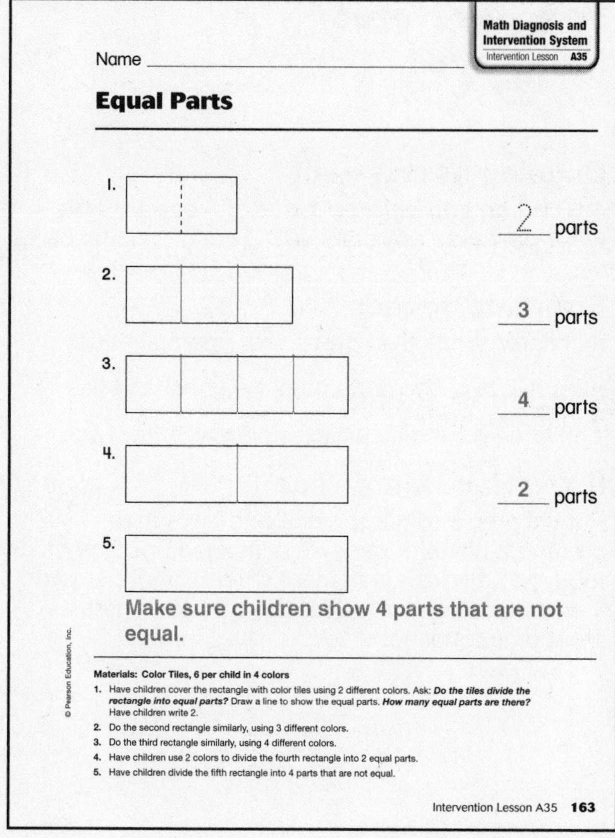

Math Diagnosis and Intervention System
Intervention Lesson A35

Name ______________________

Equal Parts

1. 2 parts
2. 3 parts
3. 4 parts
4. 2 parts
5. Make sure children show 4 parts that are not equal.

Materials: Color Tiles, 6 per child in 4 colors

1. Have children cover the rectangle with color tiles using 2 different colors. Ask: ***Do the tiles divide the rectangle into equal parts?*** Draw a line to show the equal parts. ***How many equal parts are there?*** Have children write 2.
2. Do the second rectangle similarly, using 3 different colors.
3. Do the third rectangle similarly, using 4 different colors.
4. Have children use 2 colors to divide the fourth rectangle into 2 equal parts.
5. Have children divide the fifth rectangle into 4 parts that are not equal.

Math Diagnosis and Intervention System
Intervention Lesson A35

Name ______________________

Equal Parts (continued)

Write the number of parts.
Circle **equal** or **not equal**.

6. 2 parts — (equal) / not equal
7. 4 parts — equal / (not equal)
8. 2 parts — equal / (not equal)
9. 3 parts — (equal) / not equal

Draw lines to show equal parts.

10. 4 parts
11. 2 parts

12. **Reasoning** Draw lines to show 3 different ways to make 2 equal parts.

Teacher Notes

Ongoing Assessment

Make sure children draw the lines where the color tiles meet.

Error Intervention

If children have trouble understanding equal parts,

then use A34: Halves.

If You Have More Time

Ask children to name items which are supposed to come cut into equal parts, like a loaf of bread or a pizza.

Understanding Fractions to Fourths

Math Diagnosis and Intervention System
Intervention Lesson A36

Name ____________________

Understanding Fractions to Fourths

1. 1 out of 2 equal parts
Make sure children color one of each shape

2. 3 out of 4 equal parts

3. 1 out of 3 equal parts

Materials: Crayons or markers
1. Have children color one of the equal parts in the first shape.
2. Ask: ***How many parts did you color?*** Have children write 1. Ask: ***How many equal parts in all?*** Have children write 2. Say: ***You colored 1 out of 2 equal parts or one half.***
3. Have children color 3 of the equal parts of the square. Then complete the problem similarly.
4. Have children color 1 of the equal parts of the rectangle. Then complete the problem similarly.

Intervention Lesson A36 **165**

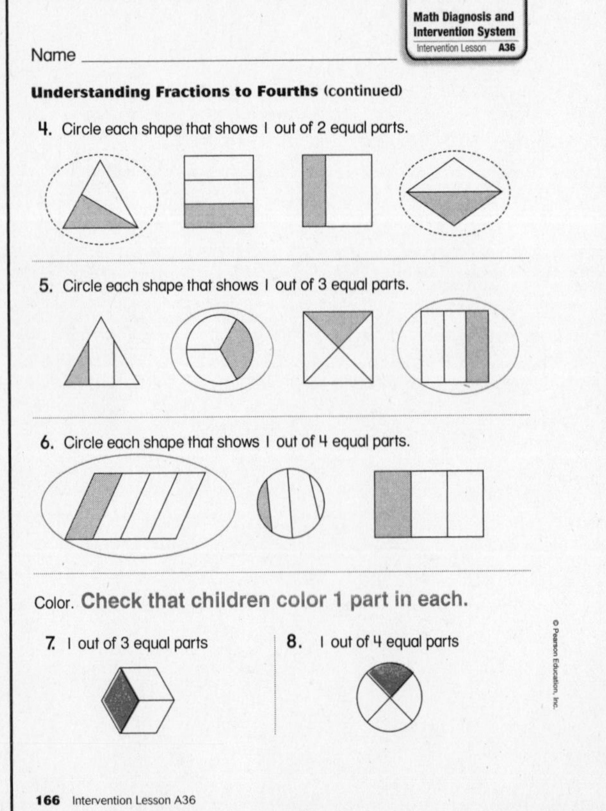
Math Diagnosis and Intervention System
Intervention Lesson A36

Name ____________________

Understanding Fractions to Fourths (continued)

4. Circle each shape that shows 1 out of 2 equal parts.

5. Circle each shape that shows 1 out of 3 equal parts.

6. Circle each shape that shows 1 out of 4 equal parts.

Color. Check that children color 1 part in each.

7. 1 out of 3 equal parts

8. 1 out of 4 equal parts

© Pearson Education, Inc.

166 Intervention Lesson A36

Teacher Notes

Ongoing Assessment

Ask: ***When you colored 1 out of 3 equal parts, what part was not colored?*** 2 out of 3 equal parts

Error Intervention

If children circle the figures with unequal parts,

then tell them the parts must be equal and use A35: Equal Parts.

If You Have More Time

Put children into groups of 4 and have them pretend a piece of paper is a lasagne or some other food they all like. Have them divide the paper into 4 equal parts and describe the part each gets as 1 out of 4 equal parts.

Fractions of a Set

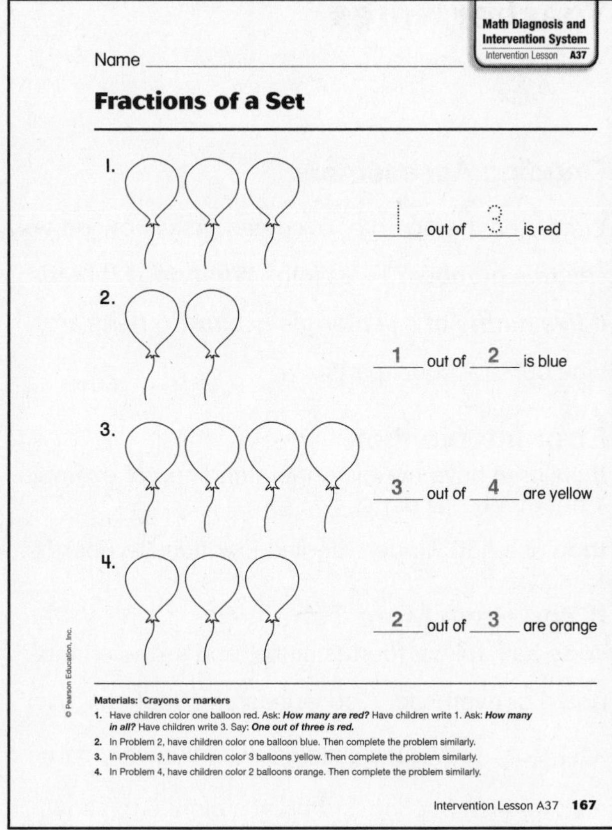

Math Diagnosis and Intervention System
Intervention Lesson A37

Name ______________________

Fractions of a Set

1. 1 out of 3 is red

2. 1 out of 2 is blue

3. 3 out of 4 are yellow

4. 2 out of 3 are orange

Materials: Crayons or markers

1. Have children color one balloon red. Ask: ***How many are red?*** Have children write 1. Ask: ***How many in all?*** Have children write 3. Say: ***One out of three is red.***
2. In Problem 2, have children color one balloon blue. Then complete the problem similarly.
3. In Problem 3, have children color 3 balloons yellow. Then complete the problem similarly.
4. In Problem 4, have children color 2 balloons orange. Then complete the problem similarly.

Intervention Lesson A37 **167**

Teacher Notes

Ongoing Assessment

To reinforce that the balloons are a set or group, ask: ***How many balloons are in the first group?*** 3 Say: ***One out of three describes a part of the group of balloons.*** Ask: ***What does 1 out 2 describe?*** It describes part of the second group of balloons.

Error Intervention

If children get confused counting the striped balls and then all the balls,

then use counters. Have the child place a counter on each striped ball, then move them away, then count them and write the number. Have the child put a counter on all the balls and repeat.

If You Have More Time

Have children name real-world situations which might have 1 out of 2, 3, or 4 different from the rest. For example, a group of children might have 1 out of 3 with blonde hair.

Math Diagnosis and Intervention System
Intervention Lesson A37

Name ______________________

Fractions of a Set (continued)

5. 1 out of 2 has stripes

6. 1 out of 4 has stripes

7. 2 out of 3 has stripes

8. 2 out of 4 has stripes

Color. **Check that children color the correct amount.**

9. 1 out of 3

10. 3 out of 4

11. **Reasoning** If 1 out of 4 is striped, then 3 out of 4 are not striped.

168 Intervention Lesson A37

Writing Fractions for Part of a Region

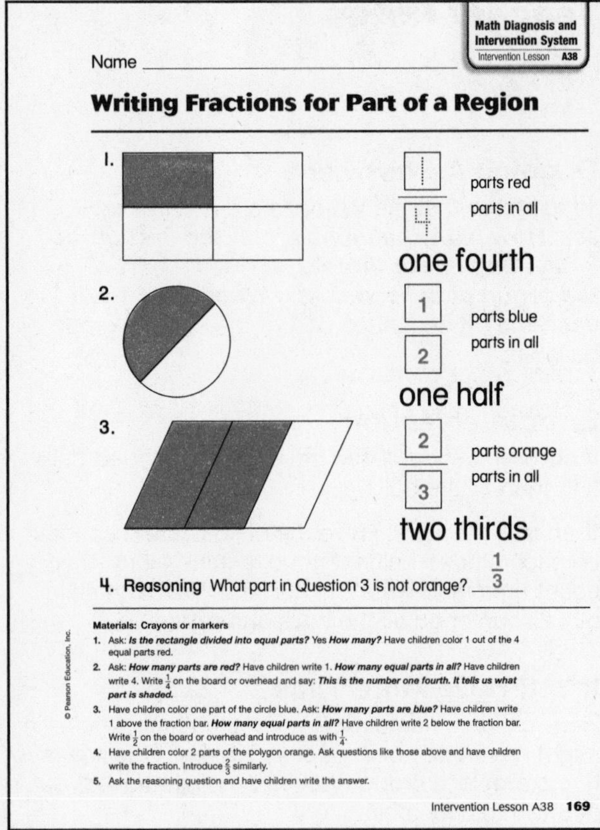

Math Diagnosis and Intervention System
Intervention Lesson A38

Name ______________________

Writing Fractions for Part of a Region

1. $\frac{1}{4}$ parts red / parts in all
one fourth

2. $\frac{1}{2}$ parts blue / parts in all
one half

3. $\frac{2}{3}$ parts orange / parts in all
two thirds

4. **Reasoning** What part in Question 3 is not orange? $\frac{1}{3}$

Materials: Crayons or markers

1. Ask: ***Is the rectangle divided into equal parts?*** Yes ***How many?*** Have children color 1 out of the 4 equal parts red.
2. Ask: ***How many parts are red?*** Have children write 1. ***How many equal parts in all?*** Have children write 4. Write $\frac{1}{4}$ on the board or overhead and say: ***This is the number one fourth. It tells us what part is shaded.***
3. Have children color one part of the circle blue. Ask: ***How many parts are blue?*** Have children write 1 above the fraction bar. ***How many equal parts in all?*** Have children write 2 below the fraction bar. Write $\frac{1}{2}$ on the board or overhead and introduce as with $\frac{1}{4}$.
4. Have children color 2 parts of the polygon orange. Ask questions like those above and have children write the fraction. Introduce $\frac{2}{3}$ similarly.
5. Ask the reasoning question and have children write the answer.

© Pearson Education, Inc.

Intervention Lesson A38 **169**

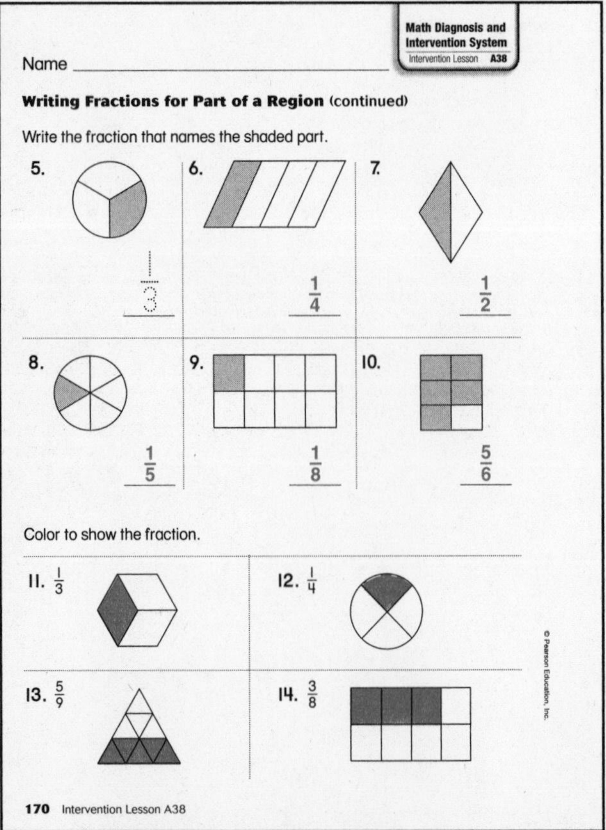

Math Diagnosis and Intervention System
Intervention Lesson A38

Name ______________________

Writing Fractions for Part of a Region (continued)

Write the fraction that names the shaded part.

5. $\frac{1}{3}$
6. $\frac{1}{4}$
7. $\frac{1}{2}$
8. $\frac{1}{5}$
9. $\frac{1}{8}$
10. $\frac{5}{6}$

Color to show the fraction.

11. $\frac{1}{3}$
12. $\frac{1}{4}$
13. $\frac{5}{9}$
14. $\frac{3}{8}$

© Pearson Education, Inc.

170 Intervention Lesson A38

Teacher Notes

Ongoing Assessment

Write $\frac{5}{9}$ on the board or overhead. Ask: ***How do you say this number?*** Five ninths ***What does it mean if five ninths of a rectangle is blue?*** 5 parts are blue out of 9 equal parts

Error Intervention

If children have trouble understanding, for example, 1 out of 4 equal parts,

then use A36: Understanding Fractions to Fourths.

If You Have More Time

Write half, thirds, fourths, fifths, and sixths on the board or overhead. Also write some fractions, such as $\frac{1}{2}, \frac{1}{4}, \frac{2}{3}, \frac{1}{5}, \frac{5}{6}$. Have children write the word name next to each fraction and draw a picture to show each.

Writing Fractions for Part of a Set

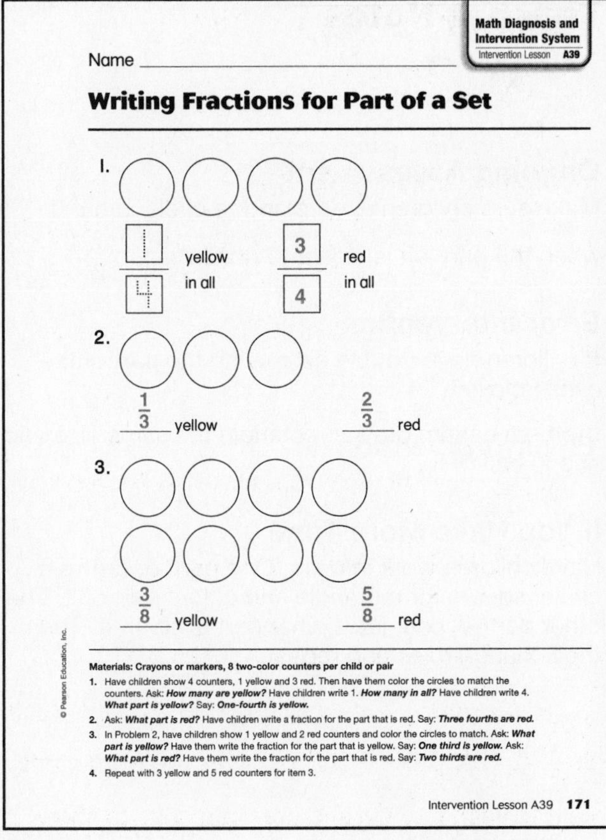

Math Diagnosis and Intervention System
Intervention Lesson A39

Name ____________________

Writing Fractions for Part of a Set

1. $\frac{1}{4}$ yellow in all $\frac{3}{4}$ red in all

2. $\frac{1}{3}$ yellow $\frac{2}{3}$ red

3. $\frac{3}{8}$ yellow $\frac{5}{8}$ red

Materials: Crayons or markers, 8 two-color counters per child or pair

1. Have children show 4 counters, 1 yellow and 3 red. Then have them color the circles to match the counters. Ask: ***How many are yellow?*** Have children write 1. ***How many in all?*** Have children write 4. ***What part is yellow?*** Say: ***One-fourth is yellow.***
2. Ask: ***What part is red?*** Have children write a fraction for the part that is red. Say: ***Three fourths are red.***
3. In Problem 2, have children show 1 yellow and 2 red counters and color the circles to match. Ask: ***What part is yellow?*** Have them write the fraction for the part that is yellow. Say: ***One third is yellow.*** Ask: ***What part is red?*** Have them write the fraction for the part that is red. Say: ***Two thirds are red.***
4. Repeat with 3 yellow and 5 red counters for item 3.

© Pearson Education, Inc.

Intervention Lesson A39 **171**

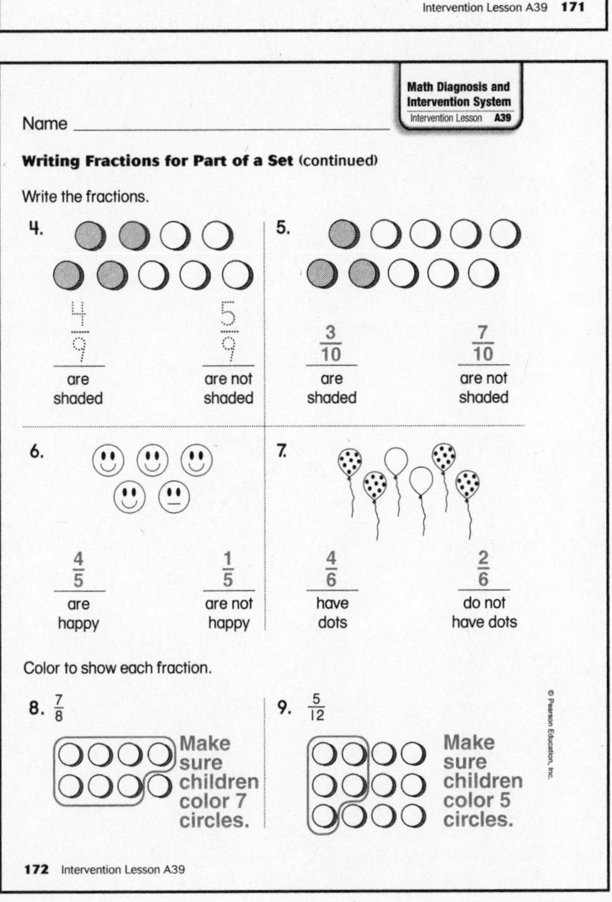

Math Diagnosis and Intervention System
Intervention Lesson A39

Name ____________________

Writing Fractions for Part of a Set (continued)

Write the fractions.

4. $\frac{4}{9}$ are shaded $\frac{5}{9}$ are not shaded

5. $\frac{3}{10}$ are shaded $\frac{7}{10}$ are not shaded

6. $\frac{4}{5}$ are happy $\frac{1}{5}$ are not happy

7. $\frac{4}{6}$ have dots $\frac{2}{6}$ do not have dots

Color to show each fraction.

8. $\frac{7}{8}$ Make sure children color 7 circles.

9. $\frac{5}{12}$ Make sure children color 5 circles.

© Pearson Education, Inc.

172 Intervention Lesson A39

Teacher Notes

Ongoing Assessment

Ask: ***What does it mean that $\frac{4}{9}$ of a group of balloons have happy faces?*** There are 4 balloons with happy faces out of 9 balloons in all.

Error Intervention

If children have difficulty describing parts of a set, **then** use A37: Fractions of a Set.

If You Have More Time

Have children make sailor-type hats out of construction paper in two different colors. Have 6 children come to the front of the room wearing their hats. Have the rest of the class write a fraction for what part has each color. Repeat with different numbers of children.

Estimating Fractions

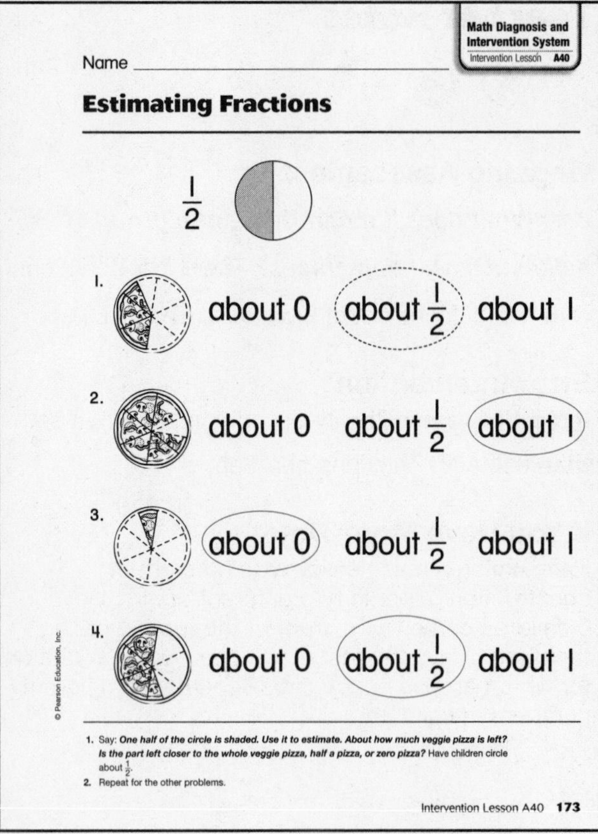

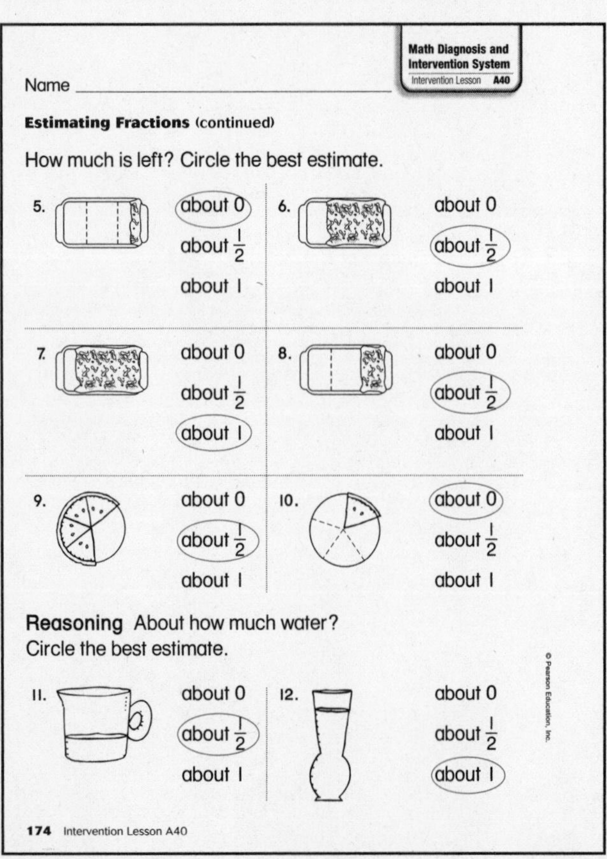

Teacher Notes

Ongoing Assessment

Make sure children understand to circle about 0 when the part left is closer to none than to $\frac{1}{2}$.

Error Intervention

If children have trouble estimating the part of the casserole left,

then have them draw a rectangle the same size and shade half of it.

If You Have More Time

Have children work in pairs. One partner draws a circle, square, or rectangle and colors part of it. The other partner estimates what part is colored. Then they change roles and repeat.

Understanding One as a Fraction

Math Diagnosis and Intervention System
Intervention Lesson **A41**

Math Diagnosis and Intervention System
Intervention Lesson A41

Name ____________________

Understanding One as a Fraction

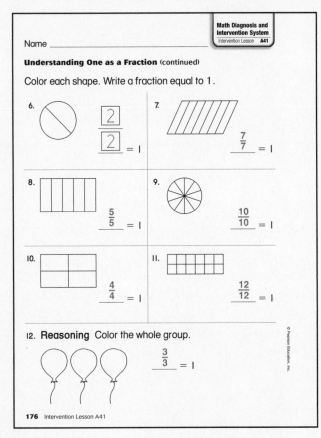

1. 4 parts red / 4 parts in all $\frac{4}{4}$ = 1

2. 3 parts blue / 3 parts in all $\frac{3}{3}$ = 1

3. 6 parts orange / 6 parts in all $\frac{6}{6}$ = 1

4. 8 parts orange / 8 parts in all $\frac{8}{8}$ = 1

5. **Reasoning** $\frac{9}{9}$ = 1

Materials: Crayons or markers

1. Have children color all 4 parts of the circle red. Ask: ***How many parts are red?*** Have children write 4. ***How many parts in all?*** Have children write 4 again. ***What fraction of the circle is red?*** Say: ***Four fourths are red.***
2. Ask: ***Is the whole circle red?*** Say: ***So, four fourths equal one whole.*** Have children write $\frac{4}{4}$.
3. Have children color all 3 parts of the square blue. Ask questions like those above.
4. Have children finish the other problems, coloring all 6 parts of the square orange and all 8 parts of the octagon yellow.

Math Diagnosis and Intervention System
Intervention Lesson A41

Name ____________________

Understanding One as a Fraction (continued)

Color each shape. Write a fraction equal to 1.

6. $\frac{2}{2}$ = 1

7. $\frac{7}{7}$ = 1

8. $\frac{5}{5}$ = 1

9. $\frac{10}{10}$ = 1

10. $\frac{4}{4}$ = 1

11. $\frac{12}{12}$ = 1

12. **Reasoning** Color the whole group.

$\frac{3}{3}$ = 1

Teacher Notes

Ongoing Assessment

Ask: ***If a pizza is divided into 8 equal slices, how many slices would it take to equal the whole pizza?*** 8 ***What fraction of the pizza equals a whole?*** $\frac{8}{8}$

Error Intervention

If children have difficulty writing fractions,

then use A38: Writing Fractions for Part of a Region.

If You Have More Time

Have children name things that come divided into equal parts. State how many equal parts it has and then say a fraction for the whole.

Equal Parts of a Whole

Name ____________________

Equal Parts of a Whole

Materials rectangular sheets of paper, 3 for each student; crayons or markers

1. Fold a sheet of paper so the two shorter edges are on top of each other, as shown at the right.

fold →

2. Open up the piece of paper. Draw a line down the fold. Color each part a different color.

The table below shows special names for the equal parts. All parts must be **equal** before you can use these special names.

3. Are the parts you colored equal in size? yes
4. How many equal parts are there? 2
5. What is the name for the parts you colored? halves

Number of Equal Parts	Name of Equal Parts
2	halves
3	thirds
4	fourths
5	fifths
6	sixths
8	eighths
10	tenths
12	twelfths

6. Fold another sheet of paper like above. Then fold it again so that it makes a long slender rectangle as shown below.
7. Open up the piece of paper. Draw lines down the folds. Color each part a different color.
8. Are the parts you colored equal in size? yes
9. How many equal parts are there? 4
10. What is the name for the parts you colored? fourths

New fold → ← Old fold

11. Fold another sheet of paper into 3 parts that are *not* equal. Open it and draw lines down the folds. In the space below, draw your rectangle and color each part a different color.

Check that students draw unequal parts.

Name ____________________

Equal Parts of a Whole (continued)

Tell if each shows parts that are equal or parts that are not equal. If the parts are equal, name them.

12. equal, fourths
13. not equal
14. equal, thirds
15. equal, eighths
16. equal, twelfths
17. not equal
18. not equal
19. equal, fifths
20. equal, halves
21. not equal
22. equal, sixths
23. not equal

24. **Reasoning** If 5 children want to equally share a large pizza and each gets 2 pieces, will they need to cut the pizza into fifths, eighths, or tenths? tenths

Teacher Notes

Ongoing Assessment

Ask: ***Looking at the names for shapes divided into 4, 5, 6, 8, 10, and 12 equal parts, what might be the name of a shape divided into seven equal parts?*** sevenths

Error Intervention

If children have trouble understanding the concept of equal parts,

then use A35: Equal parts.

If You Have More Time

Have students fold other rectangular sheets of paper and circular pieces of paper to find and name other equal parts.

Parts of a Region

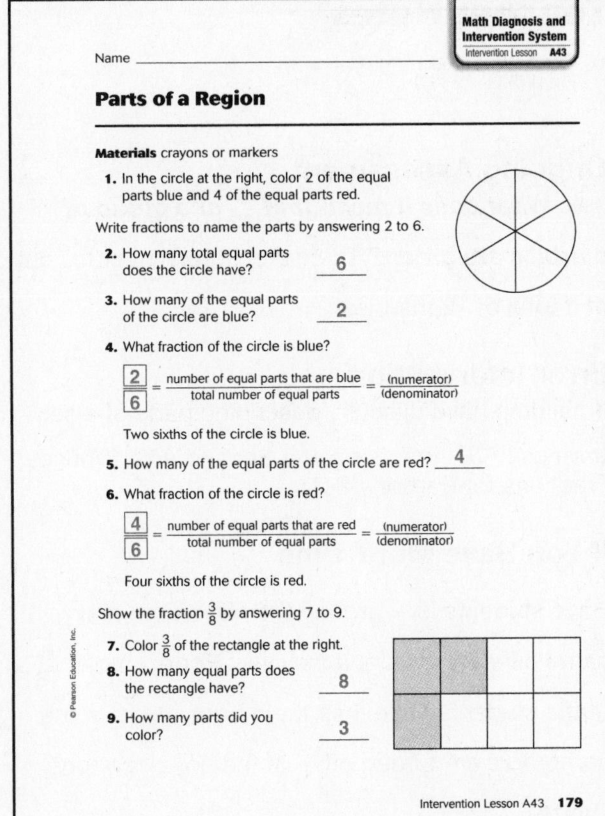

Math Diagnosis and Intervention System
Intervention Lesson A43

Name ______________________

Parts of a Region

Materials crayons or markers

1. In the circle at the right, color 2 of the equal parts blue and 4 of the equal parts red.

Write fractions to name the parts by answering 2 to 6.

2. How many total equal parts does the circle have? 6
3. How many of the equal parts of the circle are blue? 2
4. What fraction of the circle is blue?

$\frac{2}{6} = \frac{\text{number of equal parts that are blue}}{\text{total number of equal parts}} = \frac{\text{(numerator)}}{\text{(denominator)}}$

Two sixths of the circle is blue.

5. How many of the equal parts of the circle are red? 4
6. What fraction of the circle is red?

$\frac{4}{6} = \frac{\text{number of equal parts that are red}}{\text{total number of equal parts}} = \frac{\text{(numerator)}}{\text{(denominator)}}$

Four sixths of the circle is red.

Show the fraction $\frac{3}{8}$ by answering 7 to 9.

7. Color $\frac{3}{8}$ of the rectangle at the right.
8. How many equal parts does the rectangle have? 8
9. How many parts did you color? 3

© Pearson Education, Inc.

Intervention Lesson A43 **179**

Teacher Notes

Ongoing Assessment

Ask: ***Janet said she ate $\frac{4}{4}$ of an orange. Explain why Janet could have said she ate the whole orange.*** Sample answer: The orange would be cut in 4 pieces and she ate 4 pieces, so she ate the whole thing.

Error Intervention

If children have trouble writing fractions for parts of a region,

then use A36: Understanding Fractions to Fourths and A38: Writing Fractions for Part of a Region.

If You Have More Time

Have students design a rectangular flag (or rug, placemat, etc.) that is divided into equal parts. Have them color their flag and then on the back write the fractional parts of each color.

Math Diagnosis and Intervention System
Intervention Lesson A43

Name ______________________

Parts of a Region (continued)

Write the fraction for the shaded part of each region.

10. $\frac{2}{3}$
11. $\frac{1}{4}$
12. $\frac{4}{5}$
13. $\frac{1}{2}$
14. $\frac{2}{8}$
15. $\frac{2}{5}$
16. $\frac{1}{3}$
17. $\frac{3}{5}$
18. $\frac{5}{8}$

Color to show each fraction.

19. $\frac{3}{4}$
20. $\frac{5}{6}$
21. $\frac{7}{10}$

22. **Math Reasoning** Draw a picture to show $\frac{1}{3}$. Then divide each of the parts in half. What fraction of the parts does the $\frac{1}{3}$ represent now? **Check students' drawings.** $\frac{2}{6}$
23. Ben divided a pie into 8 equal pieces and ate 3 of them. How much of the pie remains? $\frac{5}{8}$

180 Intervention Lesson A43

Parts of a Set

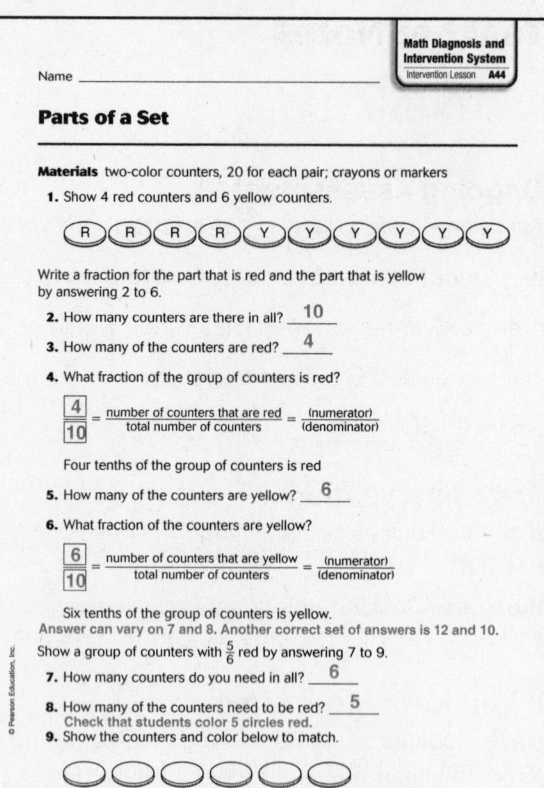

Math Diagnosis and Intervention System
Intervention Lesson A44

Name ______________________

Parts of a Set

Materials two-color counters, 20 for each pair; crayons or markers

1. Show 4 red counters and 6 yellow counters.

R R R R Y Y Y Y Y Y

Write a fraction for the part that is red and the part that is yellow by answering 2 to 6.

2. How many counters are there in all? 10
3. How many of the counters are red? 4
4. What fraction of the group of counters is red?

$\frac{4}{10} = \frac{\text{number of counters that are red}}{\text{total number of counters}} = \frac{\text{(numerator)}}{\text{(denominator)}}$

Four tenths of the group of counters is red

5. How many of the counters are yellow? 6
6. What fraction of the counters are yellow?

$\frac{6}{10} = \frac{\text{number of counters that are yellow}}{\text{total number of counters}} = \frac{\text{(numerator)}}{\text{(denominator)}}$

Six tenths of the group of counters is yellow.

Answer can vary on 7 and 8. Another correct set of answers is 12 and 10.

Show a group of counters with $\frac{5}{6}$ red by answering 7 to 9.

7. How many counters do you need in all? 6
8. How many of the counters need to be red? 5
   Check that students color 5 circles red.
9. Show the counters and color below to match.

© Pearson Education, Inc.

Intervention Lesson A44 **181**

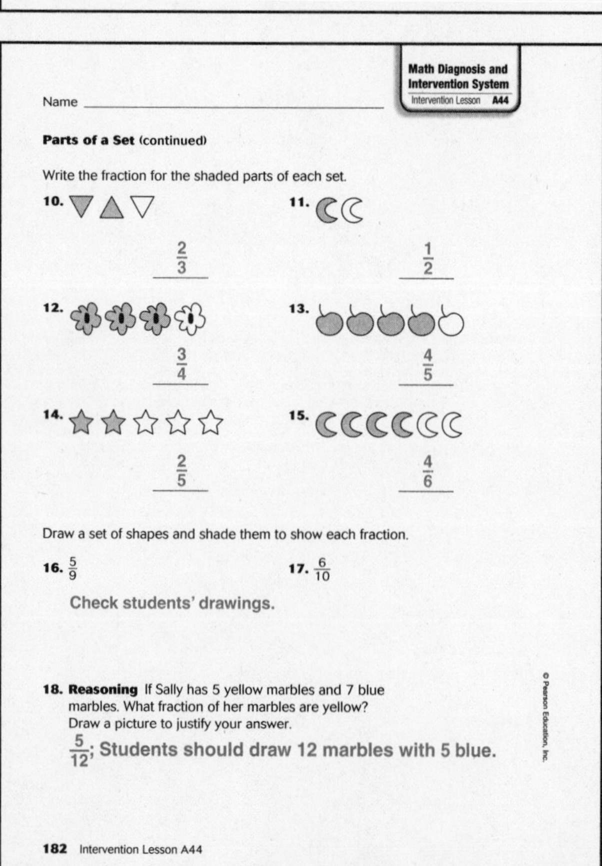

Math Diagnosis and Intervention System
Intervention Lesson A44

Name ______________________

Parts of a Set (continued)

Write the fraction for the shaded parts of each set.

10. $\frac{2}{3}$
11. $\frac{1}{2}$
12. $\frac{3}{4}$
13. $\frac{4}{5}$
14. $\frac{2}{5}$
15. $\frac{4}{6}$

Draw a set of shapes and shade them to show each fraction.

16. $\frac{5}{9}$
17. $\frac{6}{10}$

Check students' drawings.

18. **Reasoning** If Sally has 5 yellow marbles and 7 blue marbles. What fraction of her marbles are yellow? Draw a picture to justify your answer.

$\frac{5}{12}$; Students should draw 12 marbles with 5 blue.

© Pearson Education, Inc.

182 Intervention Lesson A44

Teacher Notes

Ongoing Assessment

Ask: ***What does it mean that $\frac{3}{12}$ of a group of marbles are green?*** There are 3 green marbles out of a total of 12 marbles.

Error Intervention

If children have difficulty describing parts of a set, **then** use A37: Fractions of a Set and A39: Writing Fractions for Part of a Set.

If You Have More Time

Have students look around the classroom and name different fractions they see. For example: $\frac{6}{18}$ of the students have their math book out; $\frac{2}{5}$ of the computers are turned off; $\frac{5}{9}$ of the boys have on shorts.

Fractions and Length

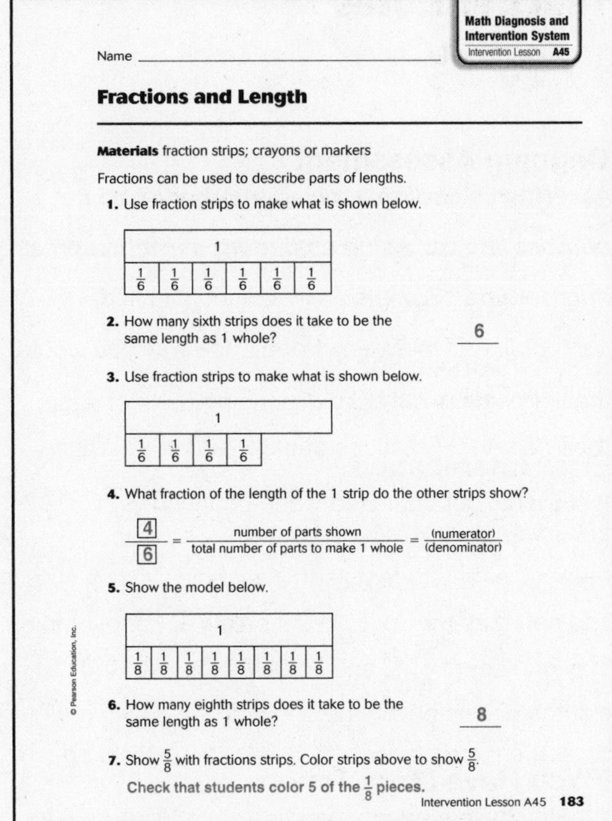

Name ____________________

Fractions and Length

Materials fraction strips; crayons or markers

Fractions can be used to describe parts of lengths.

1. Use fraction strips to make what is shown below.

1
$\frac{1}{6}$ $\frac{1}{6}$ $\frac{1}{6}$ $\frac{1}{6}$ $\frac{1}{6}$ $\frac{1}{6}$

2. How many sixth strips does it take to be the same length as 1 whole? 6

3. Use fraction strips to make what is shown below.

1
$\frac{1}{6}$ $\frac{1}{6}$ $\frac{1}{6}$ $\frac{1}{6}$

4. What fraction of the length of the 1 strip do the other strips show?

$\frac{4}{6} = \frac{\text{number of parts shown}}{\text{total number of parts to make 1 whole}} = \frac{\text{(numerator)}}{\text{(denominator)}}$

5. Show the model below.

1
$\frac{1}{8}$ $\frac{1}{8}$ $\frac{1}{8}$ $\frac{1}{8}$ $\frac{1}{8}$ $\frac{1}{8}$ $\frac{1}{8}$ $\frac{1}{8}$

6. How many eighth strips does it take to be the same length as 1 whole? 8

7. Show $\frac{5}{8}$ with fractions strips. Color strips above to show $\frac{5}{8}$.
Check that students color 5 of the $\frac{1}{8}$ pieces.

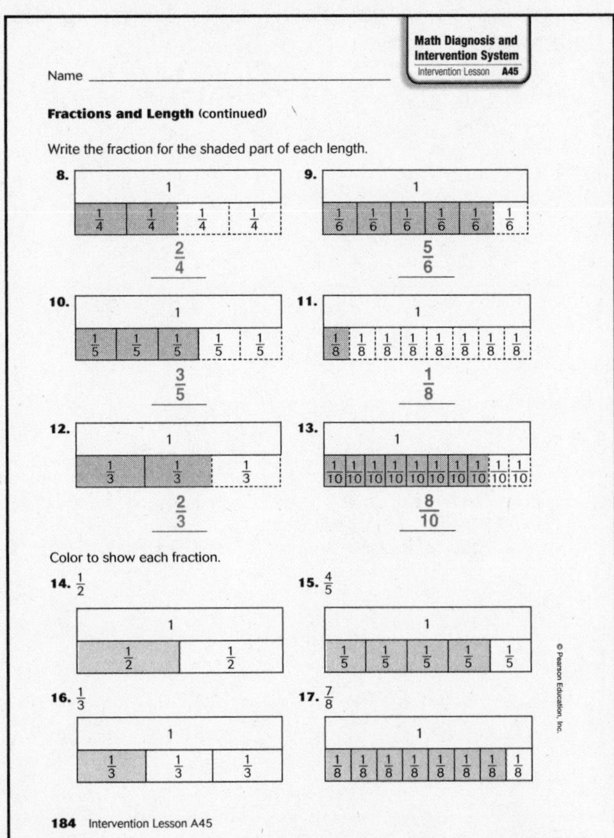

Name ____________________

Fractions and Length (continued)

Write the fraction for the shaded part of each length.

8. 1; $\frac{1}{4}$ $\frac{1}{4}$ $\frac{1}{4}$ $\frac{1}{4}$ — $\frac{2}{4}$

9. 1; $\frac{1}{6}$ $\frac{1}{6}$ $\frac{1}{6}$ $\frac{1}{6}$ $\frac{1}{6}$ $\frac{1}{6}$ — $\frac{5}{6}$

10. 1; $\frac{1}{5}$ $\frac{1}{5}$ $\frac{1}{5}$ $\frac{1}{5}$ $\frac{1}{5}$ — $\frac{3}{5}$

11. 1; $\frac{1}{8}$ $\frac{1}{8}$ $\frac{1}{8}$ $\frac{1}{8}$ $\frac{1}{8}$ $\frac{1}{8}$ $\frac{1}{8}$ $\frac{1}{8}$ — $\frac{1}{8}$

12. 1; $\frac{1}{3}$ $\frac{1}{3}$ $\frac{1}{3}$ — $\frac{2}{3}$

13. 1; $\frac{1}{10}$ $\frac{1}{10}$ $\frac{1}{10}$ $\frac{1}{10}$ $\frac{1}{10}$ $\frac{1}{10}$ $\frac{1}{10}$ $\frac{1}{10}$ $\frac{1}{10}$ $\frac{1}{10}$ — $\frac{8}{10}$

Color to show each fraction.

14. $\frac{1}{2}$ — 1; $\frac{1}{2}$ $\frac{1}{2}$

15. $\frac{4}{5}$ — 1; $\frac{1}{5}$ $\frac{1}{5}$ $\frac{1}{5}$ $\frac{1}{5}$ $\frac{1}{5}$

16. $\frac{1}{3}$ — 1; $\frac{1}{3}$ $\frac{1}{3}$ $\frac{1}{3}$

17. $\frac{7}{8}$ — 1; $\frac{1}{8}$ $\frac{1}{8}$ $\frac{1}{8}$ $\frac{1}{8}$ $\frac{1}{8}$ $\frac{1}{8}$ $\frac{1}{8}$ $\frac{1}{8}$

Teacher Notes

Ongoing Assessment

Ask: ***If Nancy has walked $\frac{7}{10}$ of the length of the trail, how much more of the trail does she have left to walk?*** $\frac{3}{10}$ of the trail

Error Intervention

If students have trouble identifying the denominator of the fraction,

then encourage them to use fraction strips to equal the length of the 1 strip to see how many total number of parts it takes to make 1 whole strip.

If You Have More Time

Have children name real-world situations which might use fractions of lengths. For example, fractions might be used to name the length of a pencil or the distance around a track in miles.

Fractions on the Number Line

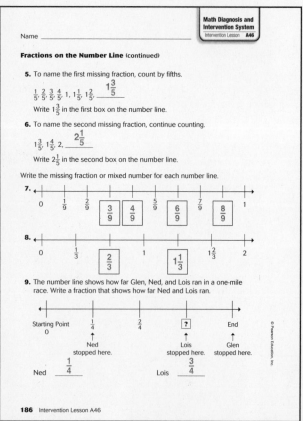

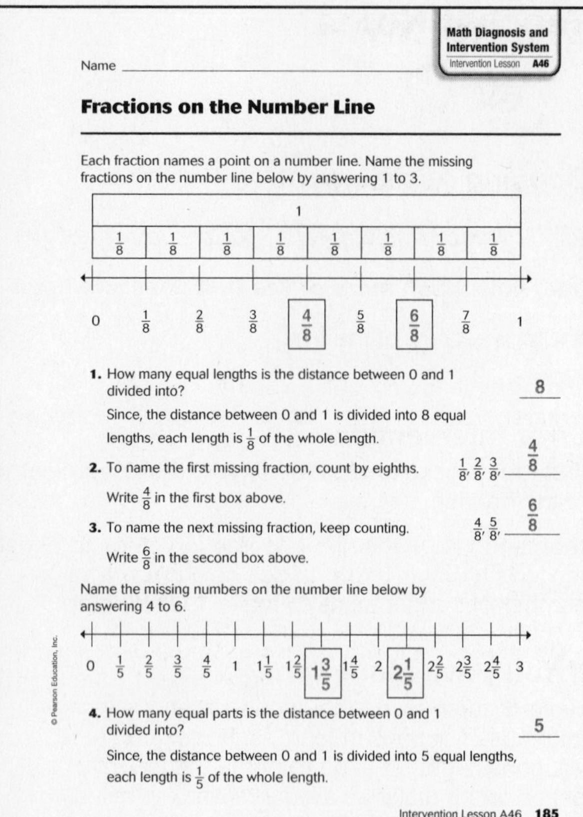

Math Diagnosis and Intervention System
Intervention Lesson A46

Name ______________________

Fractions on the Number Line

Each fraction names a point on a number line. Name the missing fractions on the number line below by answering 1 to 3.

1. How many equal lengths is the distance between 0 and 1 divided into? 8

   Since, the distance between 0 and 1 is divided into 8 equal lengths, each length is $\frac{1}{8}$ of the whole length.

2. To name the first missing fraction, count by eighths. $\frac{1}{8}, \frac{2}{8}, \frac{3}{8},$ $\frac{4}{8}$

   Write $\frac{4}{8}$ in the first box above.

3. To name the next missing fraction, keep counting. $\frac{4}{8}, \frac{5}{8},$ $\frac{6}{8}$

   Write $\frac{6}{8}$ in the second box above.

Name the missing numbers on the number line below by answering 4 to 6.

4. How many equal parts is the distance between 0 and 1 divided into? 5

   Since, the distance between 0 and 1 is divided into 5 equal lengths, each length is $\frac{1}{5}$ of the whole length.

Intervention Lesson A46 185

Math Diagnosis and Intervention System
Intervention Lesson A46

Name ______________________

Fractions on the Number Line (continued)

5. To name the first missing fraction, count by fifths.

   $\frac{1}{5}, \frac{2}{5}, \frac{3}{5}, \frac{4}{5}, 1, 1\frac{1}{5}, 1\frac{2}{5},$ $1\frac{3}{5}$

   Write $1\frac{3}{5}$ in the first box on the number line.

6. To name the second missing fraction, continue counting.

   $1\frac{3}{5}, 1\frac{4}{5}, 2,$ $2\frac{1}{5}$

   Write $2\frac{1}{5}$ in the second box on the number line.

Write the missing fraction or mixed number for each number line.

7. 0 $\frac{1}{9}$ $\frac{2}{9}$ $\frac{3}{9}$ $\frac{4}{9}$ $\frac{5}{9}$ $\frac{6}{9}$ $\frac{7}{9}$ $\frac{8}{9}$ 1

8. 0 $\frac{1}{3}$ $\frac{2}{3}$ 1 $1\frac{1}{3}$ $1\frac{2}{3}$ 2

9. The number line shows how far Glen, Ned, and Lois ran in a one-mile race. Write a fraction that shows how far Ned and Lois ran.

   Starting Point 0 — $\frac{1}{4}$ (Ned stopped here.) — $\frac{2}{4}$ — ? (Lois stopped here.) — End (Glen stopped here.)

   Ned $\frac{1}{4}$ Lois $\frac{3}{4}$

186 Intervention Lesson A46

Teacher Notes

Ongoing Assessment

Ask: ***How is finding a mixed number on a number line the same as finding a fraction on a number line?*** Sample answer: Find a mixed number like $1\frac{2}{5}$ between 1 and 2 the way you would find $\frac{2}{5}$ between 0 and 1.

Error Intervention

If students get confused when counting with fractions,

then have the students show a whole fraction strip and count as they put pieces below it. For example, they can count $\frac{1}{8}$, $\frac{2}{8}$, and so on as they put the eighths pieces below the one strip.

If You Have More Time

In pairs, have students practice counting from 0 to 5 using halves, thirds, fourths, fifths, sixths, eighths, tenths, and twelfths.

Using Models to Compare Fractions

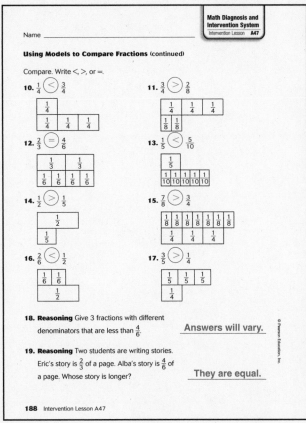

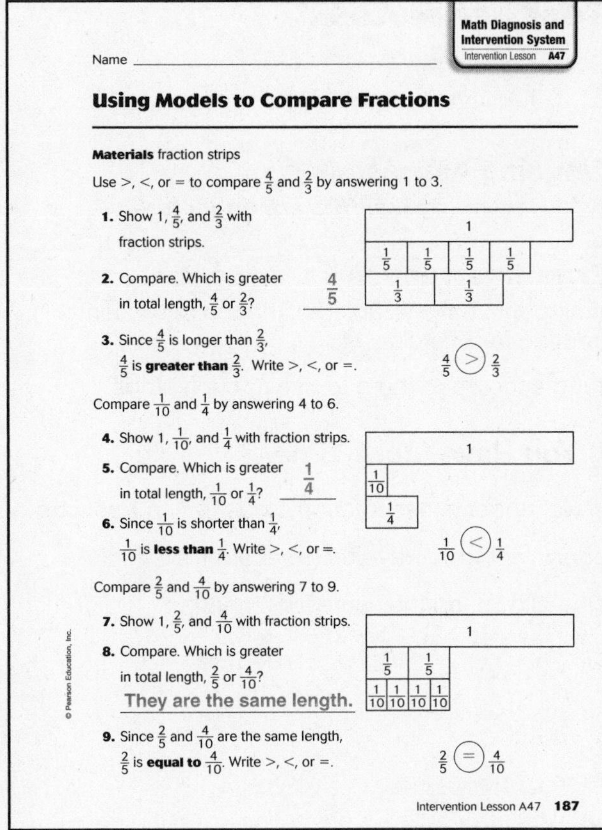

Math Diagnosis and Intervention System
Intervention Lesson A47

Name ____________________

Using Models to Compare Fractions

Materials fraction strips

Use >, <, or = to compare $\frac{4}{5}$ and $\frac{2}{3}$ by answering 1 to 3.

1. Show 1, $\frac{4}{5}$, and $\frac{2}{3}$ with fraction strips.
2. Compare. Which is greater in total length, $\frac{4}{5}$ or $\frac{2}{3}$? $\frac{4}{5}$
3. Since $\frac{4}{5}$ is longer than $\frac{2}{3}$, $\frac{4}{5}$ is **greater than** $\frac{2}{3}$. Write >, <, or =. $\frac{4}{5}$ (>) $\frac{2}{3}$

Compare $\frac{1}{10}$ and $\frac{1}{4}$ by answering 4 to 6.

4. Show 1, $\frac{1}{10}$, and $\frac{1}{4}$ with fraction strips.
5. Compare. Which is greater in total length, $\frac{1}{10}$ or $\frac{1}{4}$? $\frac{1}{4}$
6. Since $\frac{1}{10}$ is shorter than $\frac{1}{4}$, $\frac{1}{10}$ is **less than** $\frac{1}{4}$. Write >, <, or =. $\frac{1}{10}$ (<) $\frac{1}{4}$

Compare $\frac{2}{5}$ and $\frac{4}{10}$ by answering 7 to 9.

7. Show 1, $\frac{2}{5}$, and $\frac{4}{10}$ with fraction strips.
8. Compare. Which is greater in total length, $\frac{2}{5}$ or $\frac{4}{10}$? They are the same length.
9. Since $\frac{2}{5}$ and $\frac{4}{10}$ are the same length, $\frac{2}{5}$ is **equal to** $\frac{4}{10}$. Write >, <, or =. $\frac{2}{5}$ (=) $\frac{4}{10}$

Intervention Lesson A47 **187**

Math Diagnosis and Intervention System
Intervention Lesson A47

Name ____________________

Using Models to Compare Fractions (continued)

Compare. Write <, >, or =.

10. $\frac{1}{4}$ (<) $\frac{3}{4}$
11. $\frac{3}{4}$ (>) $\frac{2}{8}$
12. $\frac{2}{3}$ (=) $\frac{4}{6}$
13. $\frac{1}{5}$ (<) $\frac{5}{10}$
14. $\frac{1}{2}$ (>) $\frac{1}{5}$
15. $\frac{7}{8}$ (>) $\frac{3}{4}$
16. $\frac{2}{6}$ (<) $\frac{1}{2}$
17. $\frac{3}{5}$ (>) $\frac{1}{4}$
18. **Reasoning** Give 3 fractions with different denominators that are less than $\frac{4}{6}$. Answers will vary.
19. **Reasoning** Two students are writing stories. Eric's story is $\frac{2}{3}$ of a page. Alba's story is $\frac{4}{6}$ of a page. Whose story is longer? They are equal.

188 Intervention Lesson A47

Teacher Notes

Ongoing Assessment

Make sure children can translate simple number sentences such as 7 < 8, 4 > 2, and 6 = 6 into words.

Error Intervention

If children have difficulty with the concepts of greater than and less than, or with the symbols,

then use A27: Using >, <, and = to Compare Numbers.

If You Have More Time

Have students pretend they are each painting a board. Have the students say how much they have stained. Then use fraction strips to show and compare who has stained more. Have each student write the comparison on paper.

Using Models to Find Equivalent Fractions

Math Diagnosis and Intervention System
Intervention Lesson **A48**

Math Diagnosis and Intervention System
Intervention Lesson A48

Name ______________________

Using Models to Find Equivalent Fractions

Materials fraction strips

Find a fraction equivalent to $\frac{3}{4}$ by answering 1 to 3.

1. Show a 1 and $\frac{3}{4}$ with fraction strips.
2. How many $\frac{1}{8}$ strips does it take to equal $\frac{3}{4}$? 6

$\frac{3}{4} = \frac{6}{8}$

3. So, $\frac{3}{4}$ is equal to six $\frac{1}{8}$ strips.

Find the missing number in $\frac{1}{2} = \frac{?}{10}$, by answering 4 to 7.

The denominators of the fractions tell which fraction strips to use.

4. Show 1 and $\frac{1}{2}$ with fraction strips.
5. What is the denominator of the second fraction? 10
6. Since the denominator of the second fraction is 10, find the number of $\frac{1}{10}$ strips equal to $\frac{1}{2}$. 5
7. So, $\frac{1}{2}$ is equal to five $\frac{1}{10}$ strips.

$\frac{1}{2} = \frac{5}{10}$

Math Diagnosis and Intervention System
Intervention Lesson A48

Name ______________________

Using Models to Find Equivalent Fractions (continued)

Complete each number sentence.

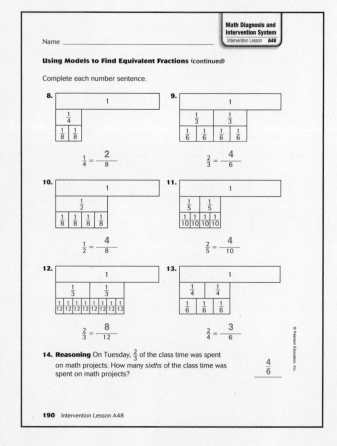

8. $\frac{1}{4} = \frac{2}{8}$
9. $\frac{2}{3} = \frac{4}{6}$
10. $\frac{1}{2} = \frac{4}{8}$
11. $\frac{2}{5} = \frac{4}{10}$
12. $\frac{2}{3} = \frac{8}{12}$
13. $\frac{2}{4} = \frac{3}{6}$

14. **Reasoning** On Tuesday, $\frac{2}{3}$ of the class time was spent on math projects. How many *sixths* of the class time was spent on math projects? $\frac{4}{6}$

Teacher Notes

Ongoing Assessment

Ask: ***How many twelfths are equal to $\frac{1}{3}$?*** $\frac{4}{12}$

Error Intervention

If students have trouble finding the equivalent fraction for Exercise 14,

then encourage them to use fraction strips.

If You Have More Time

Have students use fraction strips to find fractions equivalent to $\frac{1}{2}$. Have them record their findings. If time allows, do the same for $\frac{1}{4}$ and $\frac{3}{4}$.

Equivalent Fractions

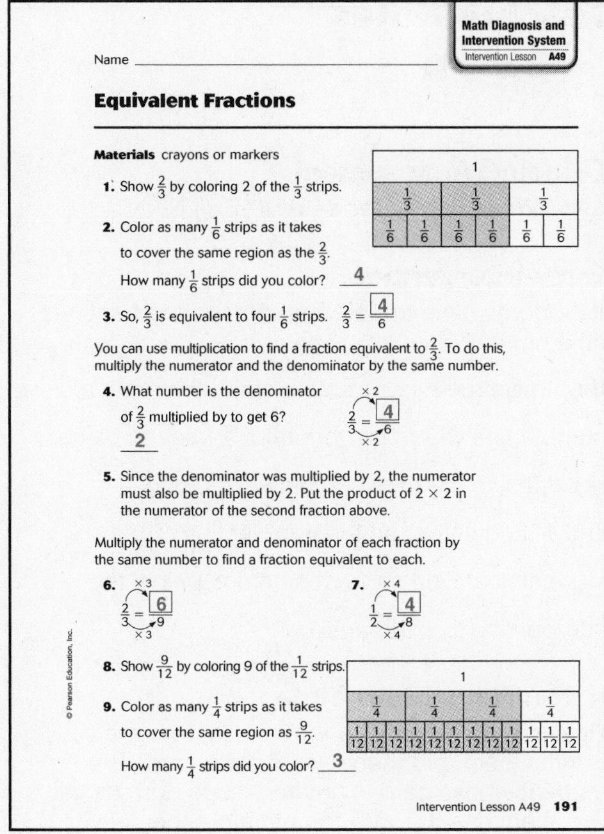

Math Diagnosis and Intervention System
Intervention Lesson A49

Name ____________________

Equivalent Fractions

Materials crayons or markers

1					
$\frac{1}{3}$		$\frac{1}{3}$		$\frac{1}{3}$	
$\frac{1}{6}$	$\frac{1}{6}$	$\frac{1}{6}$	$\frac{1}{6}$	$\frac{1}{6}$	$\frac{1}{6}$

1. Show $\frac{2}{3}$ by coloring 2 of the $\frac{1}{3}$ strips.

2. Color as many $\frac{1}{6}$ strips as it takes to cover the same region as the $\frac{2}{3}$.

How many $\frac{1}{6}$ strips did you color? 4

3. So, $\frac{2}{3}$ is equivalent to four $\frac{1}{6}$ strips. $\frac{2}{3} = \frac{4}{6}$

You can use multiplication to find a fraction equivalent to $\frac{2}{3}$. To do this, multiply the numerator and the denominator by the same number.

4. What number is the denominator of $\frac{2}{3}$ multiplied by to get 6? 2

$\times 2$: $\frac{2}{3} = \frac{4}{6}$

5. Since the denominator was multiplied by 2, the numerator must also be multiplied by 2. Put the product of 2×2 in the numerator of the second fraction above.

Multiply the numerator and denominator of each fraction by the same number to find a fraction equivalent to each.

6. $\times 3$: $\frac{2}{3} = \frac{6}{9}$

7. $\times 4$: $\frac{1}{2} = \frac{4}{8}$

1											
$\frac{1}{4}$			$\frac{1}{4}$			$\frac{1}{4}$			$\frac{1}{4}$		
$\frac{1}{12}$	$\frac{1}{12}$	$\frac{1}{12}$	$\frac{1}{12}$	$\frac{1}{12}$	$\frac{1}{12}$	$\frac{1}{12}$	$\frac{1}{12}$	$\frac{1}{12}$	$\frac{1}{12}$	$\frac{1}{12}$	$\frac{1}{12}$

8. Show $\frac{9}{12}$ by coloring 9 of the $\frac{1}{12}$ strips.

9. Color as many $\frac{1}{4}$ strips as it takes to cover the same region as $\frac{9}{12}$.

How many $\frac{1}{4}$ strips did you color? 3

© Pearson Education, Inc.

Intervention Lesson A49 **191**

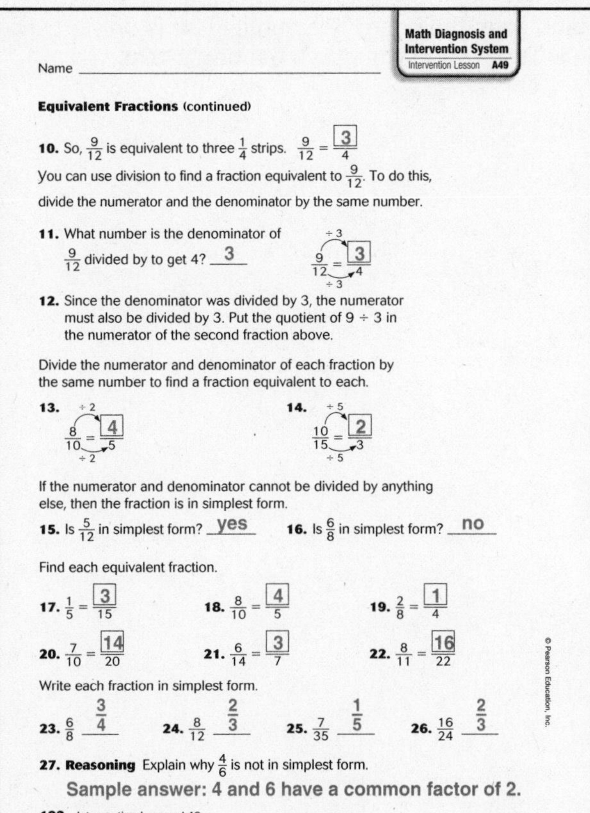

Math Diagnosis and Intervention System
Intervention Lesson A49

Name ____________________

Equivalent Fractions (continued)

10. So, $\frac{9}{12}$ is equivalent to three $\frac{1}{4}$ strips. $\frac{9}{12} = \frac{3}{4}$

You can use division to find a fraction equivalent to $\frac{9}{12}$. To do this, divide the numerator and the denominator by the same number.

11. What number is the denominator of $\frac{9}{12}$ divided by to get 4? 3

$\div 3$: $\frac{9}{12} = \frac{3}{4}$

12. Since the denominator was divided by 3, the numerator must also be divided by 3. Put the quotient of $9 \div 3$ in the numerator of the second fraction above.

Divide the numerator and denominator of each fraction by the same number to find a fraction equivalent to each.

13. $\div 2$: $\frac{8}{10} = \frac{4}{5}$

14. $\div 5$: $\frac{10}{15} = \frac{2}{3}$

If the numerator and denominator cannot be divided by anything else, then the fraction is in simplest form.

15. Is $\frac{5}{12}$ in simplest form? yes

16. Is $\frac{6}{8}$ in simplest form? no

Find each equivalent fraction.

17. $\frac{1}{5} = \frac{3}{15}$

18. $\frac{8}{10} = \frac{4}{5}$

19. $\frac{2}{8} = \frac{1}{4}$

20. $\frac{7}{10} = \frac{14}{20}$

21. $\frac{6}{14} = \frac{3}{7}$

22. $\frac{8}{11} = \frac{16}{22}$

Write each fraction in simplest form.

23. $\frac{6}{8}$ $\frac{3}{4}$

24. $\frac{8}{12}$ $\frac{2}{3}$

25. $\frac{7}{35}$ $\frac{1}{5}$

26. $\frac{16}{24}$ $\frac{2}{3}$

27. Reasoning Explain why $\frac{4}{6}$ is not in simplest form.

Sample answer: 4 and 6 have a common factor of 2.

© Pearson Education, Inc.

192 Intervention Lesson A49

Teacher Notes

Ongoing Assessment

Ask: ***Explain how you can tell $\frac{3}{7}$ is in simplest form.*** 3 and 7 have only 1 as a common factor.

Error Intervention

If students do not understand how two fractions can be equivalent,

then use H7: Using Models to Find Equivalent Fractions.

If You Have More Time

Have students create and number a cube 2, 2, 3, 3, 6, and 6. Label 8 index cards: $\frac{1}{2}$, $\frac{2}{3}$, $\frac{4}{6}$, $\frac{6}{18}$, $\frac{6}{24}$, $\frac{6}{10}$, $\frac{6}{12}$, and $\frac{3}{4}$. Shuffle the index cards. One student rolls the number cube and the other draws an index card. Both students find a fraction equivalent to the one on the index card by either multiplying or dividing by the number rolled. Have students check each others' work. Sometimes either operation can be done, sometimes only one can be used.

Comparing Fractions on the Number Line

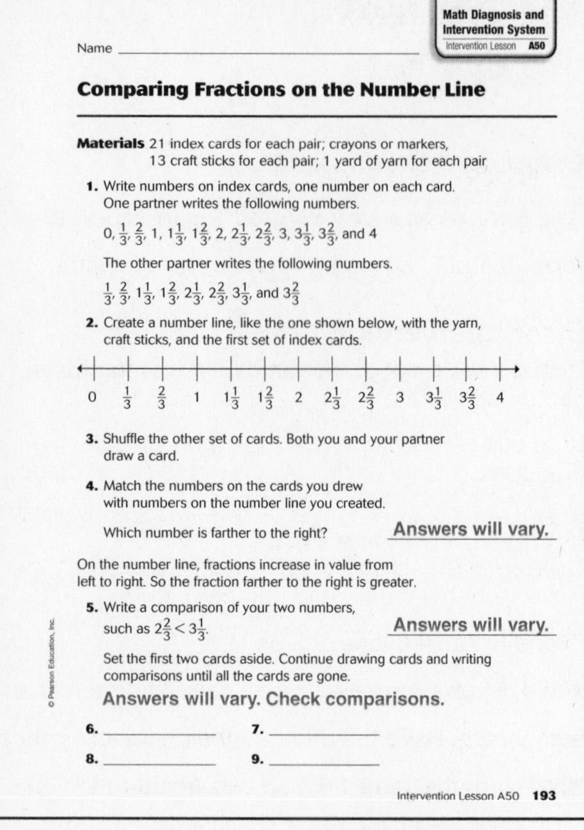

Math Diagnosis and Intervention System
Intervention Lesson A50

Name ____________________

Comparing Fractions on the Number Line

Materials 21 index cards for each pair; crayons or markers, 13 craft sticks for each pair; 1 yard of yarn for each pair

1. Write numbers on index cards, one number on each card. One partner writes the following numbers.

$0, \frac{1}{3}, \frac{2}{3}, 1, 1\frac{1}{3}, 1\frac{2}{3}, 2, 2\frac{1}{3}, 2\frac{2}{3}, 3, 3\frac{1}{3}, 3\frac{2}{3}$, and 4

The other partner writes the following numbers.

$\frac{1}{3}, \frac{2}{3}, 1\frac{1}{3}, 1\frac{2}{3}, 2\frac{1}{3}, 2\frac{2}{3}, 3\frac{1}{3}$, and $3\frac{2}{3}$

2. Create a number line, like the one shown below, with the yarn, craft sticks, and the first set of index cards.

3. Shuffle the other set of cards. Both you and your partner draw a card.

4. Match the numbers on the cards you drew with numbers on the number line you created.

Which number is farther to the right? **Answers will vary.**

On the number line, fractions increase in value from left to right. So the fraction farther to the right is greater.

5. Write a comparison of your two numbers, such as $2\frac{2}{3} < 3\frac{1}{3}$. **Answers will vary.**

Set the first two cards aside. Continue drawing cards and writing comparisons until all the cards are gone.

Answers will vary. Check comparisons.

6. ________ **7.** ________

8. ________ **9.** ________

Intervention Lesson A50 **193**

Math Diagnosis and Intervention System
Intervention Lesson A50

Name ____________________

Comparing Fractions on the Number Line (continued)

For 10–18, use the number line below. Compare. Write <, >, or =.

0 $\frac{1}{4}$ $\frac{2}{4}$ or $\frac{1}{2}$ $\frac{3}{4}$ 1 $1\frac{1}{4}$ $1\frac{2}{4}$ or $1\frac{1}{2}$ $1\frac{3}{4}$ 2 $2\frac{1}{4}$ $2\frac{2}{4}$ or $2\frac{1}{2}$ $2\frac{3}{4}$ 3

10. $\frac{3}{4} > \frac{1}{4}$ **11.** $1\frac{1}{4} < 2\frac{1}{2}$ **12.** $1\frac{1}{2} < 1\frac{3}{4}$

13. $1\frac{1}{4} > \frac{1}{4}$ **14.** $2\frac{3}{4} > 2\frac{1}{4}$ **15.** $1\frac{1}{2} = 1\frac{1}{2}$

16. $\frac{1}{4} < \frac{1}{2}$ **17.** $1\frac{3}{4} = 1\frac{3}{4}$ **18.** $\frac{3}{4} > \frac{1}{2}$

For 19–24, use the number line below. Compare. Write <, >, or =.

0 1 2 3 4

19. $\frac{2}{3} > \frac{1}{3}$ **20.** $2\frac{1}{3} > 1\frac{2}{3}$ **21.** $1\frac{1}{3} < 2\frac{1}{3}$

22. $\frac{3}{3} = 1$ **23.** $2\frac{2}{3} > 2\frac{1}{3}$ **24.** $\frac{2}{3} < 1\frac{1}{3}$

25. Reasoning Why is $2\frac{1}{8}$ greater than $1\frac{7}{8}$, even though $\frac{1}{8}$ is less than $\frac{7}{8}$?
Sample answer: The whole number part of $2\frac{1}{8}$ is greater than the whole number part of $1\frac{7}{8}$. So, $2\frac{1}{8} > 1\frac{7}{8}$.

26. Reasoning Explain how you can use the number line above to compare $6\frac{1}{3}$ and $6\frac{2}{3}$.
Sample answer: Since the whole number parts of the mixed numbers are the same, you can just compare the fractional parts. You can compare $\frac{1}{3}$ and $\frac{2}{3}$ on the number line above.

194 Intervention Lesson A50

Teacher Notes

Ongoing Assessment

Ask: ***Which is greater $4\frac{1}{4}$ or $4\frac{3}{4}$?*** $4\frac{3}{4}$

Error Intervention

If students have trouble with comparing fractions on a number line,

then have them use fraction strips to create a number line where the length of a fraction piece, like fifths, is the distance between 0 and $\frac{1}{5}$, $\frac{1}{5}$ and $\frac{2}{5}$, and so on, on the number line. Then, students can line up fraction strips below the number line to compare.

If You Have More Time

Have partners combine their cards from the activity. Shuffle them and then each draw a card. The student whose card is greater keeps both cards. (Let them use the yarn to craft a number line if needed.) If students draw cards that are equal, they each keep their card. Play until there is only 1 card left. The person with the most cards wins.

Comparing Fractions

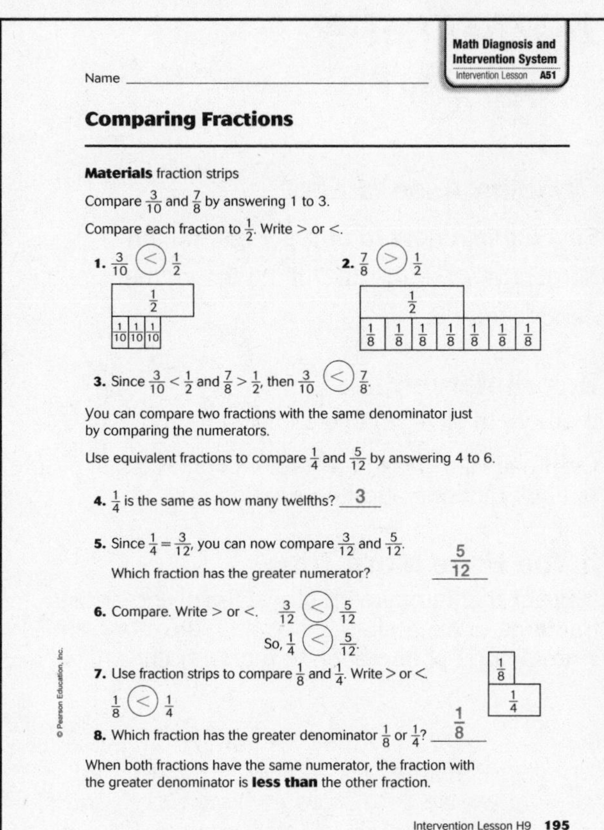

Math Diagnosis and Intervention System
Intervention Lesson A51

Name ____________________

Comparing Fractions

Materials fraction strips

Compare $\frac{3}{10}$ and $\frac{7}{8}$ by answering 1 to 3.

Compare each fraction to $\frac{1}{2}$. Write > or <.

1. $\frac{3}{10}$ (<) $\frac{1}{2}$

2. $\frac{7}{8}$ (>) $\frac{1}{2}$

3. Since $\frac{3}{10} < \frac{1}{2}$ and $\frac{7}{8} > \frac{1}{2}$, then $\frac{3}{10}$ (<) $\frac{7}{8}$.

You can compare two fractions with the same denominator just by comparing the numerators.

Use equivalent fractions to compare $\frac{1}{4}$ and $\frac{5}{12}$ by answering 4 to 6.

4. $\frac{1}{4}$ is the same as how many twelfths? 3

5. Since $\frac{1}{4} = \frac{3}{12}$, you can now compare $\frac{3}{12}$ and $\frac{5}{12}$.
Which fraction has the greater numerator? $\frac{5}{12}$

6. Compare. Write > or <. $\frac{3}{12}$ (<) $\frac{5}{12}$
So, $\frac{1}{4}$ (<) $\frac{5}{12}$.

7. Use fraction strips to compare $\frac{1}{8}$ and $\frac{1}{4}$. Write > or <.
$\frac{1}{8}$ (<) $\frac{1}{4}$

8. Which fraction has the greater denominator $\frac{1}{8}$ or $\frac{1}{4}$? $\frac{1}{8}$

When both fractions have the same numerator, the fraction with the greater denominator is **less than** the other fraction.

© Pearson Education, Inc.

Intervention Lesson H9 **195**

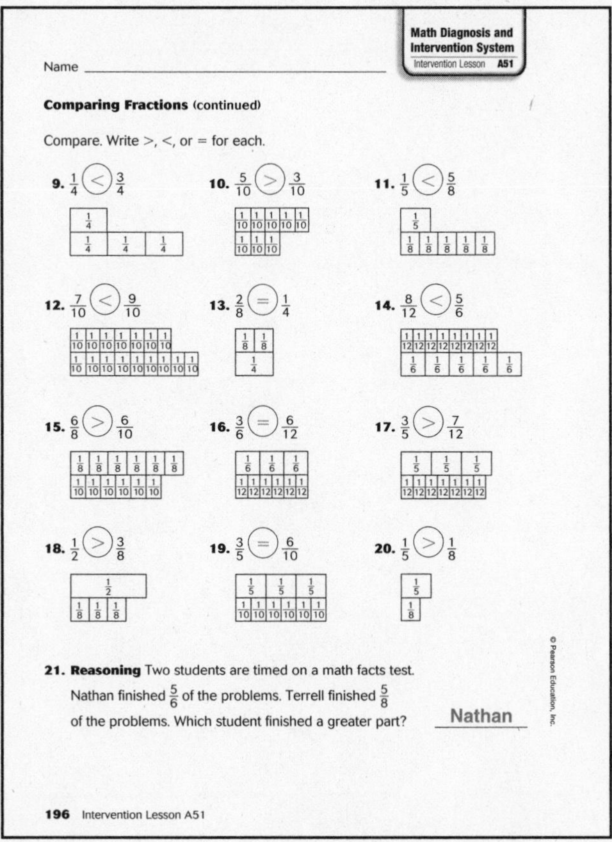

Math Diagnosis and Intervention System
Intervention Lesson A51

Name ____________________

Comparing Fractions (continued)

Compare. Write >, <, or = for each.

9. $\frac{1}{4}$ (<) $\frac{3}{4}$

10. $\frac{5}{10}$ (>) $\frac{3}{10}$

11. $\frac{1}{5}$ (<) $\frac{5}{8}$

12. $\frac{7}{10}$ (<) $\frac{9}{10}$

13. $\frac{2}{8}$ (=) $\frac{1}{4}$

14. $\frac{8}{12}$ (<) $\frac{5}{6}$

15. $\frac{6}{8}$ (>) $\frac{6}{10}$

16. $\frac{3}{6}$ (=) $\frac{6}{12}$

17. $\frac{3}{5}$ (>) $\frac{7}{12}$

18. $\frac{1}{2}$ (>) $\frac{3}{8}$

19. $\frac{3}{5}$ (=) $\frac{6}{10}$

20. $\frac{1}{5}$ (>) $\frac{1}{8}$

21. **Reasoning** Two students are timed on a math facts test. Nathan finished $\frac{5}{6}$ of the problems. Terrell finished $\frac{5}{8}$ of the problems. Which student finished a greater part? Nathan

© Pearson Education, Inc.

196 Intervention Lesson A51

Teacher Notes

Ongoing Assessment

Ask: ***How can you compare $\frac{1}{3}$ and $\frac{1}{5}$ without fraction strips and without finding a common denominator?*** Sample answer: Both of the numerators are 1, so the fraction with the greater denominator is less. So, $\frac{1}{5}$ is less than $\frac{1}{3}$.

Error Intervention

If students have trouble comparing fractions, **then** use H6: Using Models to Compare Fractions.

If You Have More Time

Have students use fraction strips to find fractions less than $\frac{1}{2}$. Have them record their findings. If time allows, do the same for fractions greater than $\frac{1}{2}$.

Adding Fractions with Like Denominators

Math Diagnosis and Intervention System
Intervention Lesson A52

Name ______________________

Adding Fractions with Like Denominators

Materials crayons or markers

Nur wove $\frac{2}{5}$ of a rug in February and $\frac{1}{5}$ of it in March.
Find what part of the rug she has finished in all by answering 1 to 4.

1. Color $\frac{2}{5}$ of the rectangle on the right.
2. Color $\frac{1}{5}$ more of the rectangle on the right.
3. How much of the rectangle did you color in all? $\frac{3}{5}$

This is the sum of $\frac{2}{5}$ and $\frac{1}{5}$. So, $\frac{2}{5} + \frac{1}{5} = \frac{3}{5}$.

4. What part of her rug has Nur finished in all? $\frac{3}{5}$

Jamal wove $\frac{2}{6}$ of a rug in February and $\frac{2}{6}$ in March.
Find what part of the rug he has finished in all by answering 5 to 11.

5. Color $\frac{2}{6}$ of the rectangle on the right.
6. Color $\frac{2}{6}$ more of the rectangle on the right.
7. How much of the rectangle did you color in all? $\frac{4}{6}$
8. What is $\frac{2}{6} + \frac{2}{6}$? $\frac{4}{6}$
9. What is a fraction equivalent to $\frac{4}{6}$, but with smaller numbers? Color the second rectangle to find out. $\frac{4}{6} = \frac{2}{3}$
10. So, $\frac{2}{6} + \frac{2}{6} = \frac{4}{6} = \frac{2}{3}$.
11. What part of his rug has Jamal finished in all? $\frac{2}{3}$

Intervention Lesson A52 **197**

Math Diagnosis and Intervention System
Intervention Lesson A52

Name ______________________

Adding Fractions with Like Denominators (continued)

12. **Reasoning** Explain how to add $\frac{1}{9} + \frac{4}{9}$.
Add the 1 and the 4 to get 5. Then, put 5 over the denominator. So, $\frac{1}{9} + \frac{4}{9} = \frac{5}{9}$.

Add.

13. $\frac{1}{3}$ | $\frac{1}{3}$
$\frac{1}{3} + \frac{1}{3} = \frac{2}{3}$

14. $\frac{1}{5}$ | $\frac{3}{5}$
$\frac{1}{5} + \frac{3}{5} = \frac{4}{5}$

15. $\frac{1}{4}$ | $\frac{2}{4}$
$\frac{1}{4} + \frac{2}{4} = \frac{3}{4}$

16. $\frac{1}{6}$ | $\frac{1}{6}$ | $\frac{1}{6}$ | $\frac{1}{6}$ | $\frac{1}{6}$
$\frac{2}{6} + \frac{3}{6} = \frac{5}{6}$

17. $\frac{2}{8} + \frac{5}{8} = \frac{7}{8}$

18. $\frac{3}{10} + \frac{2}{10} = \frac{5}{10} = \frac{1}{2}$

19. Calvin bought a gallon of yogurt. He ate $\frac{1}{6}$ gallon the first day, and $\frac{2}{6}$ gallon the second day. What fraction of the yogurt did he eat? $\frac{3}{6}$

20. Three-fifths of Mr. James' class are wearing blue jeans and white shirts. One-fifth of the class are wearing blue jeans and red shirts. One-fifth of the class are wearing brown pants and white shirts. What fraction of Mr. James' class are wearing white shirts? $\frac{4}{5}$

21. **Reasoning** What fraction would you add to $\frac{1}{3}$ to get $\frac{3}{3}$? $\frac{2}{3}$

198 Intervention Lesson A52

Teacher Notes

Ongoing Assessment

Say: ***Explain how to add $\frac{1}{6} + \frac{4}{6}$.*** Add the numerators 1 + 4 = 5. Put the 5 over the denominator 6.

Error Intervention

If students have trouble showing fractions,

then use H2: Parts of a Region, H3: Parts of a Set, or H4: Fractions and Length.

If You Have More Time

Have students make up stories involving adding fractions, draw a picture to match the story, and write a number sentence to match both.

Subtracting Fractions with Like Denominators

Math Diagnosis and Intervention System
Intervention Lesson **A53**

Name ______________________

Math Diagnosis and Intervention System
Intervention Lesson A53

Subtracting Fractions with Like Denominators

Materials crayons or markers

Tammy loves tuna bake. When she came home from school, she found $\frac{6}{8}$ of a tuna bake on the stove. She ate $\frac{1}{8}$ of it. Find how much of the tuna bake was left by answering 1 to 5.

1. Color $\frac{6}{8}$ of the rectangle on the right.
2. Cross out $\frac{1}{8}$ of the part you colored.
3. How much of the rectangle you colored is not crossed out? $\frac{5}{8}$
4. What is $\frac{6}{8} - \frac{1}{8}$? $\frac{5}{8}$
5. How much of the tuna bake was left after Tammy ate? $\frac{5}{8}$

Brad found $\frac{3}{4}$ of a submarine sandwich when he came home from school. He ate $\frac{1}{4}$ of the sandwich. Find how much of the sandwich was left by answering 6 to 12.

6. Color $\frac{3}{4}$ of the rectangle on the right.
7. Cross out $\frac{1}{4}$ of the part you colored.
8. How much of the rectangle you colored is not crossed out? $\frac{2}{4}$
9. What is $\frac{3}{4} - \frac{1}{4}$? $\frac{2}{4}$
10. What is a fraction equivalent to $\frac{2}{4}$, but with smaller numbers? Color the second rectangle to find out. $\frac{2}{4} = \frac{1}{2}$
11. So, $\frac{3}{4} - \frac{1}{4} = \frac{2}{4} = \frac{1}{2}$.
12. How much of the sandwich was left after Brad ate? $\frac{1}{2}$

Name ______________________

Math Diagnosis and Intervention System
Intervention Lesson A53

Subtracting Fractions with Like Denominators (continued)

13. **Reasoning** Explain how to subtract $\frac{5}{10} - \frac{2}{10}$.
Subtract 5 – 2 to get 3. Then, put 3 over the denominator 10. So, $\frac{5}{10} - \frac{2}{10} = \frac{3}{10}$.

Subtract.

14. $\frac{1}{6}$ | $\frac{1}{6}$ | $\frac{1}{6}$ | $\frac{1}{6}$ | $\frac{1}{6}$ |
$\frac{5}{6} - \frac{3}{6} = \frac{2}{6}$

15. $\frac{1}{5}$ | $\frac{1}{5}$ | $\frac{1}{5}$ |
$\frac{3}{5} - \frac{1}{5} = \frac{2}{5}$

16. $\frac{1}{4}$ | $\frac{1}{4}$ | $\frac{1}{4}$ |
$\frac{3}{4} - \frac{1}{4} = \frac{2}{4}$

17. $\frac{1}{5}$ | $\frac{1}{5}$ | $\frac{1}{5}$ | $\frac{1}{5}$ |
$\frac{4}{5} - \frac{2}{5} = \frac{2}{5}$

18. $\frac{4}{7} - \frac{3}{7} = \frac{1}{7}$
19. $\frac{5}{9} - \frac{4}{9} = \frac{1}{9}$
20. $\frac{7}{8} - \frac{1}{8} = \frac{6}{8} = \frac{3}{4}$
21. $\frac{4}{6} - \frac{1}{6} = \frac{3}{6} = \frac{1}{2}$

The table shows the distances run by members of a track team. Use the table for Exercises 22 and 23.

Runner	Distance in miles
Rosie	$\frac{7}{8}$
Tricia	$\frac{4}{8}$
Amy	$\frac{5}{8}$
Caro	$\frac{6}{8}$

22. How much farther did Rosie run than Tricia? $\frac{3}{8}$ mile
23. How much farther did Caro run than Tricia? $\frac{2}{8}$ or $\frac{1}{4}$ mile
24. **Reasoning** Why would it be more difficult to subtract $\frac{2}{3} - \frac{1}{6}$ than $\frac{2}{3} - \frac{1}{3}$?
$\frac{2}{3}$ and $\frac{1}{3}$ have the same denominator, and $\frac{2}{3}$ and $\frac{1}{6}$ have different denominators.

Teacher Notes

Ongoing Assessment

Make sure students do not try to subtract the denominators.

Error Intervention

If students have trouble showing fractions,

then use H2: Parts of a Region, H3: Parts of a Set, or H4: Fractions and Length.

If You Have More Time

Have students work in pairs. Have one student make up a story about subtracting fractions. Have the partner write a number sentence and solve. Then, have students change roles and repeat.

Money

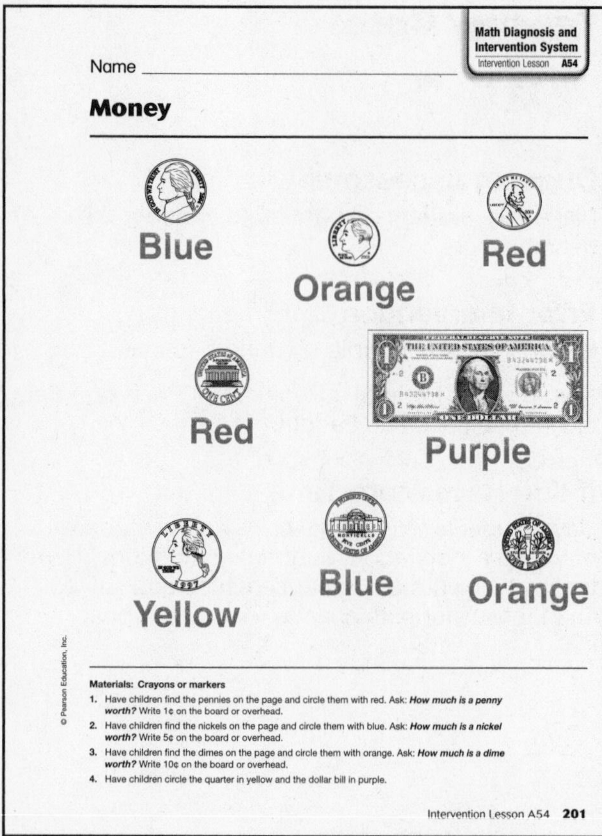

Math Diagnosis and Intervention System
Intervention Lesson A54

Name ______________________

Money

Materials: Crayons or markers

1. Have children find the pennies on the page and circle them with red. Ask: ***How much is a penny worth?*** Write 1¢ on the board or overhead.
2. Have children find the nickels on the page and circle them with blue. Ask: ***How much is a nickel worth?*** Write 5¢ on the board or overhead.
3. Have children find the dimes on the page and circle them with orange. Ask: ***How much is a dime worth?*** Write 10¢ on the board or overhead.
4. Have children circle the quarter in yellow and the dollar bill in purple.

Intervention Lesson A54 201

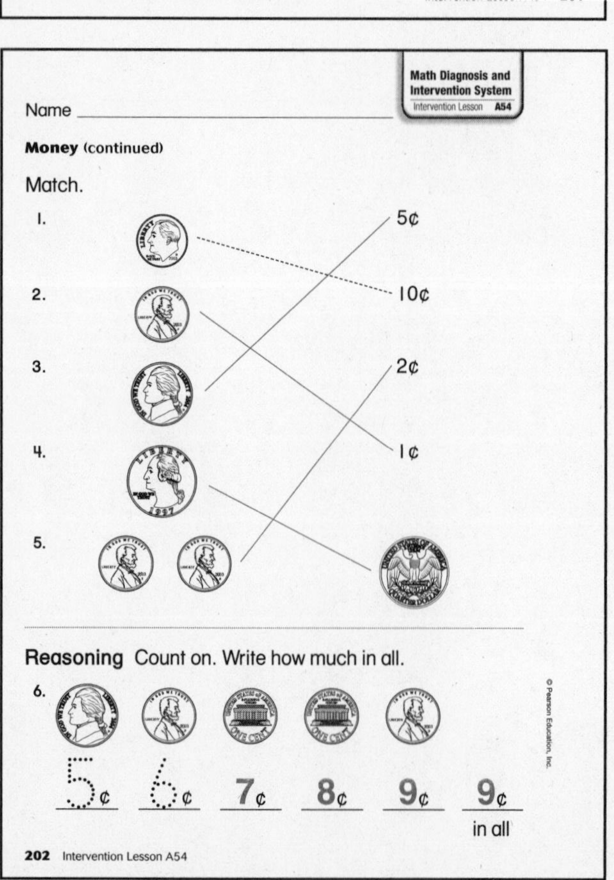

Math Diagnosis and Intervention System
Intervention Lesson A54

Name ______________________

Money (continued)

Match.

1.
2.
3.
4.
5.

5¢
10¢
2¢
1¢

Reasoning Count on. Write how much in all.

6. 5¢ 6¢ 7¢ 8¢ 9¢ 9¢ in all

202 Intervention Lesson A54

Teacher Notes

Ongoing Assessment

Make sure children can count on to do the Reasoning exercise. If they are having trouble, let them trade a nickel for 5 pennies and count.

Error Intervention

If children can not tell the coins apart from the drawings,

then let them use real coins or the coins in the manipulatives kit.

If You Have More Time

Put one of each coin in a paper bag. Let a child choose a coin without looking and then tell its name and value. Return the coin to the bag. Shake the bag and repeat until all children have had a turn.

Pennies and Nickels

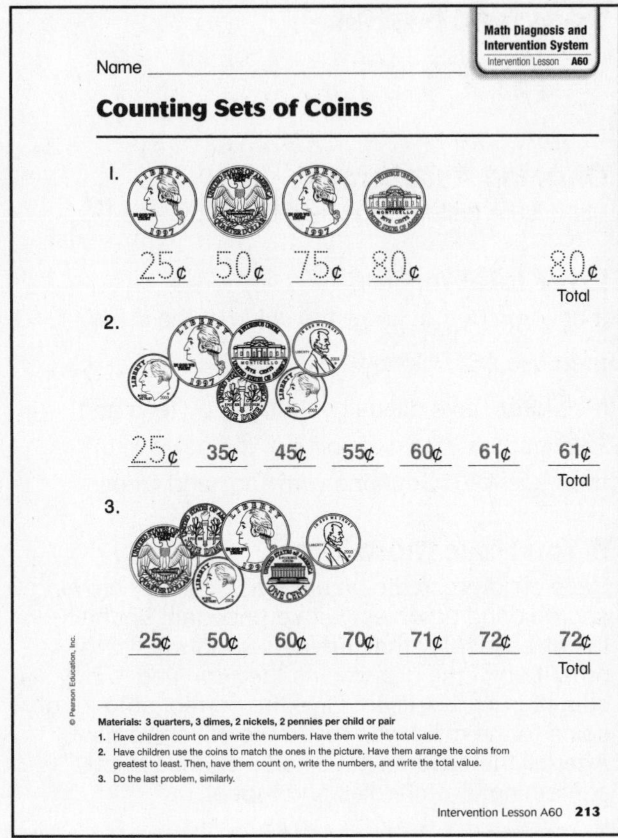

Math Diagnosis and Intervention System
Intervention Lesson **A60**

Name ______________________

Counting Sets of Coins

1. 25¢ 50¢ 75¢ 80¢ — 80¢ Total

2. 25¢ 35¢ 45¢ 55¢ 60¢ 61¢ — 61¢ Total

3. 25¢ 50¢ 60¢ 70¢ 71¢ 72¢ — 72¢ Total

Materials: 3 quarters, 3 dimes, 2 nickels, 2 pennies per child or pair

1. Have children count on and write the numbers. Have them write the total value.
2. Have children use the coins to match the ones in the picture. Have them arrange the coins from greatest to least. Then, have them count on, write the numbers, and write the total value.
3. Do the last problem, similarly.

© Pearson Education, Inc.

Intervention Lesson A60 **213**

Math Diagnosis and Intervention System
Intervention Lesson **A55**

Name ______________________

Pennies and Nickels (continued)

Count on. Write how much in all.

4. 5¢ 10¢ 11¢ 12¢ 13¢ — 13¢ in all

5. 5¢ 10¢ 15¢ 20¢ 21¢ — 21¢ in all

Circle the coins that match each price. **Arrangements may vary.**

6. 11¢

7. 15¢

JUICE

© Pearson Education, Inc.

204 Intervention Lesson A55

Teacher Notes

Ongoing Assessment

Make sure children can count on.

Error Intervention

If children do not know the value of the coins,

then use A54: Money.

If children have difficulty skip counting,

then use A16: Using Skip Counting.

If You Have More Time

Let children play store. One child puts price tags on items and the partner counts out pennies and nickels to match the price. Children can change roles and repeat.

Dimes

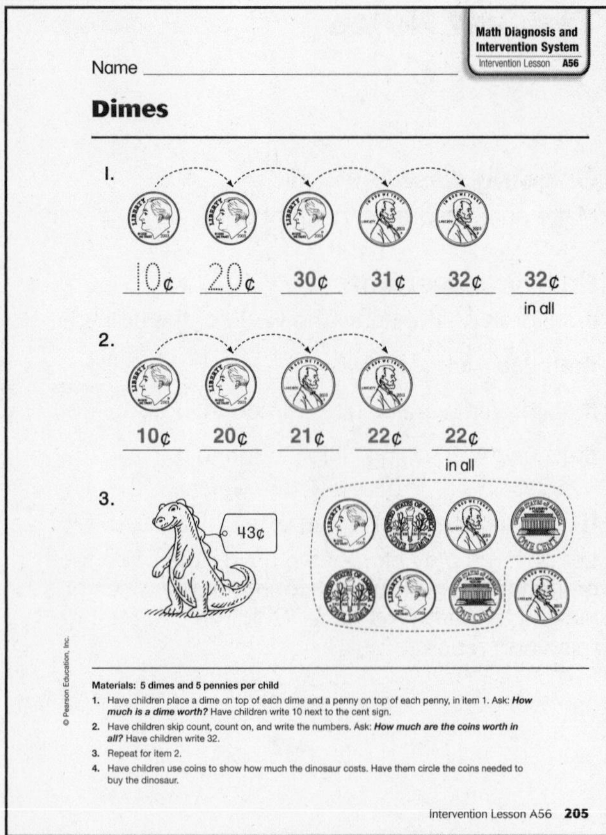

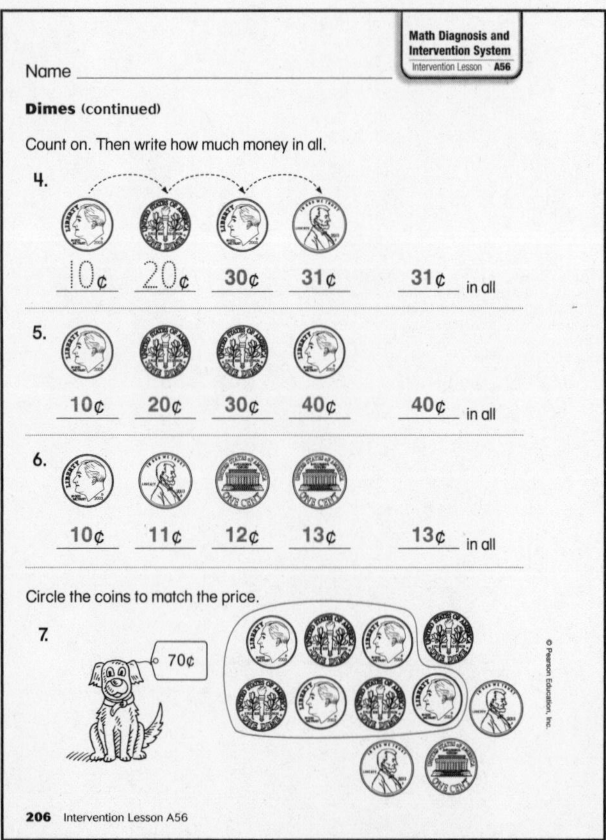

Teacher Notes

Ongoing Assessment

Make sure children can skip count by tens.

Error Intervention

If children do not know the value of the coins,

then use A54: Money.

If children have difficulty counting by tens and ones,

then use A20: Counting with Tens and Ones.

If You Have More Time

Have children create an advertisement by drawing and coloring an object with a price tag. Let half the class display their advertisements. Give the other half of the class coins they can use to buy something advertised. Give the correct amount of coins to the child who made the advertisement. After all the children have had a chance to buy something, switch roles and repeat.

Counting Pennies, Nickels, and Dimes

Math Diagnosis and Intervention System
Intervention Lesson A57

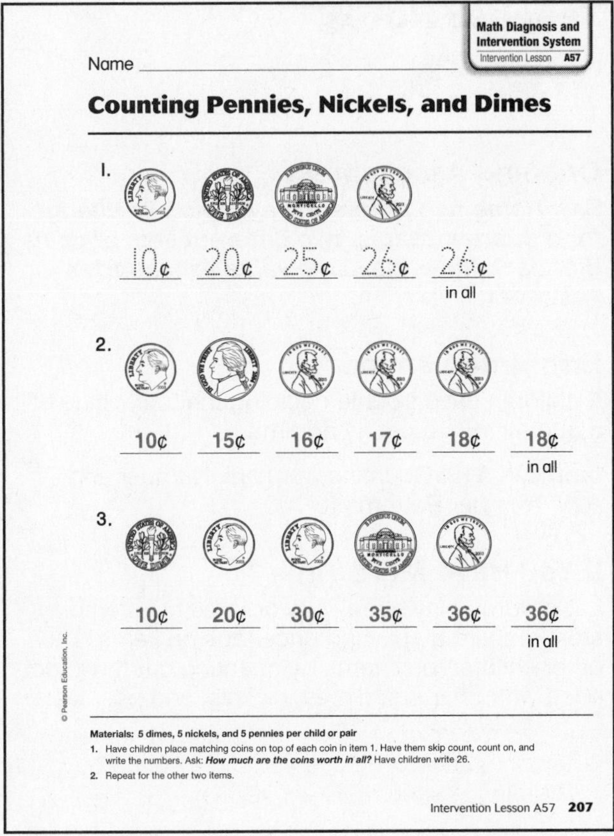

Name

Counting Pennies, Nickels, and Dimes

1. 10¢ 20¢ 25¢ 26¢ 26¢ in all

2. 10¢ 15¢ 16¢ 17¢ 18¢ 18¢ in all

3. 10¢ 20¢ 30¢ 35¢ 36¢ 36¢ in all

Materials: 5 dimes, 5 nickels, and 5 pennies per child or pair

1. Have children place matching coins on top of each coin in item 1. Have them skip count, count on, and write the numbers. Ask: *How much are the coins worth in all?* Have children write 26.
2. Repeat for the other two items.

Intervention Lesson A57 207

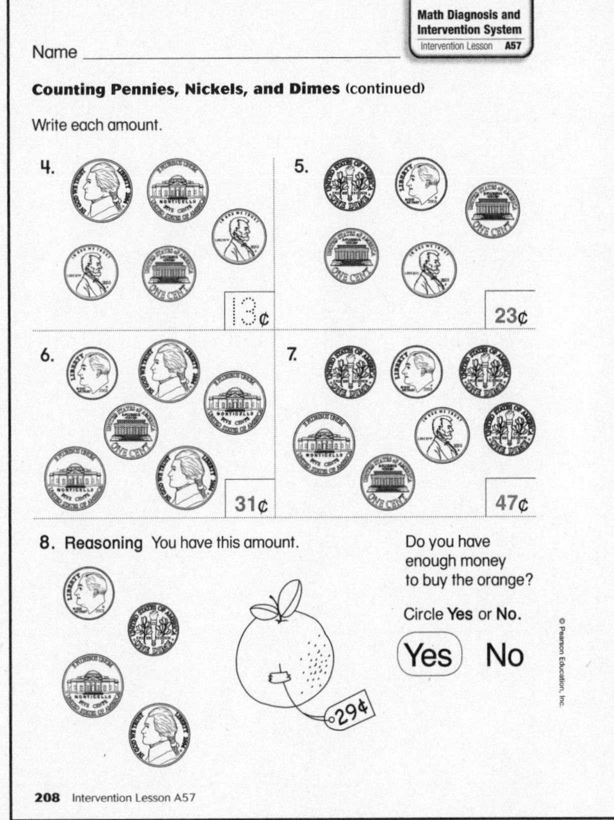

Name

Counting Pennies, Nickels, and Dimes (continued)

Write each amount.

4. 13¢
5. 23¢
6. 31¢
7. 47¢

8. Reasoning You have this amount. Do you have enough money to buy the orange? Circle Yes or No.

29¢

Yes No

208 Intervention Lesson A57

Teacher Notes

Ongoing Assessment

Make sure children know the value of each coin.

Error Intervention

If children have difficulty deciding how much a dime and nickel are worth together,

then let them trade the nickel for 5 pennies and count on from 10.

If You Have More Time

Have partners play Guess My Coins' Value. One child hides 4 coins from the pennies, nickels, and dimes. The other partner tries to guess the worth of the coins by asking yes-no questions, like *Are the coins worth more than 30 cents? Are there fewer than 2 dimes?*

Quarters

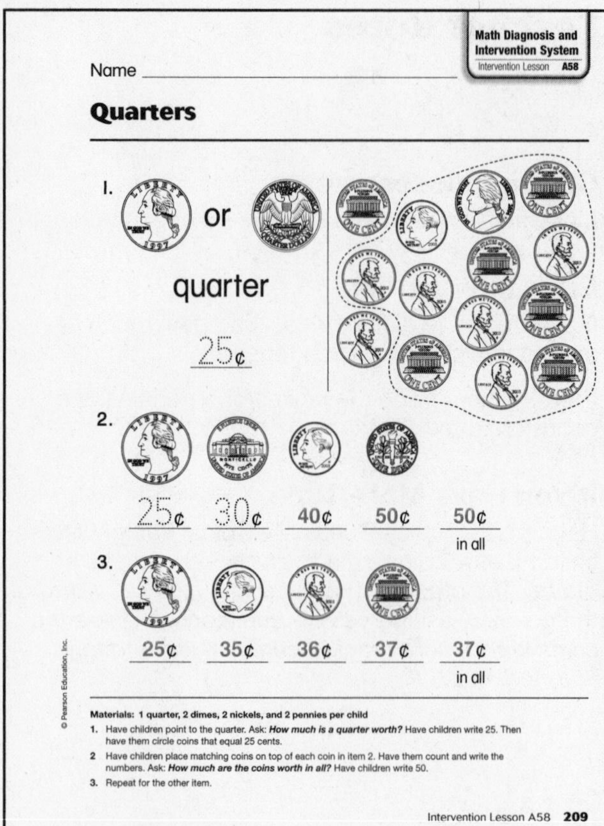

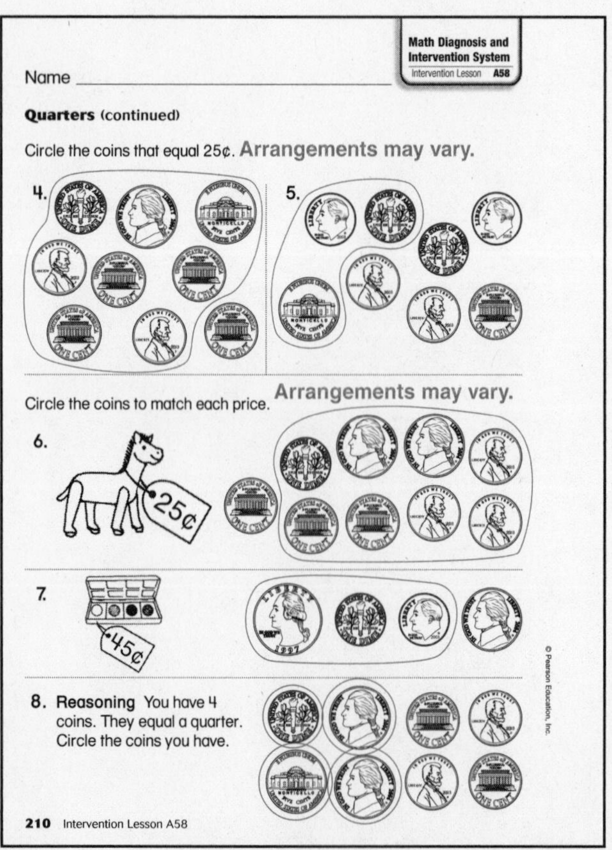

Teacher Notes

Ongoing Assessment

Say: ***Name two different ways to make change for a quarter, that is, two different sets of coins that each have the same value as a quarter.*** Answers will vary.

Error Intervention

If children have trouble deciding the total value of a quarter with a penny or dime,

then use A18: Counting from any Number and A25: Number Patterns to 100.

If You Have More Time

Let children play store. Two or three children play storekeepers by placing price tags on items. The other children buy items by counting out the exact price with quarters, dimes, nickels, and pennies.

Half-Dollars

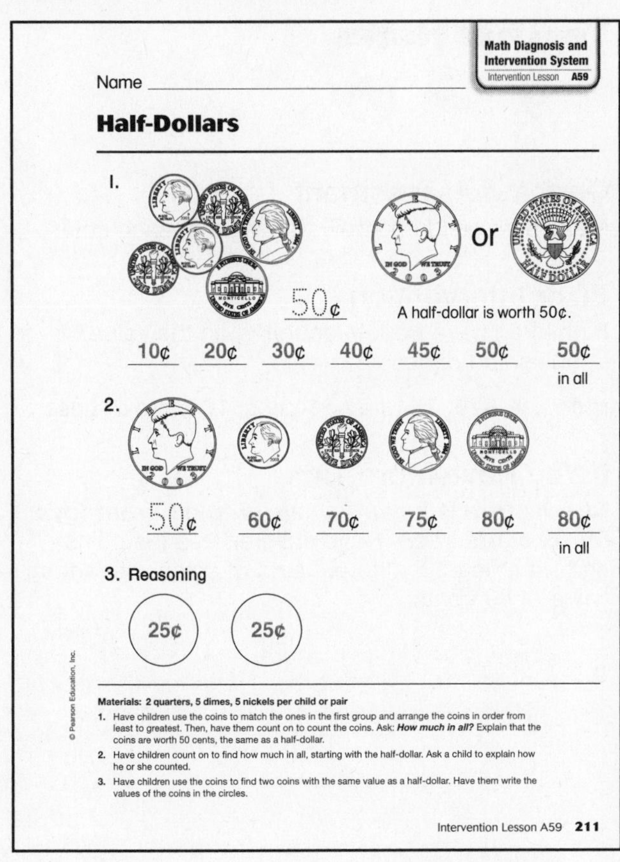

Name ____________________

Half-Dollars

1.

or

50¢ A half-dollar is worth 50¢.

10¢ 20¢ 30¢ 40¢ 45¢ 50¢ 50¢ in all

2.

50¢ 60¢ 70¢ 75¢ 80¢ 80¢ in all

3. Reasoning

25¢ 25¢

Materials: 2 quarters, 5 dimes, 5 nickels per child or pair

1. Have children use the coins to match the ones in the first group and arrange the coins in order from least to greatest. Then, have them count on to count the coins. Ask: ***How much in all?*** Explain that the coins are worth 50 cents, the same as a half-dollar.
2. Have children count on to find how much in all, starting with the half-dollar. Ask a child to explain how he or she counted.
3. Have children use the coins to find two coins with the same value as a half-dollar. Have them write the values of the coins in the circles.

Teacher Notes

Ongoing Assessment

Notice which children write 25 in the circles and which write 25¢. Show the ¢ sign to the ones who just write 25 and ask: ***What does this sign mean?*** cents

Error Intervention

If children have difficulty counting the value of the groups of coins,

then use A57: Counting Pennies, Nickels, and Dimes, and A58: Quarters.

If You Have More Time

Have children work with a partner to list at least 4 different ways to make 50 cents.

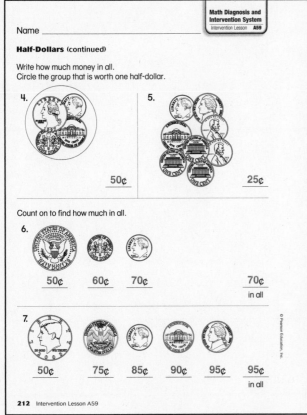

Name ____________________

Half-Dollars (continued)

Write how much money in all.
Circle the group that is worth one half-dollar.

4. 50¢

5. 25¢

Count on to find how much in all.

6. 50¢ 60¢ 70¢ 70¢ in all

7. 50¢ 75¢ 85¢ 90¢ 95¢ 95¢ in all

Counting Sets of Coins

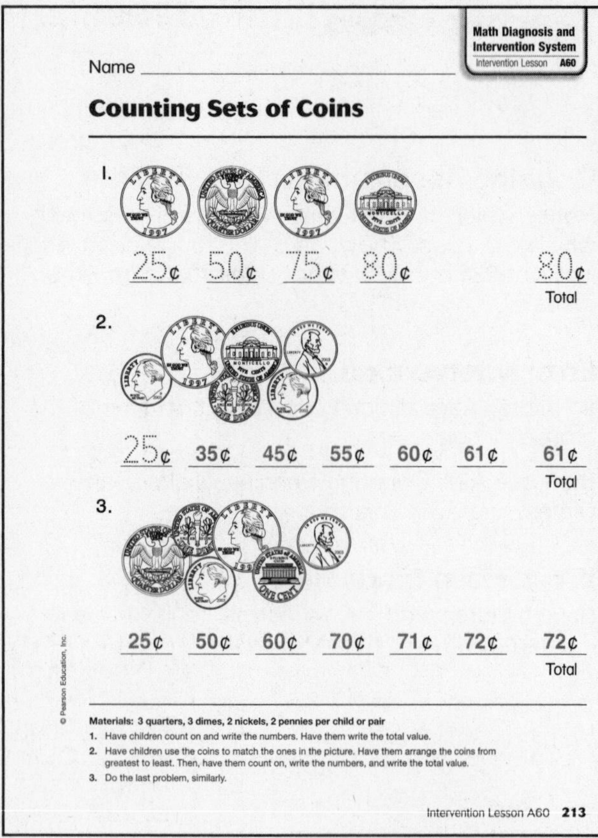

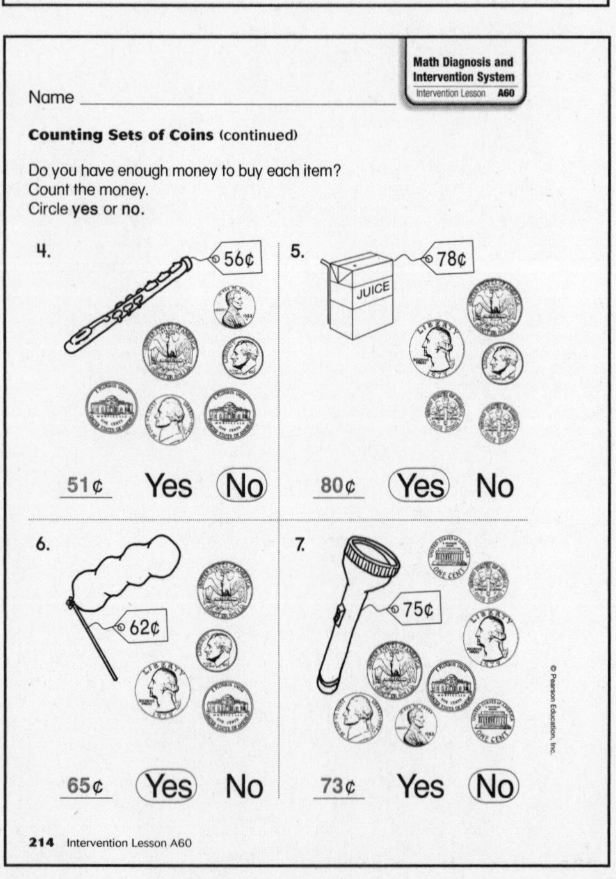

Teacher Notes

Ongoing Assessment

Make sure children know the value of each coin.

Error Intervention

If children have trouble counting on the value of pennies and dimes,

then use A26: 1 More or 1 Less, 10 More or Less.

If You Have More Time

Say: ***A store is having a sale with different toys for 89 cents each.*** Have children use the coins and list at least 5 different sets of coins with a total value of 89 cents.

Comparing Sets of Coins

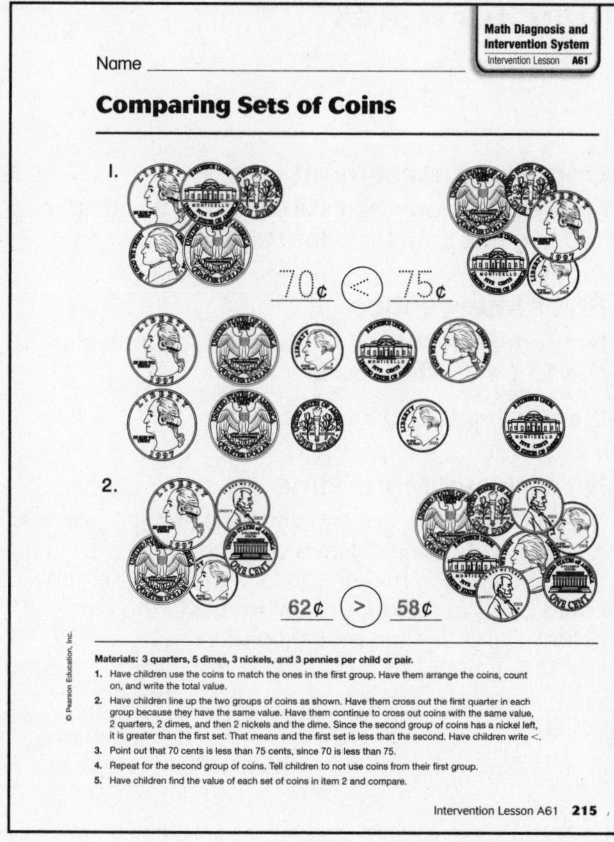
Math Diagnosis and Intervention System
Intervention Lesson A61

Name ______________________

Comparing Sets of Coins

1. 70¢ (<) 75¢

2. 62¢ (>) 58¢

Materials: 3 quarters, 5 dimes, 3 nickels, and 3 pennies per child or pair.

1. Have children use the coins to match the ones in the first group. Have them arrange the coins, count on, and write the total value.
2. Have children line up the two groups of coins as shown. Have them cross out the first quarter in each group because they have the same value. Have them continue to cross out coins with the same value, 2 quarters, 2 dimes, and then 2 nickels and the dime. Since the second group of coins has a nickel left, it is greater than the first set. That means and the first set is less than the second. Have children write <.
3. Point out that 70 cents is less than 75 cents, since 70 is less than 75.
4. Repeat for the second group of coins. Tell children to not use coins from their first group.
5. Have children find the value of each set of coins in item 2 and compare.

© Pearson Education, Inc.

Intervention Lesson A61 **215**

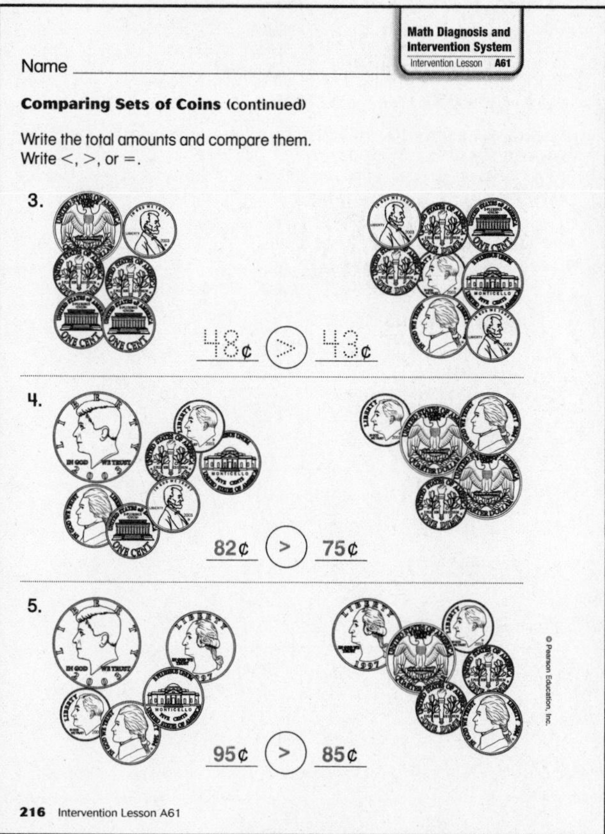
Math Diagnosis and Intervention System
Intervention Lesson A61

Name ______________________

Comparing Sets of Coins (continued)

Write the total amounts and compare them.
Write <, >, or =.

3. 48¢ (>) 43¢

4. 82¢ (>) 75¢

5. 95¢ (>) 85¢

© Pearson Education, Inc.

216 Intervention Lesson A61

Teacher Notes

Ongoing Assessment

Make sure children understand which coins have the same value. For example, make sure they know that two nickels equal a dime and that two dimes and a nickel equal a quarter.

Error Intervention

If children have trouble counting the value of groups of coins,

then use A58: Quarters and A60: Counting Sets of Coins.

If children have trouble with the < and > signs,

then use A27: Using <, >, and = to Compare Numbers.

If You Have More Time

Have children work in pairs. Put about 15 assorted coins in a paper bag. Have each child pull 5 coins from the bag without looking. Each child counts the set of coins drawn. Then they compare to decide which set is worth more. Have them return the coins to the bag and repeat.

Ways to Show the Same Amount

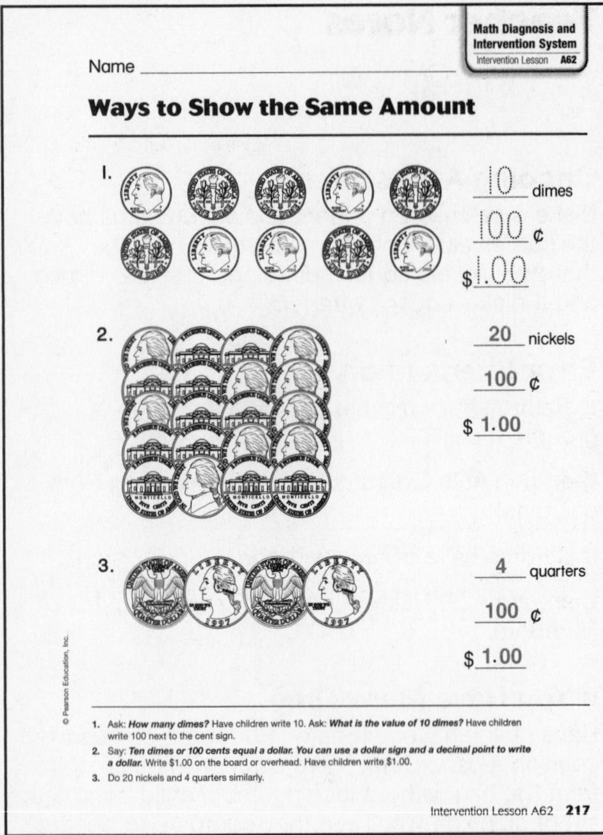

Math Diagnosis and Intervention System
Intervention Lesson A62

Name ______________________

Ways to Show the Same Amount

1. 10 dimes
100 ¢
$1.00

2. 20 nickels
100 ¢
$1.00

3. 4 quarters
100 ¢
$1.00

© Pearson Education, Inc.

1. Ask: ***How many dimes?*** Have children write 10. Ask: ***What is the value of 10 dimes?*** Have children write 100 next to the cent sign.
2. Say: ***Ten dimes or 100 cents equal a dollar. You can use a dollar sign and a decimal point to write a dollar.*** Write $1.00 on the board or overhead. Have children write $1.00.
3. Do 20 nickels and 4 quarters similarly.

Intervention Lesson A62 **217**

Math Diagnosis and Intervention System
Intervention Lesson A62

Name ______________________

Ways to Show the Same Amount (continued)

Write each amount in cents.
Then write the amount in dollars.

4. 100 ¢
$1.00

5. 100 ¢
$1.00

6. 100 ¢
$1.00

7. 100 ¢
$1.00

© Pearson Education, Inc.

218 Intervention Lesson A62

Teacher Notes

Ongoing Assessment

Make sure children can skip count by 5 and 10 to 100 and that they know the values of the coins.

Error Intervention

If children can not find the value of 4 quarters or quarters with other coins,

then let them use a hundred chart.

If You Have More Time

Make a table with columns labeled quarters, dimes, nickels, and pennies. Have children list at least 5 different ways to make a dollar. For example, they could put 3 in the quarter column, 2 in the dime column, and 5 in the penny column.

Dollars

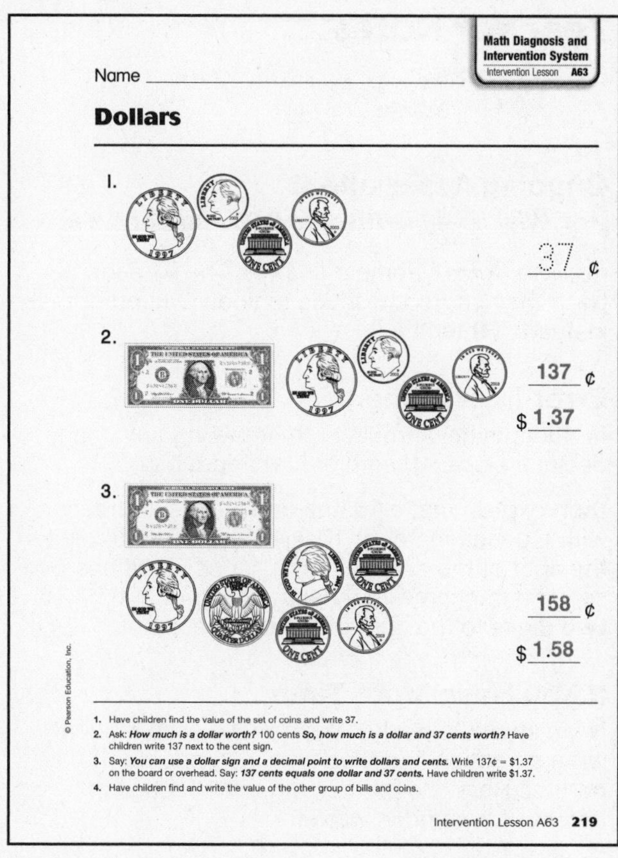

Teacher Notes

Ongoing Assessment

Make sure children put the decimal point after the dollar and read it by saying "and".

Error Intervention

If children have trouble counting the value of the coins the way they are arranged,

then let them use real coins or coins from the manipulative kit to put the coins in order. Also, use A60: Counting Sets of Coins.

If You Have More Time

Give children amounts, such as $1.48, and have them draw a dollar bill and coins to equal each amount.

Fractions and Decimals

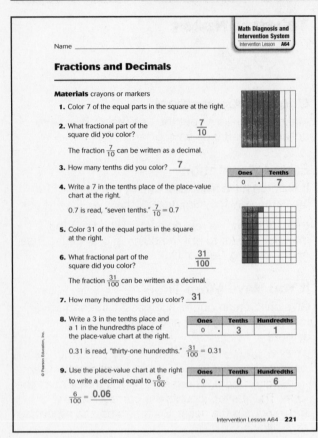

Math Diagnosis and Intervention System
Intervention Lesson A64

Name ______________________

Fractions and Decimals

Materials crayons or markers

1. Color 7 of the equal parts in the square at the right.

2. What fractional part of the square did you color? $\frac{7}{10}$

The fraction $\frac{7}{10}$ can be written as a decimal.

3. How many tenths did you color? 7

4. Write a 7 in the tenths place of the place-value chart at the right.

Ones		Tenths
0	.	7

0.7 is read, "seven tenths." $\frac{7}{10} = 0.7$

5. Color 31 of the equal parts in the square at the right.

6. What fractional part of the square did you color? $\frac{31}{100}$

The fraction $\frac{31}{100}$ can be written as a decimal.

7. How many hundredths did you color? 31

8. Write a 3 in the tenths place and a 1 in the hundredths place of the place-value chart at the right.

Ones		Tenths	Hundredths
0	.	3	1

0.31 is read, "thirty-one hundredths." $\frac{31}{100} = 0.31$

9. Use the place-value chart at the right to write a decimal equal to $\frac{6}{100}$.

Ones		Tenths	Hundredths
0	.	0	6

$\frac{6}{100} =$ 0.06

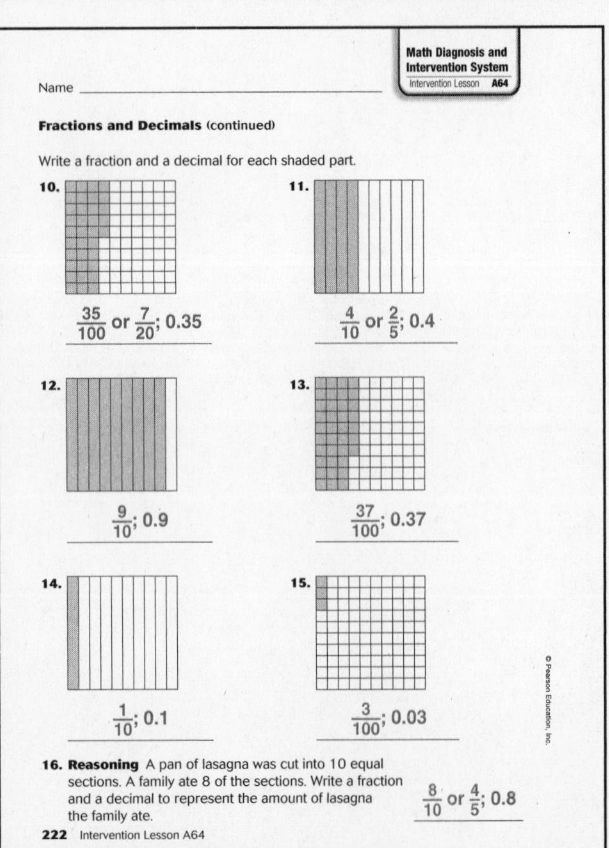
Math Diagnosis and Intervention System
Intervention Lesson A64

Name ______________________

Fractions and Decimals (continued)

Write a fraction and a decimal for each shaded part.

10. $\frac{35}{100}$ or $\frac{7}{20}$; 0.35

11. $\frac{4}{10}$ or $\frac{2}{5}$; 0.4

12. $\frac{9}{10}$; 0.9

13. $\frac{37}{100}$; 0.37

14. $\frac{1}{10}$; 0.1

15. $\frac{3}{100}$; 0.03

16. Reasoning A pan of lasagna was cut into 10 equal sections. A family ate 8 of the sections. Write a fraction and a decimal to represent the amount of lasagna the family ate. $\frac{8}{10}$ or $\frac{4}{5}$; 0.8

Teacher Notes

Ongoing Assessment

Ask: ***Why is $\frac{9}{100}$ written as 0.09 and not 0.9 in decimal form?*** Sample answer: The 9 needs to be in the hundredths place to show 9 hundredths instead of 9 tenths.

Error Intervention

If students have trouble remembering how many decimal places a tenth or hundredth has,

then explain that a 10 has **one** zero, so a fraction with a denominator of 10 will only have **one** digit to the right of the decimal point. Since a 100 has **two** zeros, a fraction with a denominator of 100 will have **two** digits to the right of the decimal point.

If You Have More Time

Have students work in pairs. Have each student write a fraction and then give the paper to the partner. Have the partner write the fraction in decimal form and in word form.

Counting Money

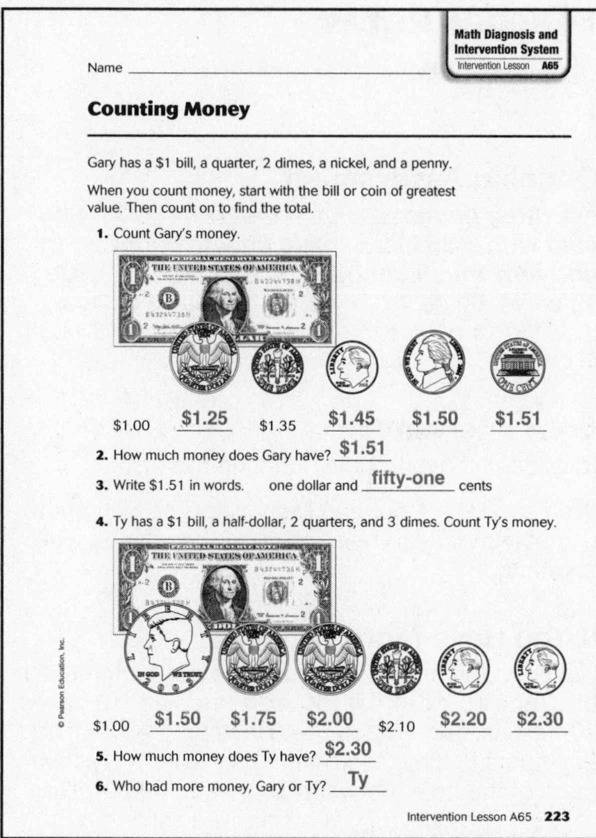

Math Diagnosis and Intervention System
Intervention Lesson A65

Name ____________________

Counting Money

Gary has a $1 bill, a quarter, 2 dimes, a nickel, and a penny.

When you count money, start with the bill or coin of greatest value. Then count on to find the total.

1. Count Gary's money.

$1.00 $1.25 $1.35 $1.45 $1.50 $1.51

2. How much money does Gary have? $1.51

3. Write $1.51 in words. one dollar and fifty-one cents

4. Ty has a $1 bill, a half-dollar, 2 quarters, and 3 dimes. Count Ty's money.

$1.00 $1.50 $1.75 $2.00 $2.10 $2.20 $2.30

5. How much money does Ty have? $2.30

6. Who had more money, Gary or Ty? Ty

© Pearson Education, Inc.

Intervention Lesson A65 **223**

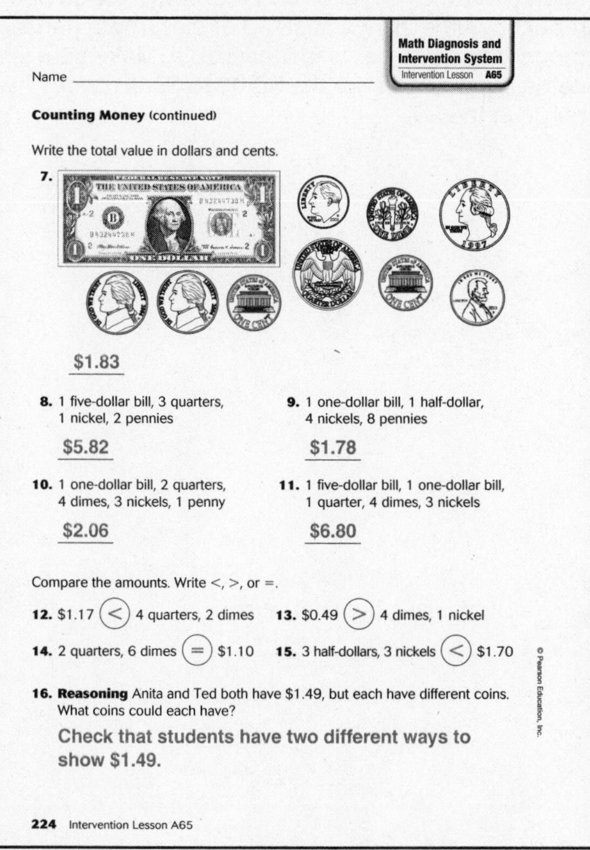

Math Diagnosis and Intervention System
Intervention Lesson A65

Name ____________________

Counting Money (continued)

Write the total value in dollars and cents.

7. $1.83

8. 1 five-dollar bill, 3 quarters, 1 nickel, 2 pennies
$5.82

9. 1 one-dollar bill, 1 half-dollar, 4 nickels, 8 pennies
$1.78

10. 1 one-dollar bill, 2 quarters, 4 dimes, 3 nickels, 1 penny
$2.06

11. 1 five-dollar bill, 1 one-dollar bill, 1 quarter, 4 dimes, 3 nickels
$6.80

Compare the amounts. Write <, >, or =.

12. $1.17 (<) 4 quarters, 2 dimes

13. $0.49 (>) 4 dimes, 1 nickel

14. 2 quarters, 6 dimes (=) $1.10

15. 3 half-dollars, 3 nickels (<) $1.70

16. Reasoning Anita and Ted both have $1.49, but each have different coins. What coins could each have?

Check that students have two different ways to show $1.49.

© Pearson Education, Inc.

224 Intervention Lesson A65

Teacher Notes

Ongoing Assessment

Ask: ***Suri has a $1 bill, 2 quarters, 3 dimes, 5 nickels, and 15 pennies. How much money does she have?*** $2.20

Error Intervention

If children have difficulty counting the value of the bills and coins,

then let them use play money and use A63: Dollars.

If children have trouble with the < and > signs,

then use A27: Using <, >, and = to Compare Numbers.

If You Have More Time

Have students work in pairs. Give partners a variety of bills and coins. Have partners sell and buy items in the classroom. The "seller" gives the price of the item. The "buyer" counts the correct amount of money out to the seller. Switch roles and repeat as time allows.

Making Change

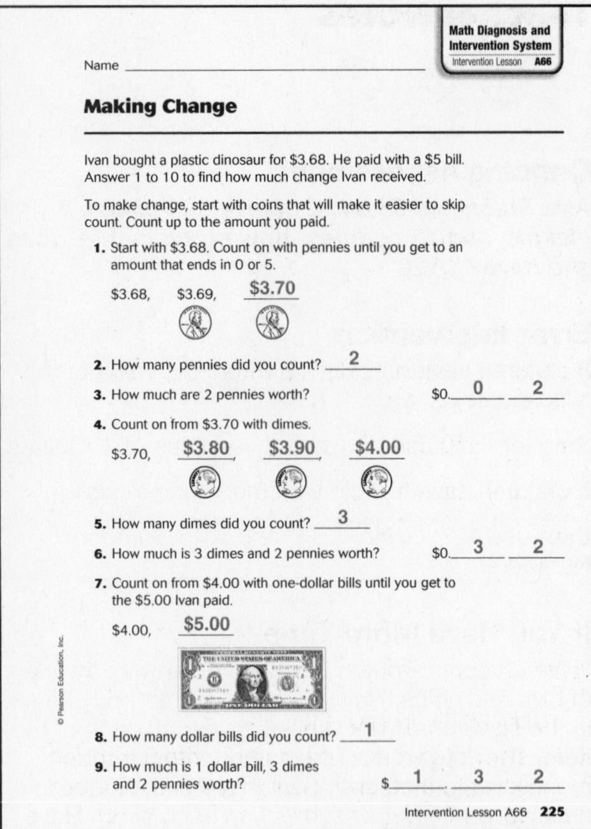

Math Diagnosis and Intervention System
Intervention Lesson A66

Name ______________________

Making Change

Ivan bought a plastic dinosaur for $3.68. He paid with a $5 bill. Answer 1 to 10 to find how much change Ivan received.

To make change, start with coins that will make it easier to skip count. Count up to the amount you paid.

1. Start with $3.68. Count on with pennies until you get to an amount that ends in 0 or 5.
   $3.68, $3.69, **$3.70**
2. How many pennies did you count? **2**
3. How much are 2 pennies worth? $0. **0** **2**
4. Count on from $3.70 with dimes.
   $3.70, **$3.80**, **$3.90**, **$4.00**
5. How many dimes did you count? **3**
6. How much is 3 dimes and 2 pennies worth? $0. **3** **2**
7. Count on from $4.00 with one-dollar bills until you get to the $5.00 Ivan paid.
   $4.00, **$5.00**
8. How many dollar bills did you count? **1**
9. How much is 1 dollar bill, 3 dimes and 2 pennies worth? $ **1**. **3** **2**

© Pearson Education, Inc.

Intervention Lesson A66 225

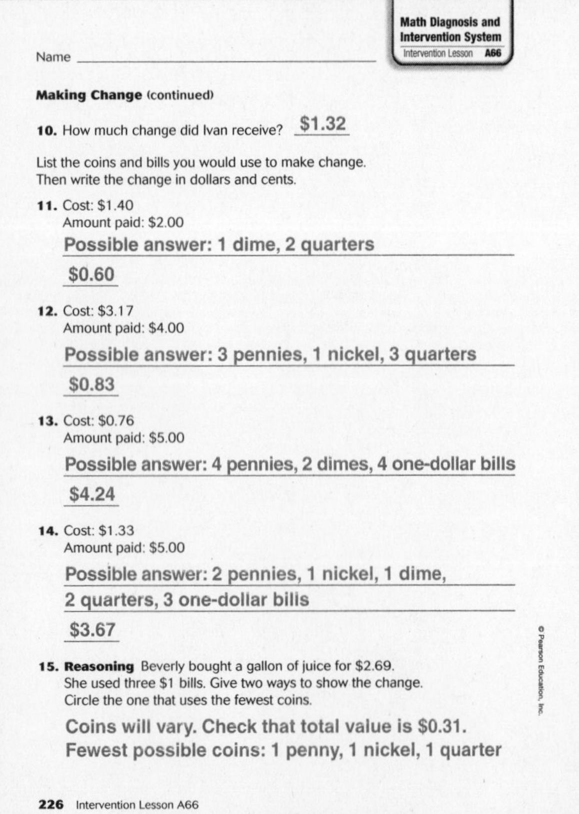

Math Diagnosis and Intervention System
Intervention Lesson A66

Name ______________________

Making Change (continued)

10. How much change did Ivan receive? **$1.32**

List the coins and bills you would use to make change. Then write the change in dollars and cents.

11. Cost: $1.40
    Amount paid: $2.00
    Possible answer: 1 dime, 2 quarters
    $0.60
12. Cost: $3.17
    Amount paid: $4.00
    Possible answer: 3 pennies, 1 nickel, 3 quarters
    $0.83
13. Cost: $0.76
    Amount paid: $5.00
    Possible answer: 4 pennies, 2 dimes, 4 one-dollar bills
    $4.24
14. Cost: $1.33
    Amount paid: $5.00
    Possible answer: 2 pennies, 1 nickel, 1 dime, 2 quarters, 3 one-dollar bills
    $3.67
15. **Reasoning** Beverly bought a gallon of juice for $2.69. She used three $1 bills. Give two ways to show the change. Circle the one that uses the fewest coins.
    Coins will vary. Check that total value is $0.31.
    Fewest possible coins: 1 penny, 1 nickel, 1 quarter

© Pearson Education, Inc.

226 Intervention Lesson A66

Teacher Notes

Ongoing Assessment

Ask: ***Meg bought a pencil that cost $0.35. She paid with a $5 bill. Explain how to count on to find how much change she received.*** 35 cents, 40 cents, 50 cents, 75 cents, 1 dollar, 2 dollars, 3 dollars, 4 dollars, 5 dollars. She received $4.65 in change.

Error Intervention

If students have trouble counting money,

then use H11: Counting Money and allow them to use play money to help visualize the change while counting.

If You Have More Time

Have students work in pairs. Give partners four $1 bills, one $5 bill, 1 half-dollar, 4 quarters, 10 dimes, 10 nickels, and 10 pennies. Have partners sell and buy items in the classroom. The "seller" gives the price of the item (between $0.01 and $9.00). The "buyer" can only pay with bills. The seller then counts out the "buyer's" change. Switch roles and repeat as time allows. Instead of classroom items, grocery ads can be used if available. Make sure items are available for the $0.01 to $9.00 price range in the ad.

Using Money to Understand Decimals

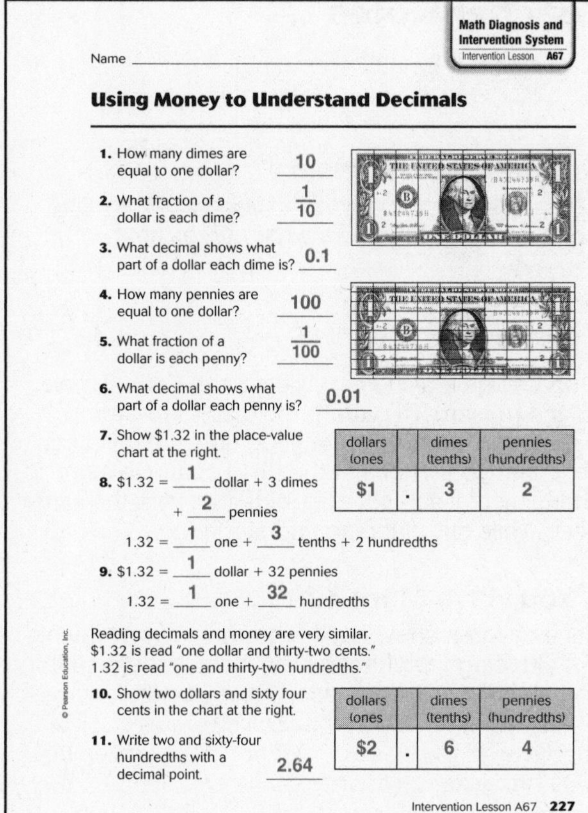
Math Diagnosis and Intervention System
Intervention Lesson A67

Name ______________________

Using Money to Understand Decimals

1. How many dimes are equal to one dollar? 10
2. What fraction of a dollar is each dime? $\frac{1}{10}$
3. What decimal shows what part of a dollar each dime is? 0.1
4. How many pennies are equal to one dollar? 100
5. What fraction of a dollar is each penny? $\frac{1}{100}$
6. What decimal shows what part of a dollar each penny is? 0.01
7. Show $1.32 in the place-value chart at the right.

dollars (ones		dimes (tenths)	pennies (hundredths)
$1	.	3	2

8. $1.32 = 1 dollar + 3 dimes + 2 pennies
   1.32 = 1 one + 3 tenths + 2 hundredths
9. $1.32 = 1 dollar + 32 pennies
   1.32 = 1 one + 32 hundredths

Reading decimals and money are very similar.
$1.32 is read "one dollar and thirty-two cents."
1.32 is read "one and thirty-two hundredths."

10. Show two dollars and sixty four cents in the chart at the right.

dollars (ones		dimes (tenths)	pennies (hundredths)
$2	.	6	4

11. Write two and sixty-four hundredths with a decimal point. 2.64

© Pearson Education, Inc.

Intervention Lesson A67 **227**

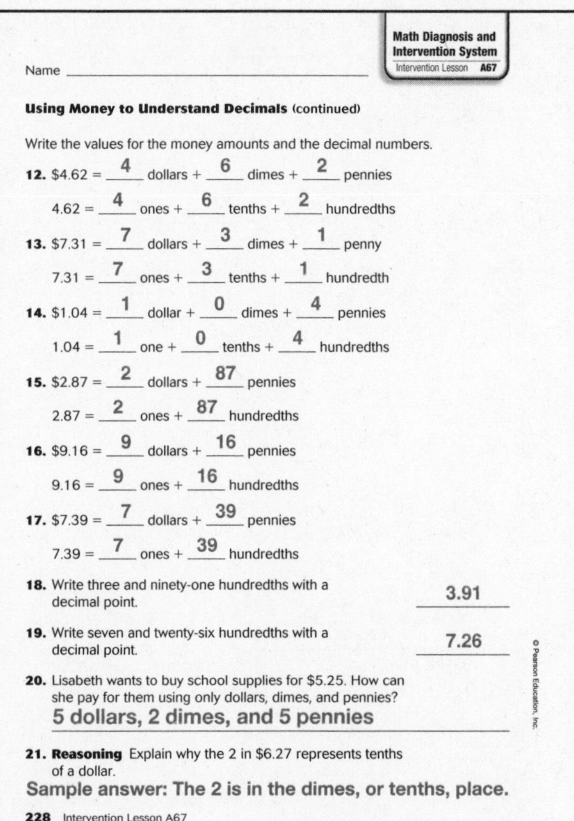
Math Diagnosis and Intervention System
Intervention Lesson A67

Name ______________________

Using Money to Understand Decimals (continued)

Write the values for the money amounts and the decimal numbers.

12. $4.62 = 4 dollars + 6 dimes + 2 pennies
    4.62 = 4 ones + 6 tenths + 2 hundredths
13. $7.31 = 7 dollars + 3 dimes + 1 penny
    7.31 = 7 ones + 3 tenths + 1 hundredth
14. $1.04 = 1 dollar + 0 dimes + 4 pennies
    1.04 = 1 one + 0 tenths + 4 hundredths
15. $2.87 = 2 dollars + 87 pennies
    2.87 = 2 ones + 87 hundredths
16. $9.16 = 9 dollars + 16 pennies
    9.16 = 9 ones + 16 hundredths
17. $7.39 = 7 dollars + 39 pennies
    7.39 = 7 ones + 39 hundredths
18. Write three and ninety-one hundredths with a decimal point. 3.91
19. Write seven and twenty-six hundredths with a decimal point. 7.26
20. Lisabeth wants to buy school supplies for $5.25. How can she pay for them using only dollars, dimes, and pennies?
    5 dollars, 2 dimes, and 5 pennies
21. **Reasoning** Explain why the 2 in $6.27 represents tenths of a dollar.
    Sample answer: The 2 is in the dimes, or tenths, place.

© Pearson Education, Inc.

228 Intervention Lesson A67

Teacher Notes

Ongoing Assessment

Ask: ***Explain why the 4 in $3.24 represents hundredths of a dollar.*** Sample answer: The 4 is in the pennies, or hundredths, place.

Error Intervention

If students have trouble with the tenths and hundredths concept,

then use H10: Fractions and Decimals.

If students have difficulty figuring out how many dimes and/or pennies there are in the money amount,

then use A57: Counting Pennies, Nickels, and Dimes and allow them to use play money while they count out the money amount.

If You Have More Time

Have students work in pairs and write 0 through 9, a decimal point, and a dollar sign on 12 index cards (one number or symbol on each card). Have one partner display 5 cards to show an amount in dollars and cents, like $5.47. Have the other partner read the amount and then say how many dollars, dimes, and pennies. Have the student remove the dollar sign, say the decimal amount, and then say how many ones, tenths, and hundredths. Have students take turns in each role with different amounts.

Patterns

Math Diagnosis and Intervention System
Intervention Lesson A68

Name ____________________

Patterns

1.

Children should color the circles red, blue, blue, red, blue, blue, red.

2.

3.

Children should color the circles red, blue, yellow, red, blue, yellow, red.

4.

Materials: Crayons or markers

1. Have a child describe the pattern. The child could say cat, dog, dog, cat, dog, dog. Ask: ***What comes next?*** Have children draw a line from the last dog to the cat.
2. Ask: ***What comes next in this similar sound pattern: meow, bark, bark, meow, bark, bark?*** Children should say meow.
3. Have children color the first circle red, the second circle blue, the third circle blue, and the fourth circle red. Ask: ***If this color pattern is similar to the cats and dogs pattern, what color comes next?*** Have children color the next circle blue. Have children finish the pattern.
4. Repeat with the next pattern. Use sounds like slosh, snap, swish. Then have children color the circles red, blue, yellow, and red. Have them finish the pattern.

© Pearson Education, Inc.

Intervention Lesson A68 **229**

Teacher Notes

Ongoing Assessment

Ask individual children to describe a pattern and explain how each knows what comes next.

Error Intervention

If children have trouble recognizing a pattern,

then imitate it using a musical beat. For example, for the mushroom pattern, do clap-clap-stomp, clap-clap-stomp, and continue until the child can do it with you. Then, let the child continue alone. Then say big-big-little, big-big-little, with the same beat, while still clapping and stomping.

If You Have More Time

Have children show each pattern with movements like clapping their hands over their heads, squatting and standing back up, and turning around.

Math Diagnosis and Intervention System
Intervention Lesson A68

Name ____________________

Patterns (continued)

Draw a line to the picture that comes next in the pattern. Then color the circles to match the pattern.

5.

Check that children color the circles correctly.

6.

© Pearson Education, Inc.

230 Intervention Lesson A68

Describing Patterns

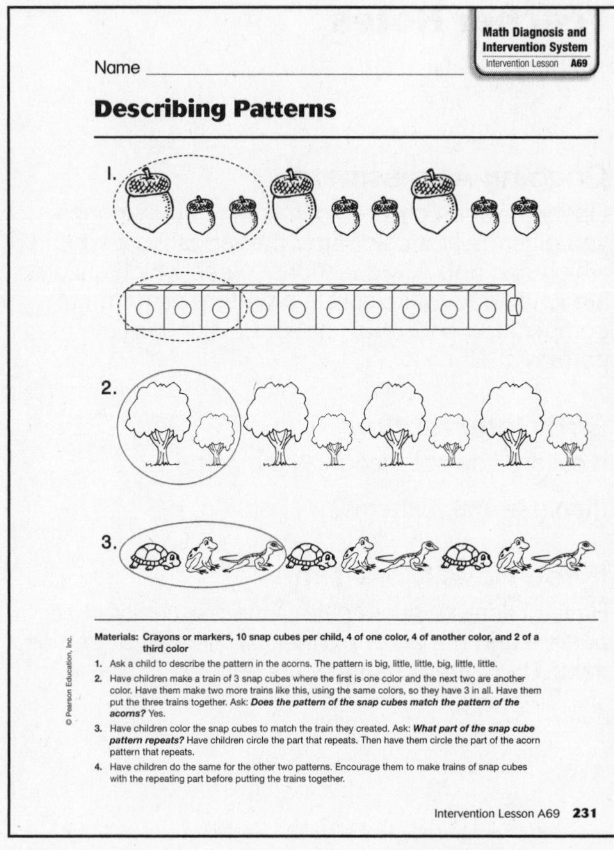

Math Diagnosis and Intervention System
Intervention Lesson A69

Name ______________________

Describing Patterns

1.

2.

3.

Materials: Crayons or markers, 10 snap cubes per child, 4 of one color, 4 of another color, and 2 of a third color

1. Ask a child to describe the pattern in the acorns. The pattern is big, little, little, big, little, little.
2. Have children make a train of 3 snap cubes where the first is one color and the next two are another color. Have them make two more trains like this, using the same colors, so they have 3 in all. Have them put the three trains together. Ask: ***Does the pattern of the snap cubes match the pattern of the acorns?*** Yes.
3. Have children color the snap cubes to match the train they created. Ask: ***What part of the snap cube pattern repeats?*** Have children circle the part that repeats. Then have them circle the part of the acorn pattern that repeats.
4. Have children do the same for the other two patterns. Encourage them to make trains of snap cubes with the repeating part before putting the trains together.

Intervention Lesson A69 **231**

Math Diagnosis and Intervention System
Intervention Lesson A69

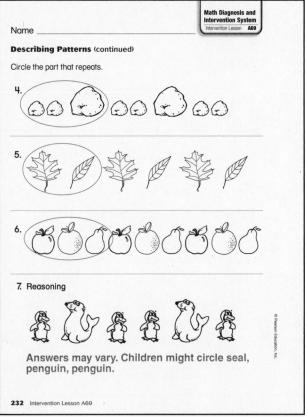

Name ______________________

Describing Patterns (continued)

Circle the part that repeats.

4.

5.

6.

7. Reasoning

Answers may vary. Children might circle seal, penguin, penguin.

232 Intervention Lesson A69

Teacher Notes

Ongoing Assessment

Make sure children make trains of snap cubes for the repeating part and then put the trains together. This will help them see how the repeating part of the pattern creates the whole.

Error Intervention

If children have difficulty describing the patterns on the second page,

then let them use snap cubes to represent the pattern.

If You Have More Time

Let children use sounds to describe each pattern, like clap-clap-stomp.

Using Patterns to Predict

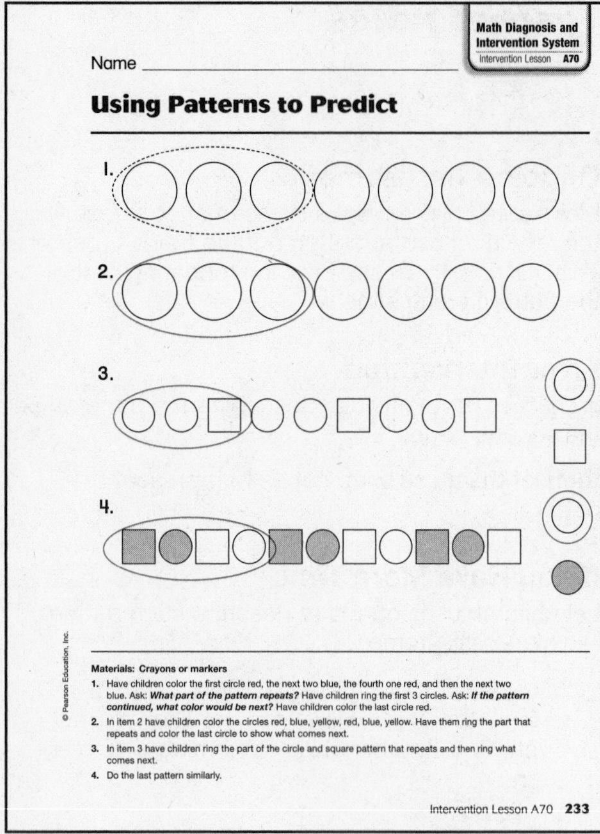
Math Diagnosis and Intervention System
Intervention Lesson A70

Name ____________________

Using Patterns to Predict

1.

2.

3.

4.

© Pearson Education, Inc.

Materials: Crayons or markers

1. Have children color the first circle red, the next two blue, the fourth one red, and then the next two blue. Ask: ***What part of the pattern repeats?*** Have children ring the first 3 circles. Ask: ***If the pattern continued, what color would be next?*** Have children color the last circle red.
2. In item 2 have children color the circles red, blue, yellow, red, blue, yellow. Have them ring the part that repeats and color the last circle to show what comes next.
3. In item 3 have children ring the part of the circle and square pattern that repeats and then ring what comes next.
4. Do the last pattern similarly.

Intervention Lesson A70 **233**

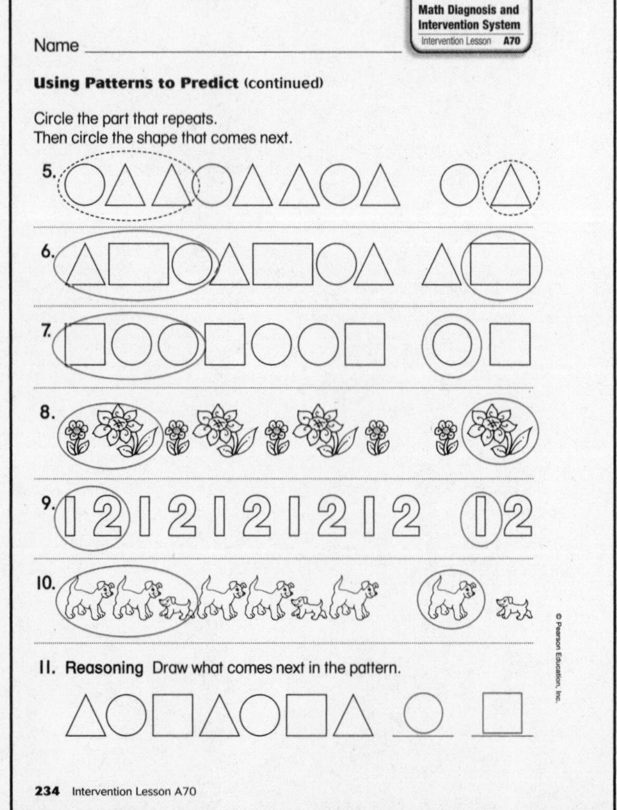
Math Diagnosis and Intervention System
Intervention Lesson A70

Name ____________________

Using Patterns to Predict (continued)

Circle the part that repeats.
Then circle the shape that comes next.

5.

6.

7.

8.

9. 1 2 1 2 1 2 1 2 1 2   1 2

10.

11. **Reasoning** Draw what comes next in the pattern.

© Pearson Education, Inc.

234 Intervention Lesson A70

Teacher Notes

Ongoing Assessment

Observe which children can finish coloring once you give the first color after the repeating part and which can not. Ask questions to see which children are waiting to make sure the pattern is not more complicated and which are not picking up the pattern at all.

Error Intervention

If children do not recognize the patterns,

then use A68: Patterns.

If You Have More Time

Have children work in pairs. One partner draws a pattern and the other partner predicts what comes next. Then, they change roles and repeat.

Extending Shape Patterns

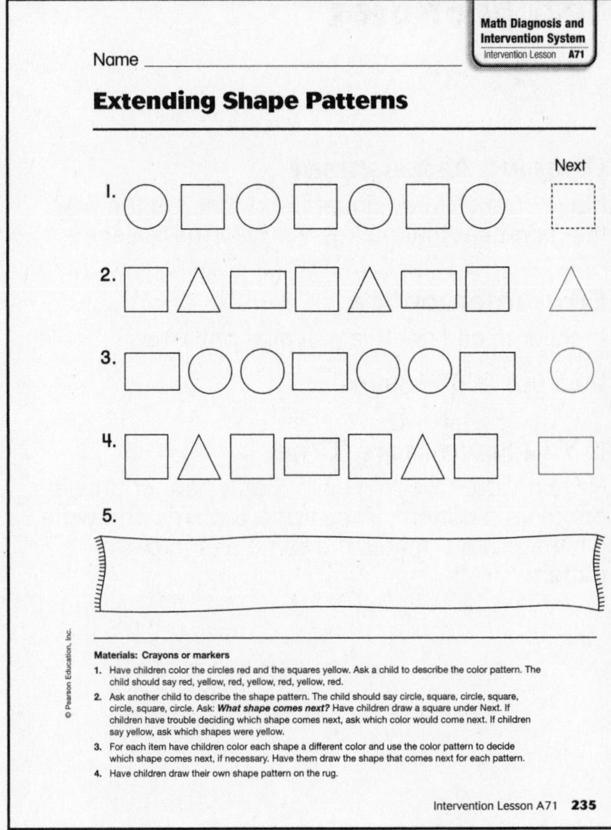

Math Diagnosis and Intervention System
Intervention Lesson A71

Name ______________________________

Extending Shape Patterns

Next

1.

2.

3.

4.

5.

Materials: Crayons or markers

1. Have children color the circles red and the squares yellow. Ask a child to describe the color pattern. The child should say red, yellow, red, yellow, red, yellow, red.
2. Ask another child to describe the shape pattern. The child should say circle, square, circle, square, circle, square, circle. Ask: ***What shape comes next?*** Have children draw a square under Next. If children have trouble deciding which shape comes next, ask which color would come next. If children say yellow, ask which shapes were yellow.
3. For each item have children color each shape a different color and use the color pattern to decide which shape comes next, if necessary. Have them draw the shape that comes next for each pattern.
4. Have children draw their own shape pattern on the rug.

© Pearson Education, Inc.

Intervention Lesson A71 **235**

Math Diagnosis and Intervention System
Intervention Lesson A71

Name ______________________________

Extending Shape Patterns (continued)

Circle the shape that comes next.

6.

7.

8.

9.

Reasoning Draw the missing shapes.

10.

11.

© Pearson Education, Inc.

236 Intervention Lesson A71

Teacher Notes

Ongoing Assessment

Make sure children can differentiate circles, squares, triangles, and rectangles.

Error Intervention

If children do not recognize the patterns,

then use A68: Patterns and A69: Describing Patterns.

If You Have More Time

Have children cut out squares, triangles, and circles from construction paper. Each child cuts out one shape. Choose children to line up at the front of the room in an order so that the shapes they made form a pattern. Have children who are seated name which shape comes next. Have a child with that shape join the ones in the front of the room. Continue for several more shapes. Then, repeat the activity with other children forming a different pattern.

Translating Patterns

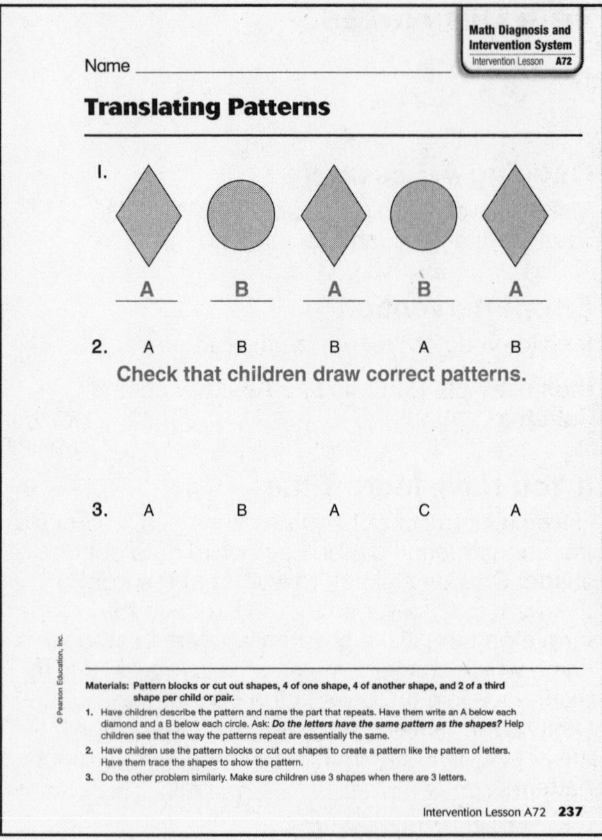

Math Diagnosis and Intervention System
Intervention Lesson A72

Name ____________________

Translating Patterns

1\. A B A B A

2\. A B B A B

Check that children draw correct patterns.

3\. A B A C A

Materials: Pattern blocks or cut out shapes, 4 of one shape, 4 of another shape, and 2 of a third shape per child or pair.

1. Have children describe the pattern and name the part that repeats. Have them write an A below each diamond and a B below each circle. Ask: ***Do the letters have the same pattern as the shapes?*** Help children see that the way the patterns repeat are essentially the same.
2. Have children use the pattern blocks or cut out shapes to create a pattern like the pattern of letters. Have them trace the shapes to show the pattern.
3. Do the other problem similarly. Make sure children use 3 shapes when there are 3 letters.

© Pearson Education, Inc.

Intervention Lesson A72 **237**

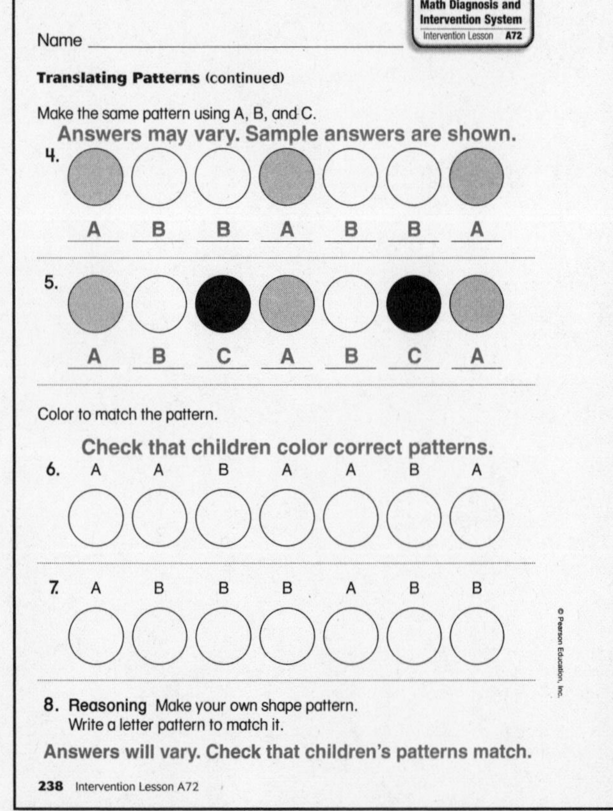

Math Diagnosis and Intervention System
Intervention Lesson A72

Name ____________________

Translating Patterns (continued)

Make the same pattern using A, B, and C.

Answers may vary. Sample answers are shown.

4\. A B B A B B A

5\. A B C A B C A

Color to match the pattern.

Check that children color correct patterns.

6\. A A B A A B A

7\. A B B B A B B

8\. **Reasoning** Make your own shape pattern. Write a letter pattern to match it.

Answers will vary. Check that children's patterns match.

© Pearson Education, Inc.

238 Intervention Lesson A72

Teacher Notes

Ongoing Assessment

Make sure children understand that it is the way things repeat that makes the patterns the same.

Error Intervention

If children can not relate similar patterns,

then use A68: Patterns.

If You Have More Time

Have children work in pairs. Each partner draws or colors a pattern. They trade patterns and write a letter pattern that is the same as the partner's pattern.

Math Diagnosis and Intervention System

Intervention Lesson **A73**

Find a Rule

Math Diagnosis and Intervention System
Intervention Lesson A73

Name ____________________

Find a Rule

1.

Teddy Bears	Bears and Dolls
2	5
3	6
5	8
6	**9**
8	**11**
9	**12**

Rule: +3

2.

Tacos	Tacos Left
3	1
4	2
6	4
9	**7**
12	**10**
14	**12**

Rule: **−2**

Materials: Two-color counters, 20 per child or pair

1. Have children show 2 counters for the teddy bears. Have them add or subtract counters until they get to 5. Ask: ***Did you add or subtract?*** Add ***How much did you add or subtract?*** 3
2. Have children show 3 red counters for the teddy bears in the second row. Have them add 3 yellow counters. Ask: ***Does the same rule, add 3, work to get 6 from 3?***
3. Have children see if the rule works to get 8 from 5. Then have them write the rule.
4. Have children use the rule to complete the table.
5. Have children show 3 counters for the tacos. Have them add or subtract counters until they get to 1. Ask if they added or subtracted and how much.
6. Have children see if the rule works for the next two rows. Then have them write the rule and use it to complete the table.

Intervention Lesson A73 **239**

Math Diagnosis and Intervention System
Intervention Lesson A73

Name ____________________

Find a Rule (continued)

Write a rule and complete each table.

3.

In	Out
6	11
7	12
9	14
10	**15**
12	**17**
15	**20**

Rule: +5

4.

In	Out
9	1
10	2
12	4
14	**6**
15	**7**
17	**9**

Rule: **−8**

5.

In	Out
6	2
8	4
9	5
10	**6**
12	**8**
14	**10**

Rule: **−4**

6.

In	Out
2	12
4	14
4	15
6	**16**
8	**18**
10	**20**

Rule: **+10**

240 Intervention Lesson A73

Teacher Notes

Ongoing Assessment

Notice which children use counters on the exercises and which do not need them.

Error Intervention

If children do not apply the same rule to every row of a table,

then write sums or differences next to the table. For example, for the teddy bears and dolls, write $2 + 3 = 5$ next to the first row, $3 + 3 = 6$ next to the second row and so on.

If You Have More Time

Let children work in pairs to create a function machine. One child writes down a rule and hides it from the other child. The second child gives the first child some counters. The first child applies the rule and returns an appropriate number of counters to the second child. They repeat this several times until the second child guesses the rule. Then, they change roles and repeat.

Repeating Patterns

Math Diagnosis and Intervention System
Intervention Lesson A74

Name ______________________

Repeating Patterns

Materials pattern blocks or shapes cut out of colored paper (10 orange squares, 10 green triangles, 10 red trapezoids) for each pair of students; 24 index cards (eight labeled 2, eight labeled 3, and eight labeled 4) for each pair of students

Look at the pattern of shapes.

1. Work with your partner to show the pattern. What is the next shape? **square**
2. Continue the pattern. What is the 14th shape? **square**
3. What is the 16th shape? **trapezoid**
4. Work with your partner and use the shapes to make a new pattern. Draw the pattern below. Draw the next four shapes.

Answers will vary. Check that patterns repeat consistently.

Look at the pattern of numbers.

3	3	2	4	3	3	2	4	3

5. Work with your partner to show the pattern. What is the next number? **3**
6. Continue the pattern. What is the 12th number? **4**
7. What is the 15th number? **2**
8. Work with your partner and use the numbers to make a new pattern. Write the pattern below. Write the next four numbers. **Answers will vary. Check that patterns repeat consistently.**

Math Diagnosis and Intervention System
Intervention Lesson A74

Name ______________________

Repeating Patterns (continued)

Draw the next three shapes to continue each pattern.

9. □ ⏢ △ ▽ □ ⏢ △ ▽ □ **⏢ △ ▽**
10. ○ □ □ ◺ ○ □ □ ◺ ○ □ **□ ◺ ○**
11. ☺ ⇧ ☺ ⇩ ☺ ⇧ ☺ ⇩ ☺ ⇧ **☺ ⇩ ☺**

Write the next three numbers to continue each pattern.

12. 1, 4, 6, 7, 1, 4, 6, 7, 1, 4, **6**, **7**, **1**
13. 8, 8, 9, 8, 8, 9, 8, 8, 9, 8, **8**, **9**, **8**
14. 3, 2, 0, 0, 3, 2, 0, 0, 3, 2, 0, **0**, **3**, **2**
15. 4, 4, 6, 6, 8, 8, 4, 4, 6, 6, 8, 8, 4, **4**, **6**, **6**
16. Create a pattern using all the shapes shown below.

□□□□○○○○

Answers will vary. Sample answer: square, circle, square, circle, square, circle, square, circle

17. Create a pattern using all the letters shown below.

T T T L L W W L W

Answers will vary. Sample answer: T L W T L W T L W

Teacher Notes

Ongoing Assessment

Ask: ***Can a pattern be formed by using only circles?*** Sample answer: Yes, if different size circles are used. The pattern could be small circle, small circle, big circle.

Error Intervention

If students can recognize the numerical patterns, but have trouble recognizing the geometric patterns,

then have students assign/label each type of shape with a different number or letter. Have them look for a pattern with the numbers. For example, the squares could be “1”, triangles “2”, and trapezoids “3”.

If students can not spell the names of the shapes,

then have students draw the shapes instead of naming them.

If You Have More Time

Have one student in each pair use the shapes or index cards to make a pattern for their partner to extend. Change roles and repeat.

Number Patterns

Math Diagnosis and Intervention System
Intervention Lesson A75

Name ______________________

Number Patterns

Find the next three numbers in the pattern 1, 3, 5, 7, 9, by answering 1 to 5.

1. Plot 1, 3, 5, 7, and 9 on the number line. Then continue to draw arrows from 3 to 5, from 5 to 7, and from 7 to 9.

0 1 2 3 4 5 6 7 8 9 10 11 12 13 14 15 16 17 18 19 20

2. How many spaces are between each number plotted on the number line? 2

3. Do you add or subtract the number of spaces to get to the next number? add

4. What is the rule for this pattern? Add 2

5. What are the next three numbers in the pattern 1, 3, 5, 7, 9? 11, 13, 15

6. Draw arrows on the number line to find the next two numbers in the following pattern.

26, 22, 18, 14, 10, 6

6 8 10 12 14 16 18 20 22 24 26

7. What is the rule for this pattern? Subtract 4.

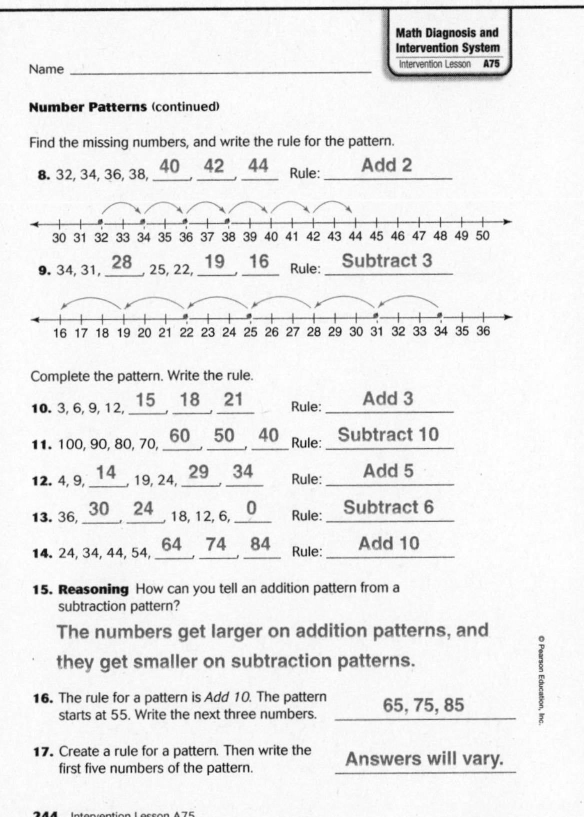

Math Diagnosis and Intervention System
Intervention Lesson A75

Name ______________________

Number Patterns (continued)

Find the missing numbers, and write the rule for the pattern.

8. 32, 34, 36, 38, 40, 42, 44 Rule: Add 2

30 31 32 33 34 35 36 37 38 39 40 41 42 43 44 45 46 47 48 49 50

9. 34, 31, 28, 25, 22, 19, 16 Rule: Subtract 3

16 17 18 19 20 21 22 23 24 25 26 27 28 29 30 31 32 33 34 35 36

Complete the pattern. Write the rule.

10. 3, 6, 9, 12, 15, 18, 21 Rule: Add 3

11. 100, 90, 80, 70, 60, 50, 40 Rule: Subtract 10

12. 4, 9, 14, 19, 24, 29, 34 Rule: Add 5

13. 36, 30, 24, 18, 12, 6, 0 Rule: Subtract 6

14. 24, 34, 44, 54, 64, 74, 84 Rule: Add 10

15. Reasoning How can you tell an addition pattern from a subtraction pattern?

The numbers get larger on addition patterns, and they get smaller on subtraction patterns.

16. The rule for a pattern is *Add 10.* The pattern starts at 55. Write the next three numbers. 65, 75, 85

17. Create a rule for a pattern. Then write the first five numbers of the pattern. Answers will vary.

© Pearson Education, Inc.

244 Intervention Lesson A75

Teacher Notes

Ongoing Assessment

Ask: ***Why should you look at the relationship between more than 1 pair of numbers before stating the rule?*** Sample answer: If the first two numbers in the pattern are 4 and 8, it could be either multiply by 2 or add 4.

Error Intervention

If students can not identify the rule of the number sequence pattern easily,

then have them write the operation sign and then the amount between each pair of numbers in the sequence. For example, +6 would be written between 8 and 14 and 14 and 20 in a sequence.

If You Have More Time

Have students make different number patterns with *Subtract 5* as a rule.

Input/Output Tables

Math Diagnosis and Intervention System
Intervention Lesson A76

Name ______________________

Input/Output Tables

1. There are 5 pennies in a nickel. Draw two sets of 5 pennies next to the row with 2 nickels, in the table below.

Nickels	Pennies
1	5
2	10
3	15
4	20
5	25
7	35
8	40

2. How many pennies equal 2 nickels? Write your answer in the table.

3. Complete the table. Draw pennies, if necessary.

4. What is the rule for the table? Multiply by 5.

5. **Reasoning** How can you find the number of pennies in 9 nickels?
Multiply 9 by 5.

6. How many pennies are in 9 nickels? 45

7. How many pennies are in 10 nickels? 50

Intervention Lesson A76 **245**

Math Diagnosis and Intervention System
Intervention Lesson A76

Name ______________________

Input/Output Tables (continued)

Complete the table. Write the rule.

8.

Number of Ants	Number of Legs
1	6
2	12
3	18
4	24
5	30

Rule: Multiply by 6

9.

Regular Price	Sale Price
$5	$3
$7	$5
$8	$6
$12	$10
$17	$15

Rule: Subtract 2

10.

My Age	My Brother's Age
9	12
10	13
12	15
15	18
20	23

Rule: Add 3

11.

Number of Packages	Number of Pencils
1	8
3	24
5	40
6	48
8	64

Rule: Multiply by 8

12.

Loaves of Bread	2	4	5	7	10
Number of Eggs Used	8	16	20	28	40

Rule: Multiply by 4

13.

Total Weight of Suitcase and Contents in Pounds	5	7	9	11	14
Content of Suitcase in Pounds	3	5	7	9	12

Rule: Subtract 2

246 Intervention Lesson A76

Teacher Notes

Ongoing Assessment

Make sure students understand that all the pairs of numbers must follow the same rule.

Error Intervention

If students have trouble finding missing values for larger numbers,

then have them add a column and label it "Think". Have them write the operation used to get from the left column to the right column for the small numbers and then continue for the larger numbers.

If You Have More Time

Have students set up a table for Dimes and Nickels. Use 1, 2, 3, 4, 5, 7, and 9 in the Dimes column.

Geometric Growth Patterns

Math Diagnosis and Intervention System
Intervention Lesson **A77**

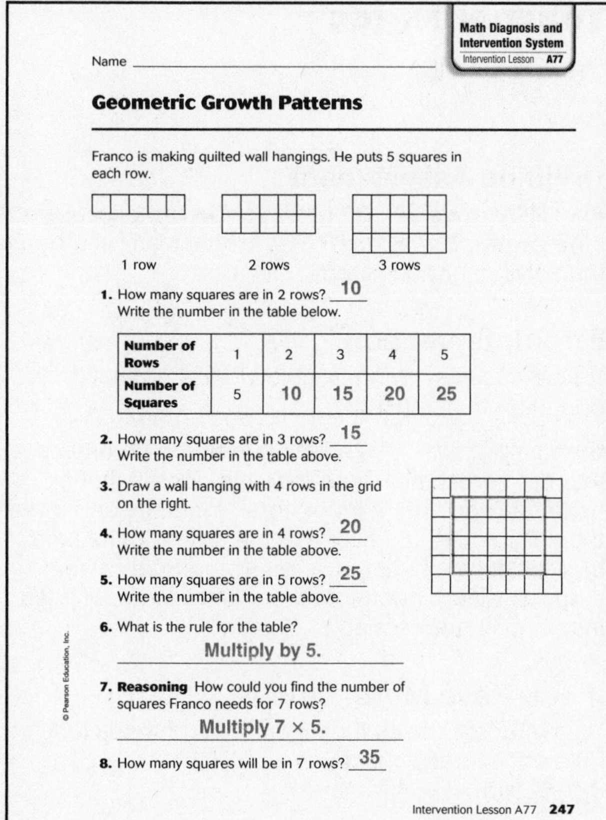

Math Diagnosis and Intervention System
Intervention Lesson A77

Name ______________________

Geometric Growth Patterns

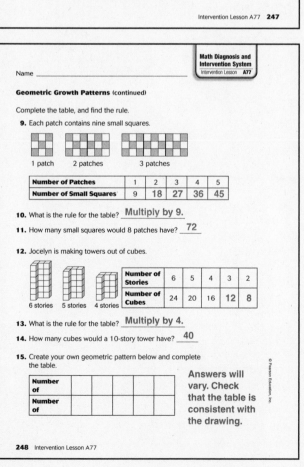

Franco is making quilted wall hangings. He puts 5 squares in each row.

1 row 2 rows 3 rows

1. How many squares are in 2 rows? 10
Write the number in the table below.

Number of Rows	1	2	3	4	5
Number of Squares	5	10	15	20	25

2. How many squares are in 3 rows? 15
Write the number in the table above.
3. Draw a wall hanging with 4 rows in the grid on the right.
4. How many squares are in 4 rows? 20
Write the number in the table above.
5. How many squares are in 5 rows? 25
Write the number in the table above.
6. What is the rule for the table?
Multiply by 5.
7. **Reasoning** How could you find the number of squares Franco needs for 7 rows?
Multiply 7 × 5.
8. How many squares will be in 7 rows? 35

Math Diagnosis and Intervention System
Intervention Lesson A77

Name ______________________

Geometric Growth Patterns (continued)

Complete the table, and find the rule.

9. Each patch contains nine small squares.

1 patch 2 patches 3 patches

Number of Patches	1	2	3	4	5
Number of Small Squares	9	18	27	36	45

10. What is the rule for the table? Multiply by 9.
11. How many small squares would 8 patches have? 72
12. Jocelyn is making towers out of cubes.

6 stories 5 stories 4 stories

Number of Stories	6	5	4	3	2
Number of Cubes	24	20	16	12	8

13. What is the rule for the table? Multiply by 4.
14. How many cubes would a 10-story tower have? 40
15. Create your own geometric pattern below and complete the table.

Number of					
Number of					

Answers will vary. Check that the table is consistent with the drawing.

Teacher Notes

Ongoing Assessment

Ask: ***What would the rule be if Franco put 6 squares in each row?*** Sample answer: Multiply by 6.

Error Intervention

If students have trouble visualizing the wall hangings with more than 4 rows,

then allow them to draw the hangings using grid paper.

If You Have More Time

Have students list places geometric patterns are found in the real world.

Translating Words to Expressions

Math Diagnosis and Intervention System
Intervention Lesson A78

Name ____________________

Translating Words to Expressions

Materials counters, 12 per student

Show each word phrase with counters. Draw a picture of your counters. Then, write a number expression for each word phrase.

	Word Phrase	Picture of your Counters	Number Expression
1.	15 pennies separated into 3 equal groups		15 ÷ 3
2.	the total of 8 pennies and 4 pennies		8 + 4
3.	4 times as many as 3 pennies		4 × 3
4.	give away 6 of 10 pennies		10 − 6
5.	6 divided into groups with 2 in each		6 ÷ 2

Math Diagnosis and Intervention System
Intervention Lesson A78

Name ____________________

Translating Words to Expressions (continued)

Write a number expression for each word phrase.

6. twice as many as 8 yards
2 × 8

7. 16 rings shared equally by 4 boys
16 ÷ 4

8. 21 separated into 7 equal groups
21 ÷ 7

9. the total of 14 boys and 15 girls
14 + 15

10. 16 fewer than 20
20 − 16

11. 3 times as far as 8 miles
3 × 8

12. 4 hours shorter than 6 hours
6 − 4

13. the total of 6, 3, and 8
6 + 3 + 8

14. 8 toys put into 2 equal groups
8 ÷ 2

15. 6 more than 7 apples
7 + 6

16. 5 fewer than 12 eggs
12 − 5

17. 3 times as many as 9 carrots
3 × 9

18. Reasoning Can you have 7 fewer than 5 dogs?
Sample answer: No; If there are only 5 dogs to start with, you can't have fewer than that.

19. Reasoning Socorra reads the phrase *18 decreased by 9* and writes the expression 9 − 18. Do you agree with Socorra's expression? Explain.
No, Socorra's expression translates to 9 decreased by 18. The correct expression is 18 − 9.

Teacher Notes

Ongoing Assessment

Ask: ***Why does 9 ÷ 3 not describe the expression "the product of 9 and 3"?*** A product is found by multiplying, not dividing.

Error Intervention

If students are having trouble identifying the operation that is used,

then help them make a list of common phrases that are sometimes used for each operation. For example, addition: sum of, total, together, and more than. Subtraction: fewer than, less, and difference of. Multiplication: times as many, product of, and times. Division: quotient of, separated into, divided into, and shared equally.

If You Have More Time

Have students write their own word phrases for different expressions, such as 5 + 10, 15 − 6, 3 × 5, and 12 ÷ 4.

Counting by Hundreds

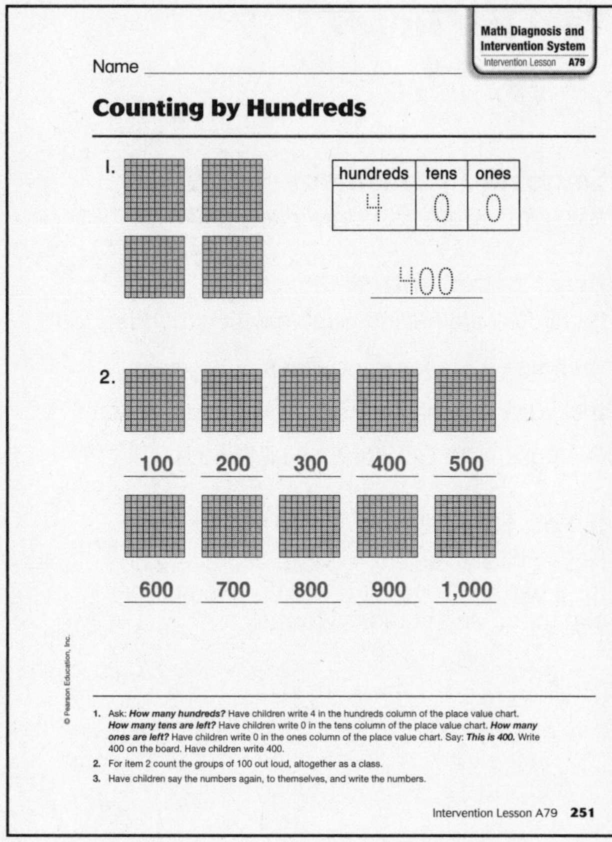

Math Diagnosis and Intervention System
Intervention Lesson A79

Name ____________________

Counting by Hundreds

1.

hundreds	tens	ones
4	0	0

400

2.

100 200 300 400 500

600 700 800 900 1,000

1. Ask: ***How many hundreds?*** Have children write 4 in the hundreds column of the place value chart. ***How many tens are left?*** Have children write 0 in the tens column of the place value chart. ***How many ones are left?*** Have children write 0 in the ones column of the place value chart. Say: ***This is 400.*** Write 400 on the board. Have children write 400.
2. For item 2 count the groups of 100 out loud, altogether as a class.
3. Have children say the numbers again, to themselves, and write the numbers.

Intervention Lesson A79 251

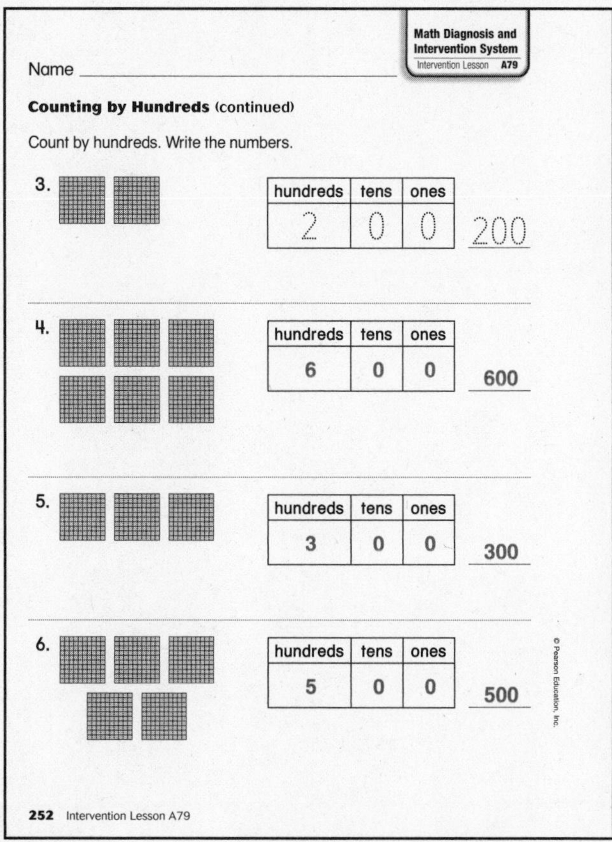

Math Diagnosis and Intervention System
Intervention Lesson A79

Name ____________________

Counting by Hundreds (continued)

Count by hundreds. Write the numbers.

3.

hundreds	tens	ones
2	0	0

200

4.

hundreds	tens	ones
6	0	0

600

5.

hundreds	tens	ones
3	0	0

300

6.

hundreds	tens	ones
5	0	0

500

252 Intervention Lesson A79

Teacher Notes

Ongoing Assessment

Have children count out loud by 100s to 1,000.

Error Intervention

If children have trouble deciding how to write a number like 500,

then tell them the first digit tells how many groups of a hundred. So if there are 5 groups of a hundred, the number is a 5, a 0, and a 0.

If You Have More Time

Have 8 children come to the front of the room. Have each child hold a hundred flat or a hundred grid drawn on grid paper. Have 8 children who are still sitting each count a hundred. For example, if the first two children standing are Maria and Jamal, the first child sitting says, "Maria makes 100," and the second child sitting says, "Jamal makes 200." Continue to 800. Select 8 different children to stand and repeat the activity.

Building Numbers to 999

Math Diagnosis and Intervention System
Intervention Lesson A80

Name ____________________

Building Numbers to 999

1\.

hundreds	tens	ones
3	5	4

354

300 + 50 + 4 = 354

2\.

hundreds	tens	ones
5	1	8

518

500 + 10 + 8 = 518

Materials: Place-value blocks, 5 hundreds, 5 tens, and 8 ones per pair or group

1. Have students show 3 hundreds, 5 tens, and 4 ones.
2. Ask: ***How many hundreds?*** Have children write 3 in the hundreds column of the place value chart. ***How many tens are left?*** Have children write 5 in the tens column of the place value chart. ***How many ones are left?*** Have children write 4 in the ones column of the place value chart. Say: ***This is 354.*** Write 354 on the board. Have students write 354.
3. Ask: ***How much is 3 hundreds?*** Have children write 300 in the first blank of the expanded form. ***How much is 5 tens?*** Have children write 50 in the second blank of the expanded form. ***How much is 4 ones?*** Have children write 4 in the third blank of the expanded form. Say: ***300 + 50 + 5 = 354***. Have students write 354.
4. Do item 2 similarly.

Intervention Lesson A80 **253**

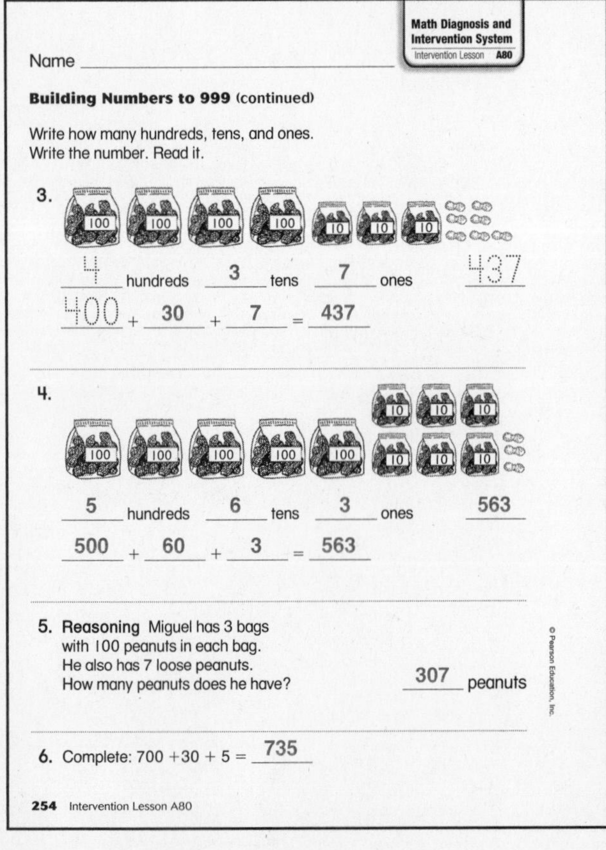
Math Diagnosis and Intervention System
Intervention Lesson A80

Name ____________________

Building Numbers to 999 (continued)

Write how many hundreds, tens, and ones.
Write the number. Read it.

3\. 4 hundreds 3 tens 7 ones 437

400 + 30 + 7 = 437

4\. 5 hundreds 6 tens 3 ones 563

500 + 60 + 3 = 563

5\. **Reasoning** Miguel has 3 bags with 100 peanuts in each bag. He also has 7 loose peanuts. How many peanuts does he have? 307 peanuts

6\. Complete: 700 +30 + 5 = 735

254 Intervention Lesson A80

Teacher Notes

Ongoing Assessment

Ask: ***How many hundreds are in 643?*** 6

Error Intervention

If children are having trouble with expanded form,

then use A24: Tens and Ones.

If children are having trouble with hundreds,

then use A79: Counting by Hundreds.

If You Have More Time

Have children select a group of place-value blocks for a partner to count and write the number in expanded and standard forms.

Reading and Writing Numbers to 999

Math Diagnosis and Intervention System
Intervention Lesson A81

Name ____________________

Reading and Writing Numbers to 999

Number Words		
Ones	Teens	Tens
1 one	11 eleven	10 ten
2 two	12 twelve	20 twenty
3 three	13 thirteen	30 thirty
4 four	14 fourteen	40 forty
5 five	15 fifteen	50 fifty
6 six	16 sixteen	60 sixty
7 seven	17 seventeen	70 seventy
8 eight	18 eighteen	80 eighty
9 nine	19 nineteen	90 ninety

1. three hundred sixty-one
   300 + 60 + __1__
   = __361__

2. four hundred fifty-eight
   400 + __50__ + __8__
   = __458__

3. 236 = 200 + __30__ + __6__
   __two__ hundred __thirty-six__

4. 549 = 500 + __40__ + __9__
   __five__ hundred __forty-nine__

1. Ask: ***The number three hundred sixty-one can be written as 300 plus 60 plus what?*** Have the students write the 1 in the blank.
2. Say: ***What does 300 plus 60 plus 1 equal?*** Write 361 on the board. Have students write 361.
3. Have children do item 2 similarly.
4. Write 236 on the board or overhead. Have children write the number in expanded form. Avoid saying two hundred thirty-six.
5. Ask a child how to say the number written on the board or overhead. Say: ***To write 236, write the number of hundreds and the word hundred. Then write the 36 as you did for two-digit numbers. Thirty hyphen six.*** Have children write two in the blank before hundred and thirty-six in the blank after.
6. Have children do item 4 similarly.

Intervention Lesson A81 **255**

Math Diagnosis and Intervention System
Intervention Lesson A81

Name ____________________

Reading and Writing Numbers to 999 (continued)

Write each number in expanded and standard form.

5. four hundred twelve
   __400__ + __10__ + __2__
   = __412__

6. eight hundred seventy
   __800__ + __70__ + __0__
   = __870__

7. three hundred fifty-one
   __300__ + __50__ + __1__
   = __351__

8. nine hundred four
   __900__ + __0__ + __4__
   = __904__

Write the number in expanded form and in words.

9. 238 = __200__ + __30__ + __8__
   __two hundred thirty-eight__

10. 667 = __600__ + __60__ + __7__
    __six hundred sixty-seven__

11. 540 = __500__ + __40__ + __0__
    __five hundred forty__

12. 415 = __400__ + __10__ + __5__
    __four hundred fifteen__

256 Intervention Lesson A81

Teacher Notes

Ongoing Assessment

Observe that the children are not using the word "and" after the word "hundred". Example: five hundred and sixty-seven

Error Intervention

If children are having trouble with number words for numbers less than 100,

then use A29: Number Words to Twenty and A30: Number Words.

If You Have More Time

Have children work in groups of 3. Each group should label 9 index cards 1 through 9. Shuffle and place the cards face down. Each child picks a card. Have the children each write two different three-digit numbers with the digits on the cards. Then have them write all of the group's variations in expanded and word form.

Changing Numbers by Hundreds and Tens

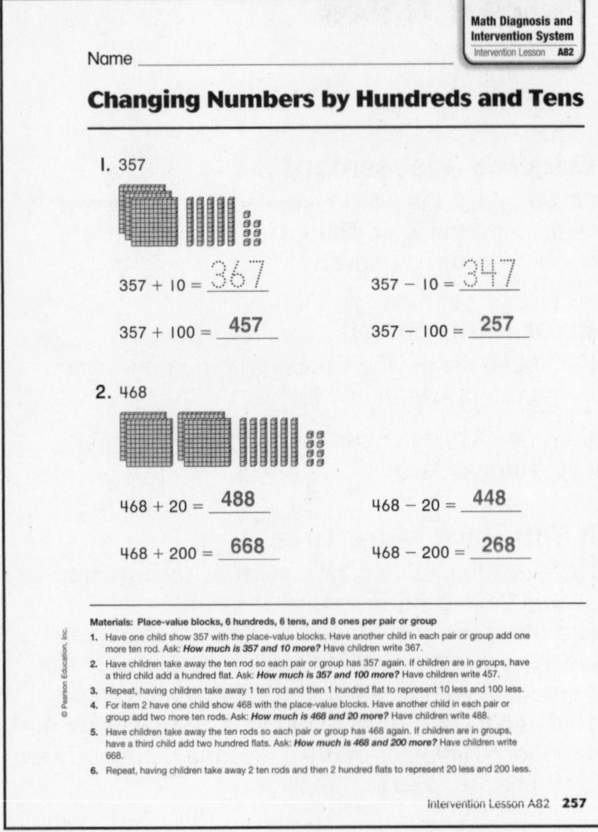

Math Diagnosis and Intervention System
Intervention Lesson A82

Name ____________________

Changing Numbers by Hundreds and Tens

1. 357

357 + 10 = 367 357 − 10 = 347

357 + 100 = 457 357 − 100 = 257

2. 468

468 + 20 = 488 468 − 20 = 448

468 + 200 = 668 468 − 200 = 268

Materials: Place-value blocks, 6 hundreds, 6 tens, and 8 ones per pair or group

1. Have one child show 357 with the place-value blocks. Have another child in each pair or group add one more ten rod. Ask: ***How much is 357 and 10 more?*** Have children write 367.
2. Have children take away the ten rod so each pair or group has 357 again. If children are in groups, have a third child add a hundred flat. Ask: ***How much is 357 and 100 more?*** Have children write 457.
3. Repeat, having children take away 1 ten rod and then 1 hundred flat to represent 10 less and 100 less.
4. For item 2 have one child show 468 with the place-value blocks. Have another child in each pair or group add two more ten rods. Ask: ***How much is 468 and 20 more?*** Have children write 488.
5. Have children take away the ten rods so each pair or group has 468 again. If children are in groups, have a third child add two hundred flats. Ask: ***How much is 468 and 200 more?*** Have children write 668.
6. Repeat, having children take away 2 ten rods and then 2 hundred flats to represent 20 less and 200 less.

© Pearson Education, Inc.

Intervention Lesson A82 **257**

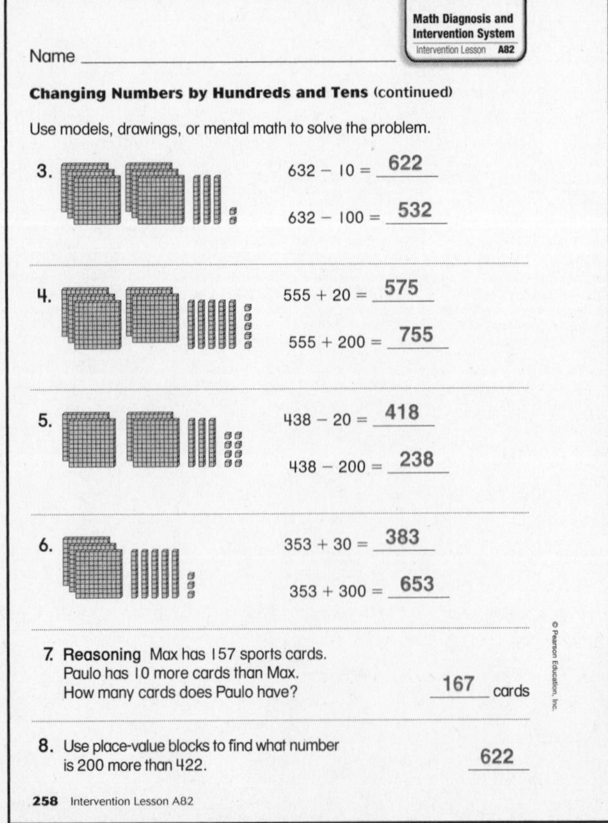

Math Diagnosis and Intervention System
Intervention Lesson A82

Name ____________________

Changing Numbers by Hundreds and Tens (continued)

Use models, drawings, or mental math to solve the problem.

3. 632 − 10 = 622
632 − 100 = 532

4. 555 + 20 = 575
555 + 200 = 755

5. 438 − 20 = 418
438 − 200 = 238

6. 353 + 30 = 383
353 + 300 = 653

7. **Reasoning** Max has 157 sports cards. Paulo has 10 more cards than Max. How many cards does Paulo have? 167 cards

8. Use place-value blocks to find what number is 200 more than 422. 622

© Pearson Education, Inc.

258 Intervention Lesson A82

Teacher Notes

Ongoing Assessment

Observe to see which children figure out to add or subtract the amount mentally and which children continue using the blocks or drawings.

Error Intervention

If children do not have models to use,

then encourage students to draw in the flats or rods that are being added, or cross out the flats or rods that are being subtracted.

If children have trouble finding 10 more or less,

then use A26: 1 More or 1 Less, 10 More or Less.

If children have trouble finding 100 more or less,

then use A79: Counting by Hundreds.

If You Have More Time

Show advertisements with prices of items in the hundreds (washer/dryers, electronics). Have children work in pairs. Have one partner be a salesperson that offers an extra special discount. The salesperson can say something like "Just for you I will take $10 off the price of the washer." The buyer then calculates the extra special sale price. Switch roles and repeat with different prices.

Patterns with Numbers on Hundreds Charts

Math Diagnosis and Intervention System
Intervention Lesson A83

Name ______________________

Patterns with Numbers on Hundreds Charts

210	220	230	240	250	260	270	280	290	300
310	320	330	340	350	360	370	380	390	400
410	420	430	440	450	460	470	480	490	500
510	520	530	540	550	560	570	580	590	600

1. 430 + 10 = **440**
2. 430 − 10 = **420**
3. 430 + 100 = **530**
4. 430 − 100 = **330**
5. 220 + 10 = **230**
6. 480 + 100 = **580**
7. 370 − 10 = **360**
8. 550 − 100 = **450**

9.

47	48	**49**
57	**58**	59
67	68	**69**

10.

470	**480**	490
570	580	**590**
670	680	690

1. Have children find 430 on the chart. For item 1 Say: ***To find the number that is 10 more than 430, move 1 space right.*** Ask: ***What number is 10 more than 430?*** Have children write 440. For item 2 Say: ***To find the number that is 10 less than 430, move 1 space left from 430.*** Ask: ***What number is 10 less than 430?*** Have children write 420.
2. For items 3 and 4 Say: ***To find the number that is 100 more than 430, move 1 row down from 430.*** Ask: ***What number is 100 more than 430?*** Have children write 530. Say: ***To find the number that is 100 less than 430, move 1 row up from, 430*** Ask: ***What number is 100 less than 430?*** Have children write 330.
3. Have children do items 5 to 8 similarly.
4. Have children complete the chart in item 9. Say: ***In the chart in item 9, numbers change by one as you move left and right. How do the numbers change as you move left and right in the chart in item 10?*** By 10s ***In the chart in item 9, numbers change by ten as you move up and down rows. How do the numbers change as you move up and down rows in the chart in item 10?*** By 100s
5. Have children use the chart in item 9 to help them complete the chart in item 10.

Intervention Lesson A83 **259**

Math Diagnosis and Intervention System
Intervention Lesson A83

Name ______________________

Patterns with Numbers on Hundreds Charts (continued)

Use the hundreds chart to complete.

410	420	430	440	450	460	470	480	490	500
510	520	530	540	550	560	570	580	590	600
610	620	630	640	650	660	670	680	690	700
710	720	730	740	750	760	770	780	790	800
810	820	830	840	850	860	870	880	890	900

11. 690 + 10 = **700**
12. 530 + 100 = **630**
13. 850 − 10 = **840**
14. 720 − 100 = **620**
15. 740 + 100 = **840**
16. 870 − 10 = **860**

Find the missing numbers.

17.

65	**66**	**67**
75	76	77
85	**86**	87

18.

650	**660**	670
750	760	**770**
850	860	870

19.

21	22	23
31	32	**33**
41	42	**43**

20.

210	**220**	230
310	**320**	330
410	420	430

260 Intervention Lesson A83

Teacher Notes

Ongoing Assessment

Ask: ***What number is 10 more than 340?*** 350
What number is 100 less than 760? 660

Error Intervention

If children are having trouble remembering which way to move on a hundreds chart,

then encourage children to draw an arrow pointing up and write "− 100", draw an arrow pointing to the right and write "+ 10", draw an arrow pointing down and write "+ 100", and draw an arrow pointing left and write "− 10".

If You Have More Time

In pairs have children play I'm Thinking of a Number with a partner. One child writes down a three-digit number and says: I'm thinking of a number. One hundred more than my number is 450. What is my number? The other partner says the number. Then, they change roles and repeat.

Comparing Numbers to 999

Math Diagnosis and Intervention System
Intervention Lesson **A84**

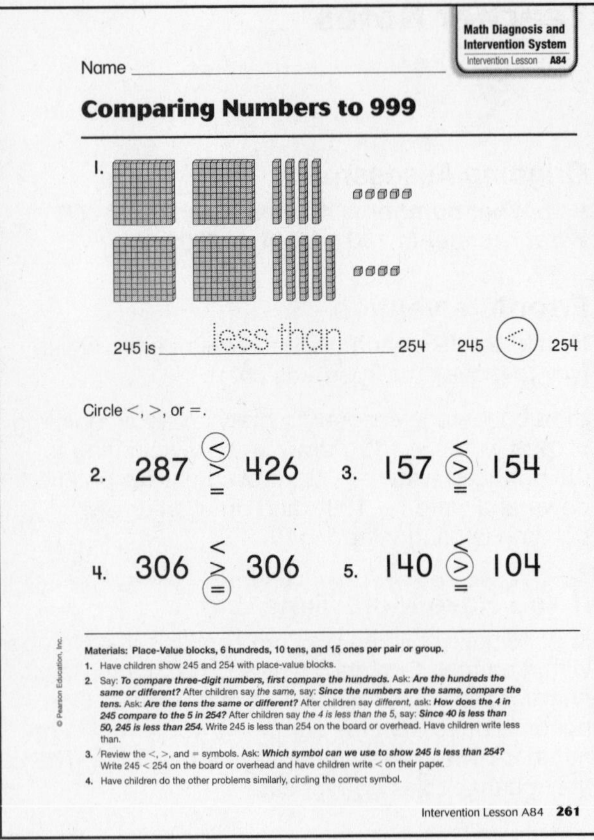

Math Diagnosis and Intervention System
Intervention Lesson A84

Name ______________________

Comparing Numbers to 999

1.

245 is less than 254 245 (<) 254

Circle <, >, or =.

2. 287 (<) 426
3. 157 (>) 154
4. 306 (=) 306
5. 140 (>) 104

Materials: Place-Value blocks, 6 hundreds, 10 tens, and 15 ones per pair or group.

1. Have children show 245 and 254 with place-value blocks.
2. Say: ***To compare three-digit numbers, first compare the hundreds.*** Ask: ***Are the hundreds the same or different?*** After children say *the same*, say: ***Since the numbers are the same, compare the tens.*** Ask: ***Are the tens the same or different?*** After children say *different*, ask: ***How does the 4 in 245 compare to the 5 in 254?*** After children say *the 4 is less than the 5*, say: ***Since 40 is less than 50, 245 is less than 254.*** Write 245 is less than 254 on the board or overhead. Have children write less than.
3. Review the <, >, and = symbols. Ask: ***Which symbol can we use to show 245 is less than 254?*** Write 245 < 254 on the board or overhead and have children write < on their paper.
4. Have children do the other problems similarly, circling the correct symbol.

Math Diagnosis and Intervention System
Intervention Lesson A84

Name ______________________

Comparing Numbers to 999 (continued)

Compare. Write <, >, or =.

6. 294 (<) 346	7. 603 (>) 598	8. 803 (<) 903
9. 450 (=) 450	10. 163 (<) 173	11. 295 (>) 259
12. 372 (>) 327	13. 500 (<) 501	14. 438 (>) 348
15. 704 (<) 740	16. 912 (>) 911	17. 443 (=) 443
18. 621 (>) 612	19. 801 (=) 801	20. 172 (<) 182
21. 278 (<) 287	22. 350 (>) 349	23. 986 (>) 968

Reasoning Use the clues to find each number.

24. It is greater than 836.
It is less than 841.
It has a 9 in the ones place.

The number is 839.

25. It is greater than 297.
It is less than 302.
It has a 1 in the ones place.

The number is 301.

Teacher Notes

Ongoing Assessment

Make sure children understand hundreds, tens, and ones.

Error Intervention

If children have difficulty with the concepts of greater than and less than, or with the symbols,

then use A27: Using >, <, and = to Compare Numbers.

If You Have More Time

Have children make a deck of cards made out of index cards. The deck should include the digits 1 to 9, four times each. Have each partner draw 3 cards, and place them face up in the order they were drawn, to form a three-digit number. Then have the children compare numbers. The child with a greater number gets a point. If the numbers are equal, both children get a point. Repeat until all cards are used. The child with the most points wins.

Before, After, and Between

Math Diagnosis and Intervention System
Intervention Lesson A85

Name ____________________

Before, After, and Between

211	212	213	214	215	216	217	218	219	210
221	222	223	224	225	226	227	228	229	230
231	232	233	234	235	236	237	238	239	240
241	242	243	244	245	246	247	248	249	250

1. 227 is one before 228. 227 is one after 226.
2. 227 is between 226 and 228.
3. 227 is ten before 237. 227 is ten after 217.
4. 239 is one before 240. 239 is one after 238.
5. 239 is between 238 and 240.
6. 239 is ten before 249. 239 is ten after 229.

1. Say: ***Put your finger on 227. Two hundred twenty-seven is one before what number?*** Have children write 228.
2. Say: ***Put your finger on 227. Two hundred twenty-seven is one after what number?*** Have children write 226.
3. Say: ***If 227 is one before 228 and one after 226, then 227 is between which two numbers?*** Have children write 226 and 228.
4. Say: ***Put your finger on 227. Two hundred twenty-seven is ten before what number?*** Have children write 237.
5. Say: ***Put your finger on 227. Two hundred twenty-seven is ten after what number?*** Have children write 217.
6. Do the other problem similarly.

Math Diagnosis and Intervention System
Intervention Lesson A85

Name ____________________

Before, After, and Between (continued)

Write the number that comes **after**.

7. 208, 209   516, 517   823, 824
8. 548, 549   163, 164   849, 850
9. 275, 276   789, 790   376, 377

Write the number that comes **before**.

10. 325, 326   150, 151   642, 643
11. 184, 185   439, 440   987, 988
12. 711, 712   505, 506   809, 810

Write the number that comes **between**.

13. 704, 705, 706   415, 416, 417
14. 521, 522, 523   649, 650, 651
15. 174, 175, 176   806, 807, 808

Teacher Notes

Ongoing Assessment

Make sure children can rote count to 999.

Error Intervention

If children have difficulty with the concepts of before, after, and between, even for 2-digit numbers,

then use A19: Before, After, and Between.

If You Have More Time

Have pairs play Guess My Number. One child writes down a three-digit number. The other child asks questions such as, *What is the number before your number?* Or *What two numbers is your number between?* After the first child answers, the second child says the number. Then, they change roles and repeat.

Ordering Numbers to 999

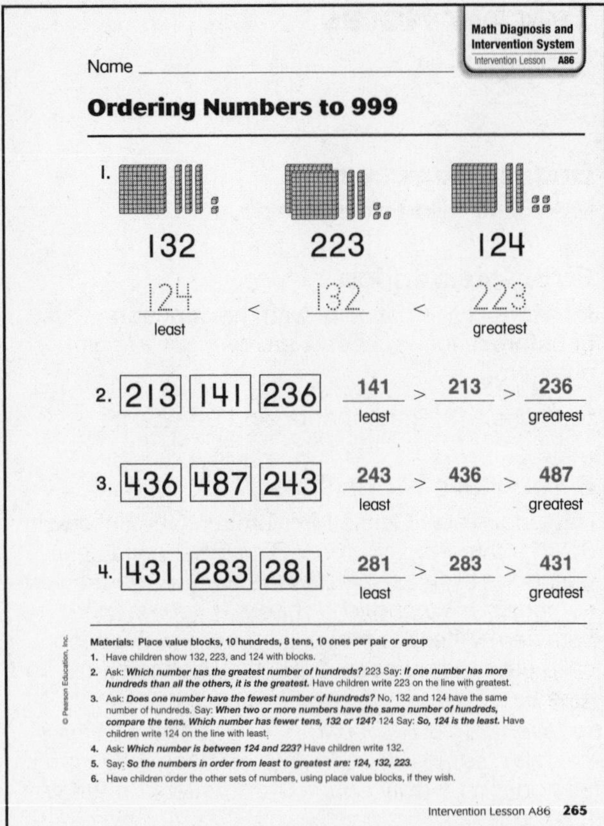

Math Diagnosis and Intervention System
Intervention Lesson A86

Name ____________________

Ordering Numbers to 999

1. 132 223 124

124 < 132 < 223
least greatest

2. 213 141 236 — 141 > 213 > 236 (least, greatest)

3. 436 487 243 — 243 > 436 > 487 (least, greatest)

4. 431 283 281 — 281 > 283 > 431 (least, greatest)

Materials: Place value blocks, 10 hundreds, 8 tens, 10 ones per pair or group

1. Have children show 132, 223, and 124 with blocks.
2. Ask: ***Which number has the greatest number of hundreds?*** 223 Say: ***If one number has more hundreds than all the others, it is the greatest.*** Have children write 223 on the line with greatest.
3. Ask: ***Does one number have the fewest number of hundreds?*** No, 132 and 124 have the same number of hundreds. Say: ***When two or more numbers have the same number of hundreds, compare the tens. Which number has fewer tens, 132 or 124?*** 124 Say: ***So, 124 is the least.*** Have children write 124 on the line with least.
4. Ask: ***Which number is between 124 and 223?*** Have children write 132.
5. Say: ***So the numbers in order from least to greatest are: 124, 132, 223.***
6. Have children order the other sets of numbers, using place value blocks, if they wish.

Math Diagnosis and Intervention System
Intervention Lesson A86

Name ____________________

Ordering Numbers to 999 (continued)

Write the numbers in order from **least** to **greatest**.

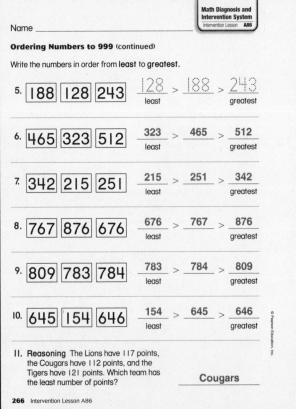

5. 188 128 243 — 128 > 188 > 243 (least, greatest)

6. 465 323 512 — 323 > 465 > 512 (least, greatest)

7. 342 215 251 — 215 > 251 > 342 (least, greatest)

8. 767 876 676 — 676 > 767 > 876 (least, greatest)

9. 809 783 784 — 783 > 784 > 809 (least, greatest)

10. 645 154 646 — 154 > 645 > 646 (least, greatest)

11. **Reasoning** The Lions have 117 points, the Cougars have 112 points, and the Tigers have 121 points. Which team has the least number of points? **Cougars**

Teacher Notes

Ongoing Assessment

Make sure children start by looking at the hundreds.

Error Intervention

If children have difficulty with the concept of ordering,

then use A28: Ordering Three Numbers, A85: Before After, and Between, A84: Comparing Numbers to 999, and A83: Patterns with Numbers on Hundreds Charts.

If You Have More Time

Put children in groups of 4. Have 3 children each write a different three-digit number on a half sheet of paper and then physically line up in any order. Have the fourth child reorganize the children to show the numbers in order from least to greatest. Continue until each person in the group gets to be the reorganizer. If two of the students write the same number have the reorganizer put them one in front of the other.

Numbers to 999 on the Number Line

Math Diagnosis and Intervention System
Intervention Lesson **A87**

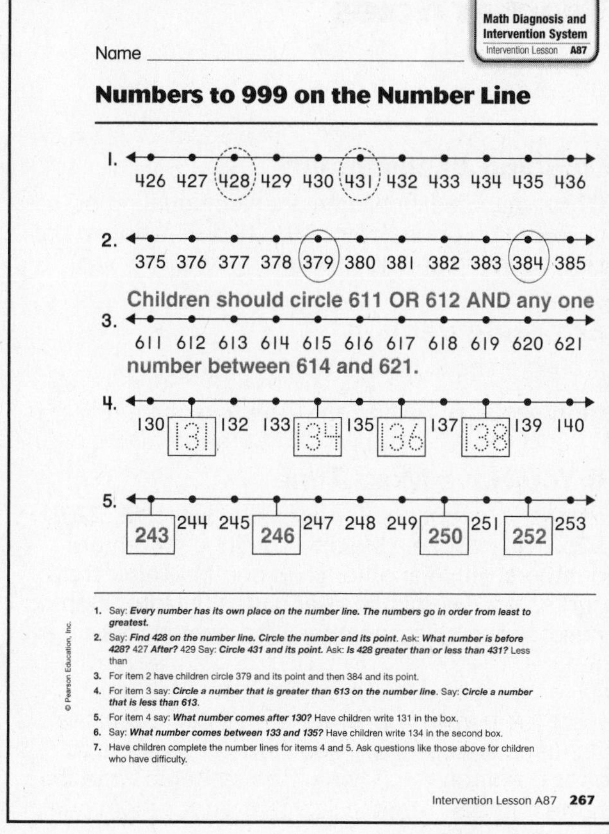
Math Diagnosis and Intervention System
Intervention Lesson A87

Name ______________________

Numbers to 999 on the Number Line

1. 426 427 428 429 430 431 432 433 434 435 436

2. 375 376 377 378 379 380 381 382 383 384 385

Children should circle 611 OR 612 AND any one

3. 611 612 613 614 615 616 617 618 619 620 621

number between 614 and 621.

4. 130 131 132 133 134 135 136 137 138 139 140

5. 243 244 245 246 247 248 249 250 251 252 253

1. Say: ***Every number has its own place on the number line. The numbers go in order from least to greatest.***
2. Say: ***Find 428 on the number line. Circle the number and its point***. Ask: ***What number is before 428?*** 427 ***After?*** 429 Say: ***Circle 431 and its point.*** Ask: ***Is 428 greater than or less than 431?*** Less than
3. For item 2 have children circle 379 and its point and then 384 and its point.
4. For item 3 say: ***Circle a number that is greater than 613 on the number line***. Say: ***Circle a number that is less than 613***.
5. For item 4 say: ***What number comes after 130?*** Have children write 131 in the box.
6. Say: ***What number comes between 133 and 135?*** Have children write 134 in the second box.
7. Have children complete the number lines for items 4 and 5. Ask questions like those above for children who have difficulty.

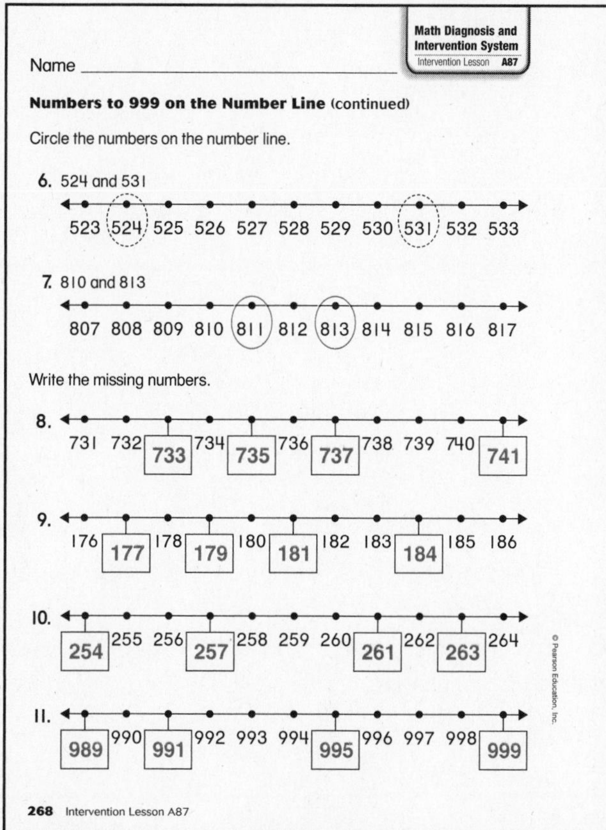
Math Diagnosis and Intervention System
Intervention Lesson A87

Name ______________________

Numbers to 999 on the Number Line (continued)

Circle the numbers on the number line.

6. 524 and 531

523 524 525 526 527 528 529 530 531 532 533

7. 810 and 813

807 808 809 810 811 812 813 814 815 816 817

Write the missing numbers.

8. 731 732 733 734 735 736 737 738 739 740 741

9. 176 177 178 179 180 181 182 183 184 185 186

10. 254 255 256 257 258 259 260 261 262 263 264

11. 989 990 991 992 993 994 995 996 997 998 999

Teacher Notes

Ongoing Assessment

Make sure children can rote count to 999.

Error Intervention

If children have trouble locating larger numbers on a number line,

then use A32: Numbers to 100 on a Number Line.

If children have trouble identifying the missing numbers,

then use A85: Before, After, and Between.

If You Have More Time

Each partner will need 11 index cards, 11 counters and 1 yard of yarn. Have one partner write the numbers 346 through 356 on index cards. Have another partner write the numbers 782 through 792 on index cards. Have partners sit with their backs to each other. Have each partner place their yarn on the floor and evenly space the counters on the yarn (to represent a number line and points). Then have each place their index cards on the floor, in order, below each counter. Each child then removes 3 of the cards. Have partners switch places and identify what numbers are missing. Partners go back to their number lines, replace the missing cards and remove 3 different ones. Children switch places and identify missing cards.

Skip Counting on the Number Line

Math Diagnosis and Intervention System
Intervention Lesson **A88**

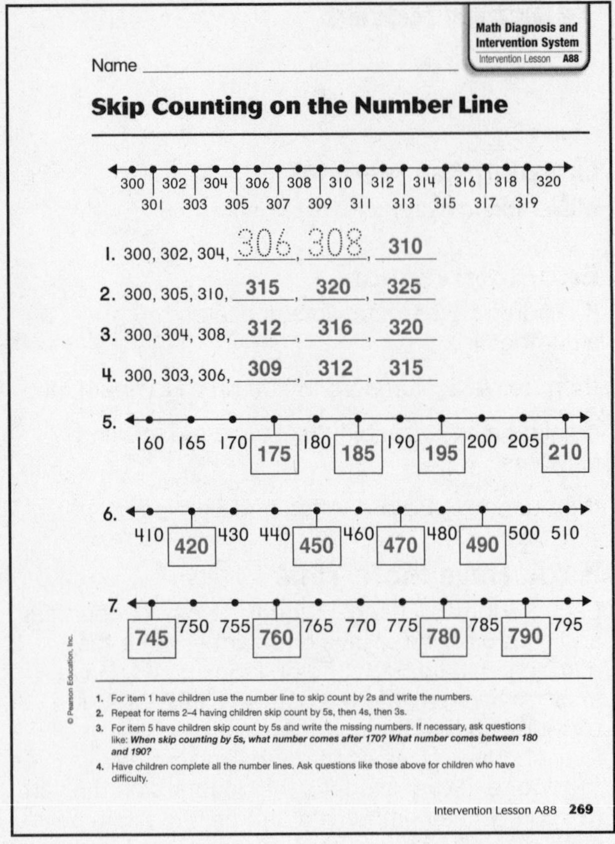

Math Diagnosis and Intervention System
Intervention Lesson A88

Name ______________________

Skip Counting on the Number Line

300 301 302 303 304 305 306 307 308 309 310 311 312 313 314 315 316 317 318 319 320

1. 300, 302, 304, 306, 308, 310
2. 300, 305, 310, 315, 320, 325
3. 300, 304, 308, 312, 316, 320
4. 300, 303, 306, 309, 312, 315
5. 160 165 170 175 180 185 190 195 200 205 210
6. 410 420 430 440 450 460 470 480 490 500 510
7. 745 750 755 760 765 770 775 780 785 790 795

1. For item 1 have children use the number line to skip count by 2s and write the numbers.
2. Repeat for items 2–4 having children skip count by 5s, then 4s, then 3s.
3. For item 5 have children skip count by 5s and write the missing numbers. If necessary, ask questions like: ***When skip counting by 5s, what number comes after 170? What number comes between 180 and 190?***
4. Have children complete all the number lines. Ask questions like those above for children who have difficulty.

© Pearson Education, Inc.

Intervention Lesson A88 **269**

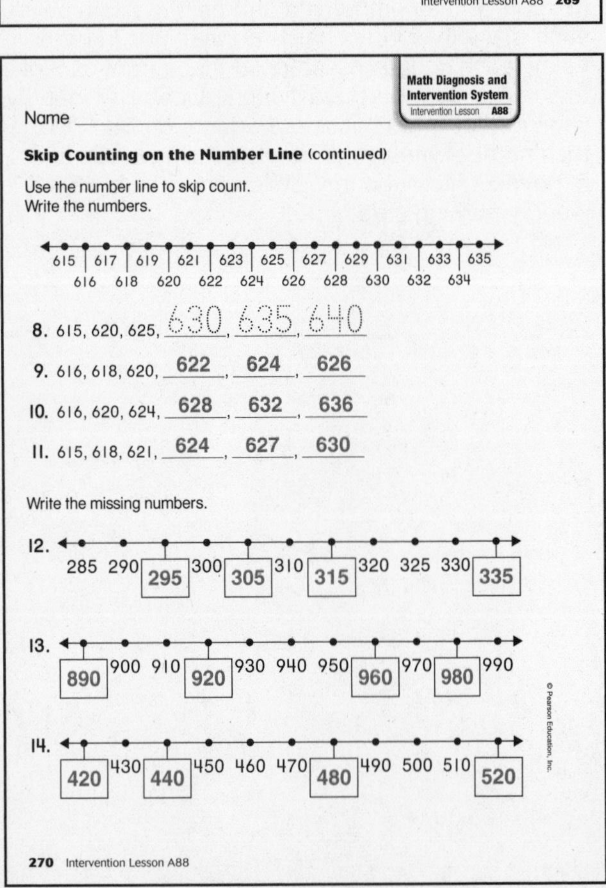

Math Diagnosis and Intervention System
Intervention Lesson A88

Name ______________________

Skip Counting on the Number Line (continued)

Use the number line to skip count.
Write the numbers.

615 616 617 618 619 620 621 622 623 624 625 626 627 628 629 630 631 632 633 634 635

8. 615, 620, 625, 630, 635, 640
9. 616, 618, 620, 622, 624, 626
10. 616, 620, 624, 628, 632, 636
11. 615, 618, 621, 624, 627, 630

Write the missing numbers.

12. 285 290 295 300 305 310 315 320 325 330 335
13. 890 900 910 920 930 940 950 960 970 980 990
14. 420 430 440 450 460 470 480 490 500 510 520

© Pearson Education, Inc.

270 Intervention Lesson A88

Teacher Notes

Ongoing Assessment

Observe to see if children are skip counting or counting on or back 5 or 10. Children who are not skip counting should take a long time to finish.

Error Intervention

If children have trouble skip counting,

then use A16: Using Skip Counting.

If You Have More Time

Start skip counting. For example, say: ***215, 220, 225***. The choose a child to continue for 3 more numbers. Have another child continue after that and so on. Then, start over with a different starting number and skip count by a different number.

Ways to Show Numbers

Name ______________________

Ways to Show Numbers

Materials 124 craft sticks and 13 rubber bands, per pair, or place-value blocks, 124 ones, 12 tens, and 1 hundred block per pair

There are various ways to show 124. Answer 1 to 9 to learn how.

If using craft sticks: use rubber bands to put the craft sticks in as many groups of 10 as possible. If using place-value blocks: trade groups of 10 ones for tens with place-value blocks.

1. How many groups of ten are there? 12

2. How many ones are left? 4

Wrap 10 groups of ten craft sticks to make a hundred or trade 10 tens place-value blocks for a hundred block.

3. How many hundreds are there? 1

4. How many tens are left? 2

5. How many ones are left? 4

6. How many in all? 124

The number 124 is written in standard form.

7. 124 = 1 hundred 2 tens 4 ones or 12 tens 4 ones

8. In expanded form, 124 is written 100 + 20 + 4.

9. In words, 124 is written one hundred twenty-four.

There are various ways to write 238. Answer 10 to 12.

10. 238 = 2 hundreds 3 tens 8 ones or 23 tens 8 ones

11. In expanded form, 238 is written 200 + 30 + 8.

12. In words, 238 is written two hundred thirty-eight.

Name ______________________

Ways to Show Numbers (continued)

Write each number in standard form.

13. 243

14. 518

Write each number in expanded form.

15. 462 400 + 60 + 2 **16.** 853 800 + 50 + 3

17. 321 300 + 20 + 1 **18.** 760 700 + 60

Write each number as groups of tens and ones only. You may use place-value blocks to help.

19. 427 42 tens 7 ones **20.** 933 93 tens 3 ones

21. 106 10 tens 6 ones **22.** 514 51 tens 4 ones

Write each number in standard form.

23. six hundred twenty-two 622 **24.** eight hundred ten 810

Write each number in words.

25. 210 two hundred ten

26. 782 seven hundred eighty-two

27. 105 one hundred five

28. 316 three hundred sixteen

Teacher Notes

Ongoing Assessment

Ask: ***How many tens and ones are in 486?***
48 tens and 6 ones

Error Intervention

If students have trouble remembering the difference between value and place,

then explain to students that the value of an object is how much money it is worth, so the value of a digit is how much it is worth. The place that a digit is in can be compared to the place that you put your math book. It is a location. The place you will find a digit might be in the hundreds, tens, or ones place.

If You Have More Time

Have students write other three-digit numbers in expanded form.

Rounding to the Nearest Ten and Hundred

Math Diagnosis and Intervention System
Intervention Lesson **A90**

Name ____________

Rounding to the Nearest Ten and Hundred

Materials 8 inches of yarn per pair

To round 77 to the nearest ten, answer 1 to 6.

1. Plot 73 on the number line below.

(Number line from 70 to 80, with 75 marked; 73 and 77 plotted.)

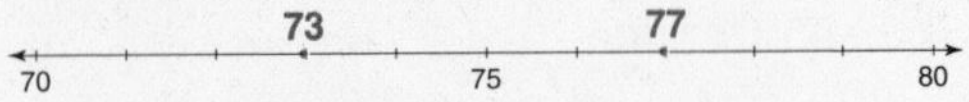

2. Use the yarn to help you decide whether 73 is closer to 70 or 80. Which is it closer to? 70

3. So, what is 73 rounded to the nearest ten? 70

4. Plot 77 on the number line above.

5. Use the yarn to help you decide whether 77 is closer to 70 or 80. Which is it closer to? 80

6. So, what is 77 rounded to the nearest ten? 80

To round 336 to the nearest hundred, answer 7 to 12.

7. Plot 380 on the number line below.

(Number line from 300 to 400, with 350 marked; 336 and 380 plotted.)

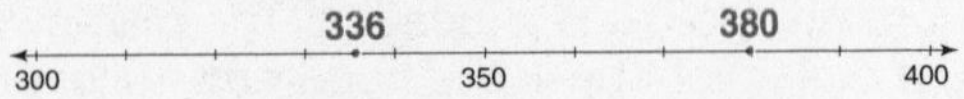

8. Use the yarn to help you decide whether 380 is closer to 300 or 400. Which is it closer to? 400

9. So, what is 380 rounded to the nearest hundred? 400

10. Plot 336 on the number line above.

11. Use the yarn to help you decide whether 336 is closer to 300 or 400. Which is it closer to? 300

12. So, what is 336 rounded to the nearest hundred? 300

Math Diagnosis and Intervention System
Intervention Lesson **A90**

Name ____________

Rounding to the Nearest Ten and Hundred (continued)

Round 459 to the nearest hundred by answering 13 to 17.

13. What digit is in the hundreds place in 459? 4

14. What digit is to the right of the 4? 5

15. Is the digit to the right of 4 less than 5, or is it 5 or greater? 5 or greater

If the digit to the right of the number is 5 or more, the number rounds up. If the digit is less than 5, the number rounds down.

16. Do you need to round 459 up or down? Up

17. Change the 4 to the next higher digit and change the 5 and 9 to 0s. So, what is 459 rounded to the nearest hundred? 500

Round to the nearest ten.

18. 54	**19.** 37	**20.** 81	**21.** 65
50	40	80	70

Round to the nearest hundred.

22. 609	**23.** 351	**24.** 491	**25.** 850
600	400	500	900

26. A rancher has 43 cattle in his herd. To the nearest ten, how many cattle are in the rancher's herd? 40

27. A new computer costs $876. To the nearest hundred, how many dollars does the computer cost? $900

28. Reasoning Round 549 to the nearest hundred and round 551 to the nearest hundred. Do you get the same answers? Explain.

No; 549 should be rounded down to 500 since $4 < 5$; 551 should be rounded up to 600 since $5 \geq 5$.

Teacher Notes

Ongoing Assessment

Ask: ***What are all the numbers that round to 600 when rounded to the nearest hundred?*** 550 to 649

Error Intervention

If students have trouble remembering what digits cause a number to round up or down,

then have the students write "0, 1, 2, 3, 4: Round Down" and "5, 6, 7, 8, 9: Round Up" on the top of their page.

If You Have More Time

Have students list all the two-digit numbers that stay the same when rounding to the nearest ten (the multiples of 10) and all the three-digit numbers that stay the same when rounding to the nearest hundred (the multiples of 100).

Reading and Writing 4-Digit Numbers

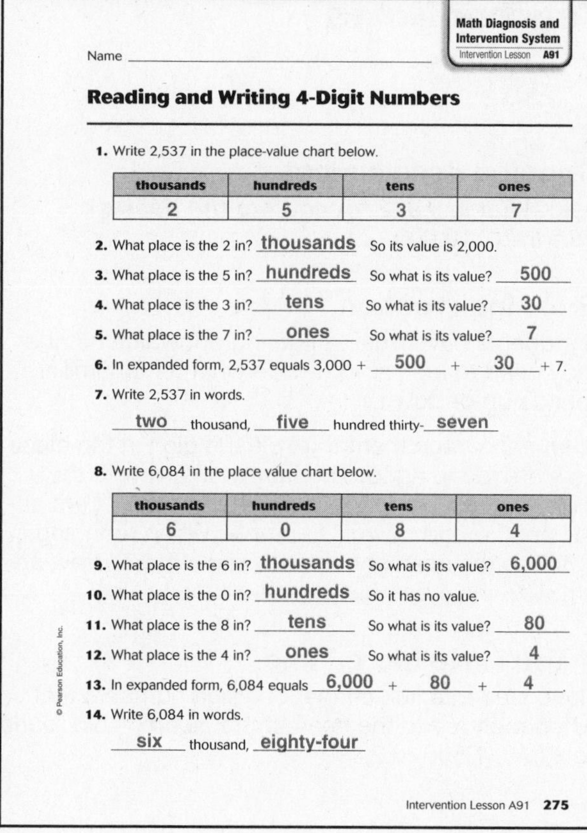

Math Diagnosis and Intervention System
Intervention Lesson A91

Name ______________________

Reading and Writing 4-Digit Numbers

1. Write 2,537 in the place-value chart below.

thousands	hundreds	tens	ones
2	5	3	7

2. What place is the 2 in? thousands So its value is 2,000.
3. What place is the 5 in? hundreds So what is its value? 500
4. What place is the 3 in? tens So what is its value? 30
5. What place is the 7 in? ones So what is its value? 7
6. In expanded form, 2,537 equals 3,000 + 500 + 30 + 7.
7. Write 2,537 in words.
   two thousand, five hundred thirty-seven
8. Write 6,084 in the place value chart below.

thousands	hundreds	tens	ones
6	0	8	4

9. What place is the 6 in? thousands So what is its value? 6,000
10. What place is the 0 in? hundreds So it has no value.
11. What place is the 8 in? tens So what is its value? 80
12. What place is the 4 in? ones So what is its value? 4
13. In expanded form, 6,084 equals 6,000 + 80 + 4.
14. Write 6,084 in words.
    six thousand, eighty-four

© Pearson Education, Inc.

Intervention Lesson A91 **275**

Math Diagnosis and Intervention System
Intervention Lesson A91

Name ______________________

Reading and Writing 4-Digit Numbers (continued)

Write each number in standard form.

15. 1,000 + 500 + 20 + 7
    1,527
16. nine thousand, four hundred
    9,400
17. 8,000 + 100 + 30
    8,130
18. five thousand, six hundred one
    5,601
19. 4,000 + 500 + 2
    4,502
20. six thousand, eight hundred ninety
    6,890

Write each number in expanded form.

21. 3,716
    3,000 + 700 + 10 + 6
22. 2,091
    2,000 + 90 + 1

Write the value of the underlined digit.

23. 1,8<u>6</u>3 — 60
24. <u>9</u>,504 — 9,000
25. 5,12<u>9</u> — 9
26. <u>1</u>83 — 100

27. Write 3,995 in words.
    three thousand, nine hundred ninety-five
28. Write 4,716 in words.
    four thousand, seven hundred sixteen
29. Use the digits 1, 5, 7, and 3. Write the greatest possible four-digit number using each of the digits only once. 7,531
30. **Reasoning** What number would make the number sentence 5,000 + 800 + ■ + 6 = 5,826 true? 20

© Pearson Education, Inc.

276 Intervention Lesson A91

Teacher Notes

Ongoing Assessment

Ask: ***What is 6,001 in expanded form?*** 6,000 + 1

Error Intervention

If students have trouble placing the comma in the correct position while writing a number in word form,

then explain to the students that commas belong in the same place in word form as they do in standard form.

If You Have More Time

Have students work in pairs and use index cards. Have them write a four-digit number in standard form on one card and the same number in a different form on another. Make 10 pairs of different four-digit numbers. Students shuffle the cards and arrange them in a face-down array. One student turns over two cards and keeps them if they match. If the cards do not match, the cards are turned back over and it is the other student's turn. Continue until all cards are matched.

Numbers Halfway Between and Rounding

Math Diagnosis and Intervention System
Intervention Lesson A92

Name ______________________

Numbers Halfway Between and Rounding

Answer 1 and 2 to find the number that is halfway between 200 and 300.

200 210 220 230 240 250 260 270 280 290 300

1. Use your pencil to draw a hop from 200 to 210, and then backwards from 300 to 290. Repeat one hop on each side until the hops meet at a point. Draw a dot where they meet. This is the number that is halfway between 200 and 300.
2. What number is halfway between 200 and 300? 250

Round 6,375 to the nearest hundred by answering 3 to 7.

3. What number is halfway between 6,300 and 6,400? 6,350
4. Is 6,375 greater than or less than the halfway number? greater than
5. Plot 6,375 on the number line below.

6,375

6,300 6,310 6,320 6,330 6,340 6,350 6,360 6,370 6,380 6,390 6,400

6. Is 6,375 closer to 6,300 or 6,400? 6,400
7. So, what is 6,375 rounded to the nearest hundred? 6,400

Round 7,824 to the nearest thousand without using a number line. Answer 8 to 12.

8. What digit is in the thousands place in 7,824? 7
9. What digit is to the right of the 7? 8
10. Is the digit to the right of 7 less than 5 or is it 5 or greater? 5 or greater

Intervention Lesson A92 277

Math Diagnosis and Intervention System
Intervention Lesson A92

Name ______________________

Numbers Halfway Between and Rounding (continued)

If the digit to the right of the number is 5 or more, the number rounds up. If the digit is less than 5, the number rounds down.

11. When you round 7,824 to the nearest thousand, do you need to round the 7 up or down? Up
12. Change the 7 to the next higher digit and change the other digits to 0s. So, what is 7,824 rounded to the nearest thousand? 8,000

Find the number halfway between each pair of numbers.

13. 70 and 80 — 75
14. 500 and 600 — 550
15. 2,000 and 3,000 — 2,500

Round each number to the nearest ten.

16. 4,769 — 4,770
17. 8,274 — 8,270
18. 6,616 — 6,620
19. 995 — 1,000

Round each number to the nearest hundred.

20. 3,248 — 3,200
21. 9,929 — 9,900
22. 1,372 — 1,400
23. 2,050 — 2,100

Round each number to the nearest thousand.

24. 5,604 — 6,000
25. 7,487 — 7,000
26. 2,868 — 3,000
27. 6,452 — 6,000

28. **Reasoning** If 4,500 is halfway between 4,000 and 5,000, why does 4,509 round up to 5,000 when rounding to the nearest thousand?

Answers will vary. Sample answer: 4,509 is 9 more than 4,500, so it is closer to 5,000.

278 Intervention Lesson A92

Teacher Notes

Ongoing Assessment

Ask: ***What is 9,972 rounded to the nearest hundred?*** 10,000

Error Intervention

If students have trouble figuring out which number they need to look at to decide whether a number rounds up or down,

then encourage them to circle the digit in the place they are rounding to. Then draw an arrow to the digit to the right. Then have that digit say, "I am a "4" and I round down." Example: When rounding 5,349 to the nearest hundred, circle the 3, draw an arrow to the 4 and have the 4 do the talking.

If You Have More Time

Have students find all the four-digit numbers that when rounded to the nearest thousand would round to 2,000. 1,500 to 2,499

Comparing and Ordering Numbers

Name ______________________

Comparing and Ordering Numbers

Seth's class collected 1,382 cans during the food drive. Yolanda's class collected 1,357 cans of food. Determine whose class collected more by answering 1 to 6.

1. Write 1,382 and 1,357 in the place value chart.

thousands	hundreds	tens	ones
1	3	8	2
1	3	5	7

2. Use <, >, or = to compare the thousands. 1,000 = 1,000

3. Since the thousands are equal, compare the hundreds. 300 = 300

4. Since the hundreds are equal, compare the tens. 80 > 50

5. Since 80 > 50, Which value is greater, 1,382 or 1,357? 1,382

6. Whose class collected more cans of food? Seth's

Zoe scored 3,496 points, Mario scored 2,908 points, and Kim scored 3,520 points. Determine who scored the most points by answering 7 to 12.

7. Write 3,496, 2,908, and 3,520 in the place value chart.

thousands	hundreds	tens	ones
3	4	9	6
2	9	0	8
3	5	2	0

8. Compare the thousands. Since 2,000 < 3,000, what is the least number? 2,908

Name ______________________

Comparing and Ordering Numbers (continued)

9. Use the chart you completed in 7 to compare the hundreds of the other two numbers. 400 < 500

10. Since 400 < 500, then is 3,496 greater than or less than 3,520? less than

11. What are the numbers in order from least to greatest?
2,908, 3,496, 3,520

12. Who scored the most points? Kim

Compare. Write >, <, or =.

13. 514 (>) 512 **14.** 394 (>) 349 **15.** 809 (=) 809

16. 1,078 (>) 178 **17.** 236 (<) 2,036 **18.** 7,530 (>) 7,240

19. 9,089 (<) 9,098 **20.** 4,517 (<) 5,417 **21.** 3,728 (>) 3,727

Write the numbers in order from **least** to **greatest.**

22. 428 418 422 — 418; 422; 428

23. 1,234 134 123 — 123; 134; 1,234

24. 5,619 5,691 569 — 569; 5,619; 5,691

25. 1,010 1,001 1,100 — 1,001; 1,010; 1,100

26. Reasoning What is the smallest digit that makes 1,328 > 1,■28 true? 0

27. Daniella has 1,241 trading cards. Mark has 1,099 trading cards. Who has more cards? Daniella

28. Maria scored 3,950 points playing a video game. Leigh scored 3,590 points. Kathy scored 3,905. Order their scores from least to greatest.
Leigh, 3,590; Kathy, 3,905; Maria, 3,950

Teacher Notes

Ongoing Assessment

Ask: ***How can you tell that 6,879 is greater than 6,789?*** Since the thousands are the same, compare the hundreds: 8 is greater than 7, so 6,879 is greater than 6,789.

Error Intervention

If students have trouble comparing two numbers when they are written next to each other horizontally,

then encourage them to write one number above the other, making sure they are lining up corresponding place values.

If You Have More Time

Have students write ordering problems for a partner to solve.

Place-Value Patterns

Math Diagnosis and Intervention System
Intervention Lesson A94

Name ______

Place-Value Patterns

Materials 4 pieces of centimeter grid paper, crayons, markers, or colored pencils

Show 1,200 with grid paper by answering 1 to 8.

1. In the upper left corner of your grid paper, color a 10 by 10 square like the one on the right.
2. How many small squares did you color? 100
3. Since 1,000 = 10 hundreds, show the 1,000 in 1,200 by coloring nine more 10 by 10 squares on your grid paper, to make 10 in all. Check student's drawing.
4. Show the 200 in 1,200 by coloring two more 10 by 10 squares on your grid paper. Check student's drawing.
5. All the 10 by 10 squares together show 1,200. How many 10 by 10 squares do you have? 12
6. 1,200 = 12 hundreds
7. How many tens are in each 10 by 10 square? 10
8. So, 1,200 = 120 tens and 1,200 = 1,200 ones.

Math Diagnosis and Intervention System
Intervention Lesson A94

Name ______

Place-Value Patterns (continued)

Fill in the blanks to name each number in two different ways.

9. 200
2 hundreds
20 tens

10. 840
84 tens
840 ones

11. 1,600
16 hundreds
160 tens

12. 3,200
32 hundreds
320 tens

13. 700
7 hundreds
70 tens

14. 820
82 tens
820 ones

15. 1,300
13 hundreds
130 tens

16. 570
57 tens
570 ones

17. 1,400
14 hundreds
140 tens

18. How many tens are in 40? 4 400? 40 4,000? 400
19. The state fair ordered 2,200 new cages for the rabbit barn. How many stacks would there be if there were 100 cages in each stack? 22
20. The school cafeteria has 900 lunch trays. How many stacks of trays are there if each stack has 10 trays in it? 90
21. **Reasoning** What is the next number in this pattern?
2,377 2,477 2,577 2,677
Explain how you know.
The hundreds place is increasing by 1 each time.

Teacher Notes

Ongoing Assessment

Ask: ***How can you name 5,000 using hundreds? tens? ones?*** 50 hundreds; 500 tens; 5,000 ones

Error Intervention

If students have trouble understanding that there are ten 10s in 100,

then encourage them to use their knowledge of counting by 10 to actually count each column of 10.

If You Have More Time

Have students use numbers to name a number in different ways. Give an example like the one that follows. Then have them do the same for other three- and four-digit numbers.

$$2{,}500 = 25 \times 1{,}000$$
$$250 \times 10$$
$$2{,}500 \times 1$$

Name ___________________________________

Zero to Five

0000

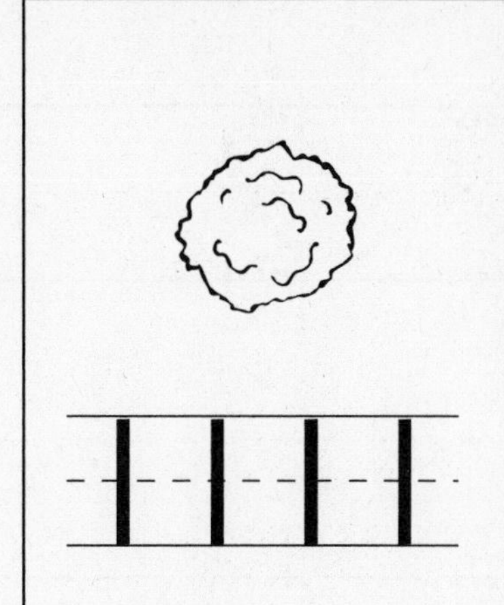

1111

2222

3333

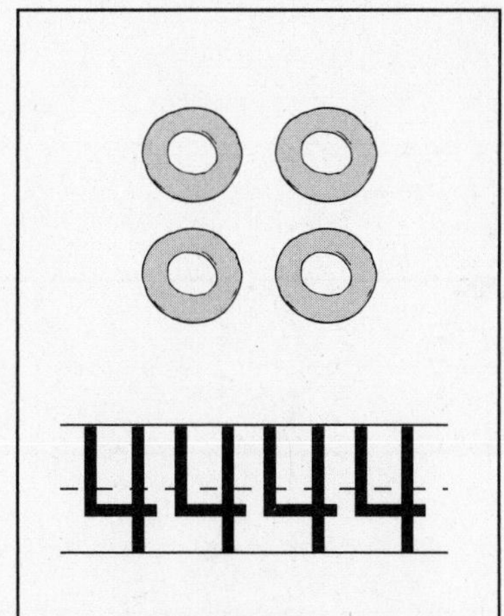

4444

5555

Materials: 7 sheets of construction paper per child, writing paper, yarn, glue, assorted materials to glue onto paper such as stickers, beans, pasta, cotton balls, cereal, and buttons

1. Cut the writing paper into strips and tape one strip to the bottom of each piece of construction paper. Punch 2 holes in the side of each page to use to bind the Number Books together. Make enough so each child has 6 pages with writing paper and one page without.
2. Show one sheet of paper and ask: ***How many objects are glued to this page?*** After children say zero, have them practice writing zero.
3. Have children glue one object to another page and practice writing 1.
4. Ask the children to glue one more object on the next page and practice writing 2.
5. Continue up to 5.
6. Let children make a cover for their "Number Book." Tie the books together by threading yarn through the punched holes.

Name ______________________________

Zero to Five (continued)

How many?

1. 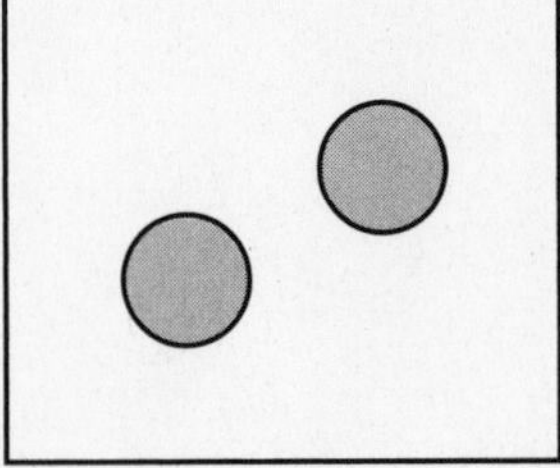

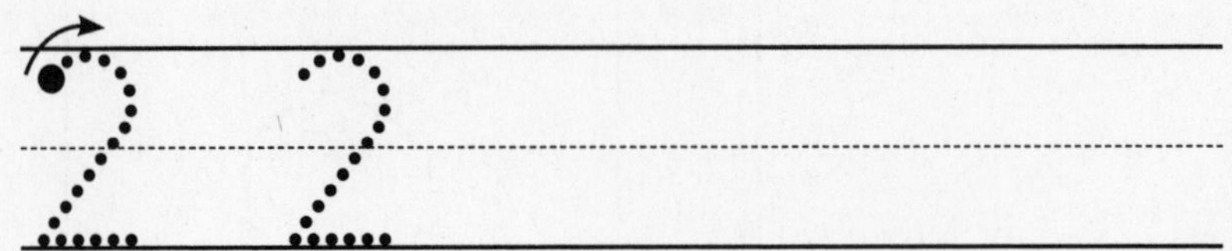

2. 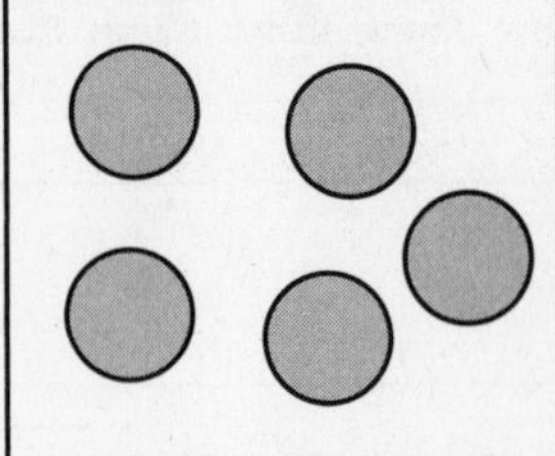

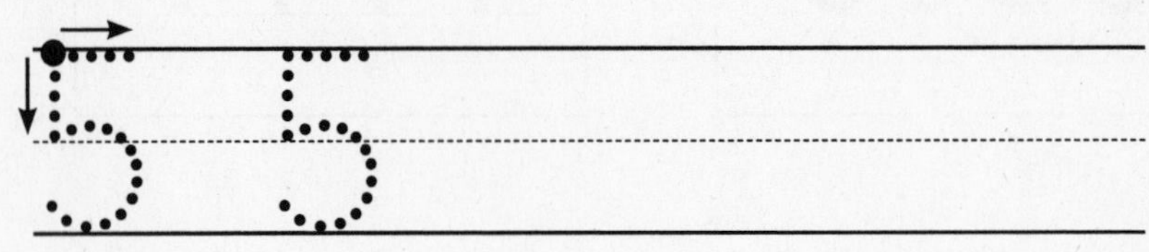

3. 

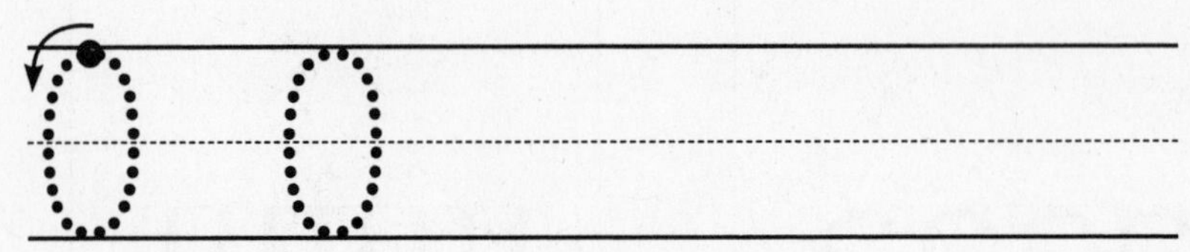

4. 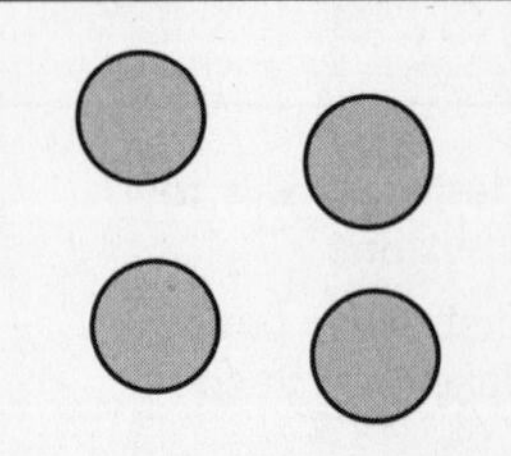

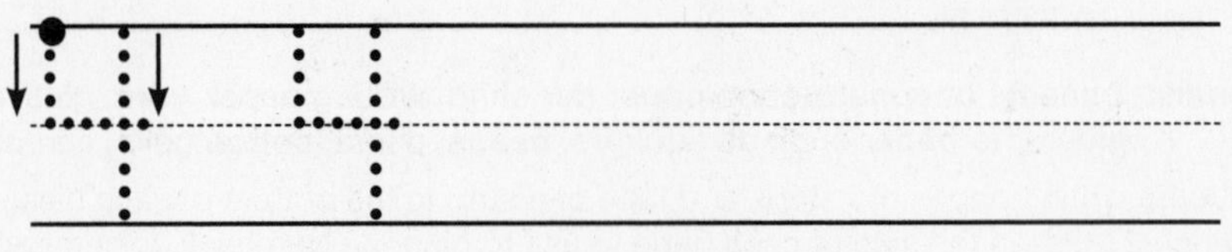

Name ______________________

More and Fewer

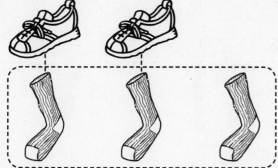

I.

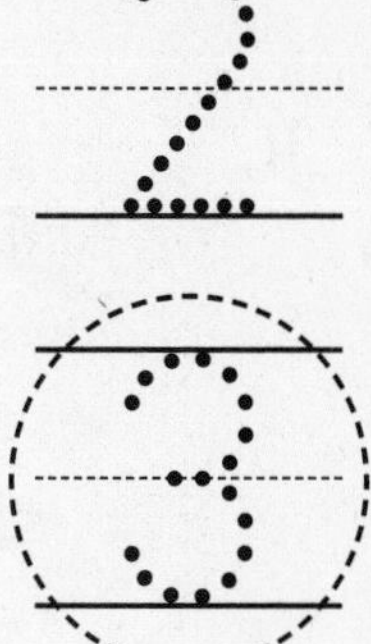

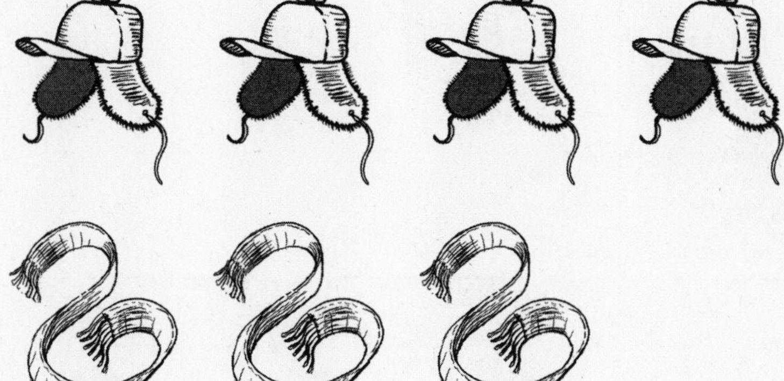

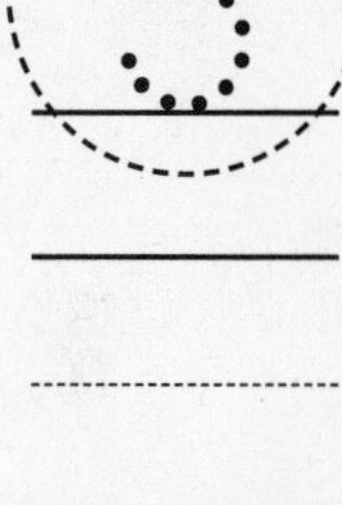

2.

3.

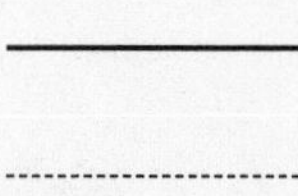

Materials:

1. Have children draw a line from each object in one group to an object in the other group and circle the group that has more.
2. Have children count the objects and write the numbers for how many objects are in each group. Then have them circle the number which is more.
3. Do the same for the other two problems.

Name ______________________________

More and Fewer (continued)

How many? Circle the group with fewer objects.
Circle the number which is less.

4. 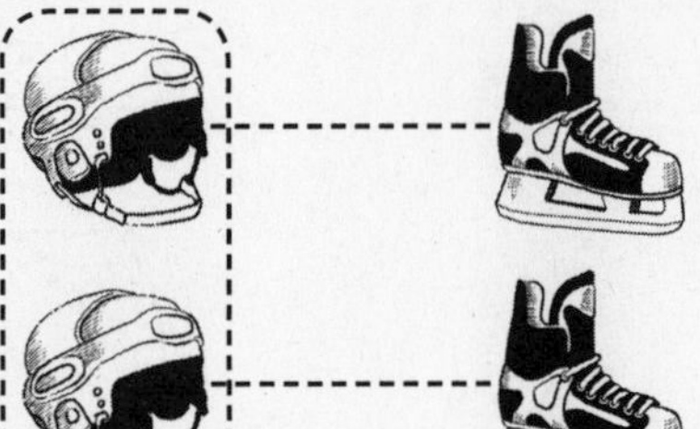

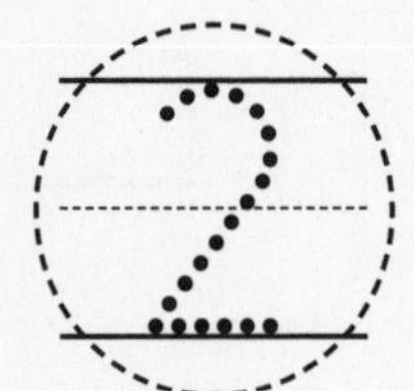
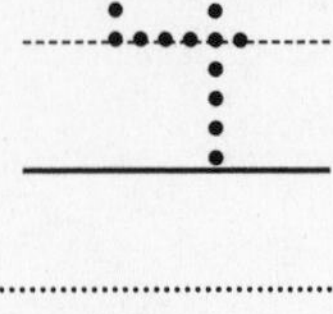

2 4

5. 

____ ____

6. 

____ ____

7. 

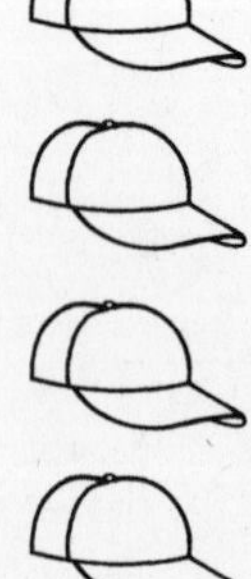

____ ____

Name ______________________________

Six to Ten

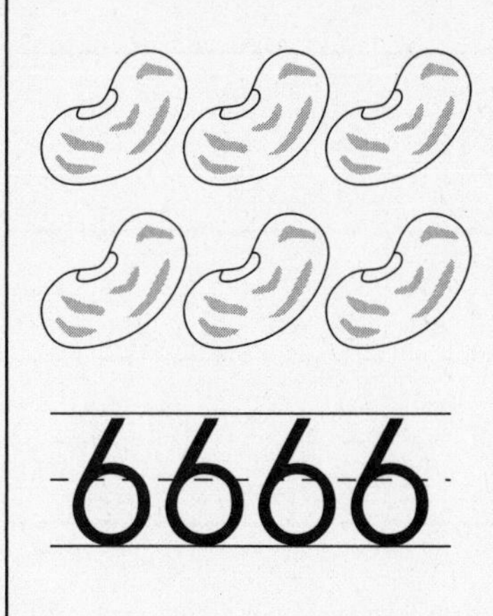

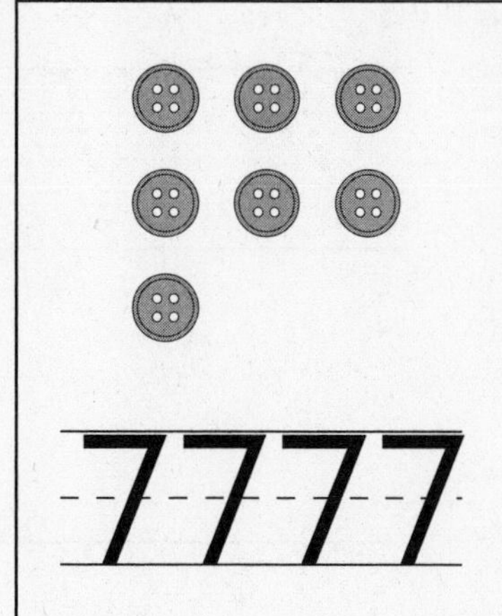

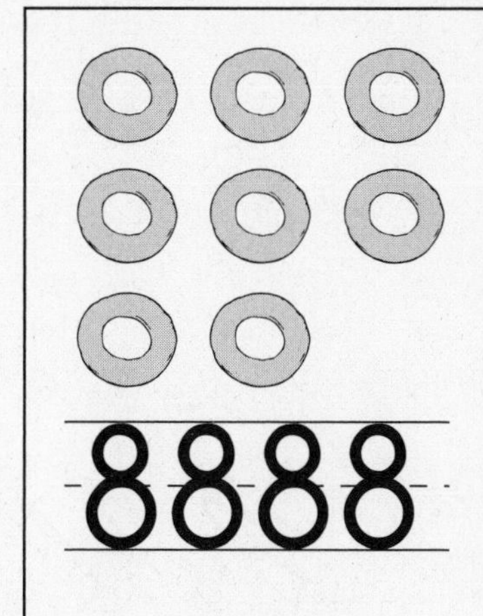

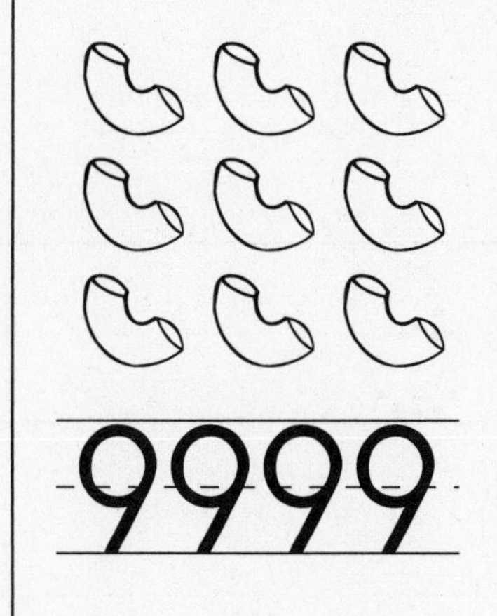

Materials: 5 sheets of construction paper per child, writing paper, yarn, glue, assorted materials to glue onto paper such as stickers, beans, pasta, cotton balls, cereal, and buttons

1. Cut the writing paper into strips and tape one strip to the bottom of each piece of construction paper. Punch 2 holes in the side of each page to use to bind the Number Books together. Make enough so each child has 5 pages with writing paper. If you did not do activity A1, include one more sheet per child, with holes, but without writing paper.
2. Show a page with 5 objects. Ask: ***How many objects are glued to this page?***
3. Have children glue six objects on a page and practice writing 6.
4. Have children glue one more object on the next page and practice writing 7.
5. Continue up to 10.
6. Let children make a cover for their "Number Book" or attach these pages to the book created in activity A1. Tie the books together by threading yarn through the punched holes.

Name ______________________________

Six to Ten (continued)

How many?

1. 

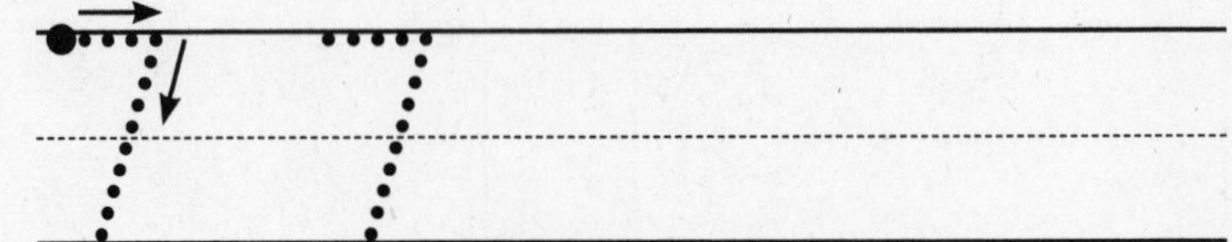

2. 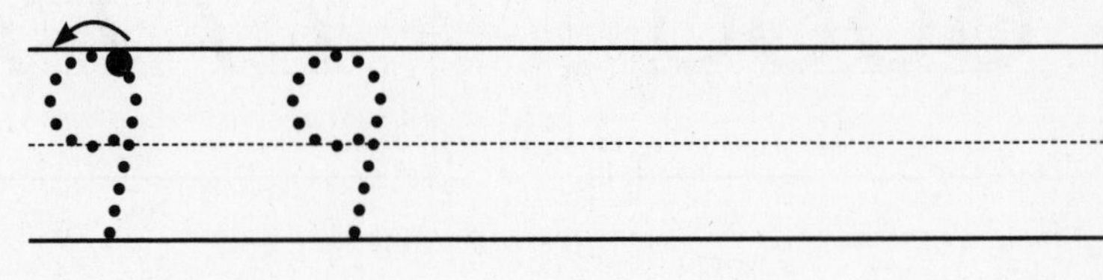

3. 

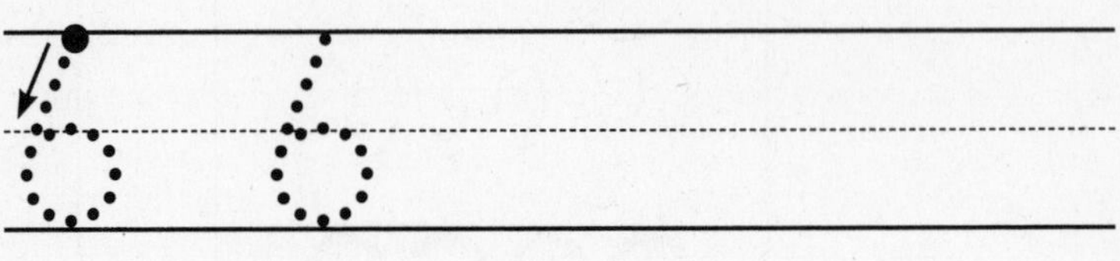

4. 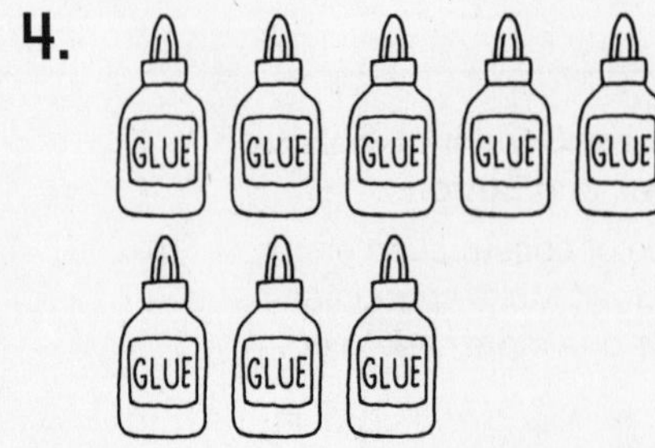

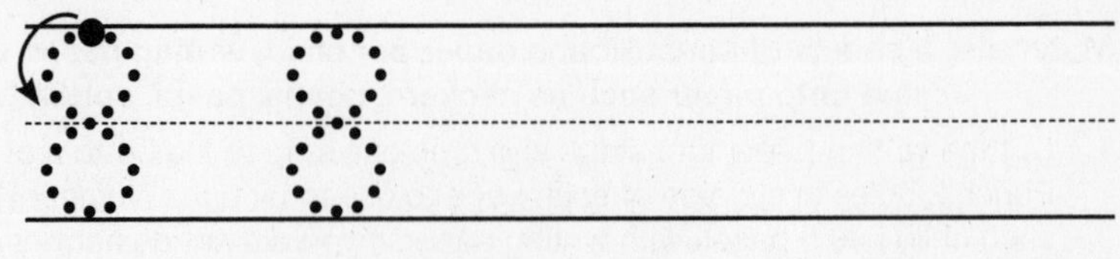

Name ________________________

Comparing Numbers

1.

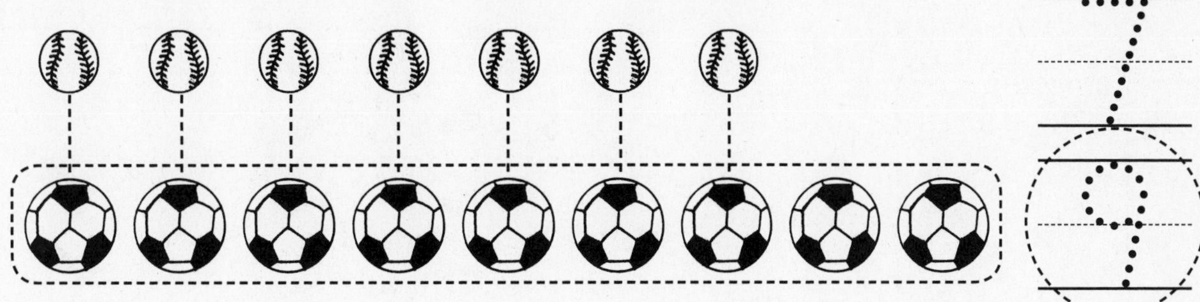

2.

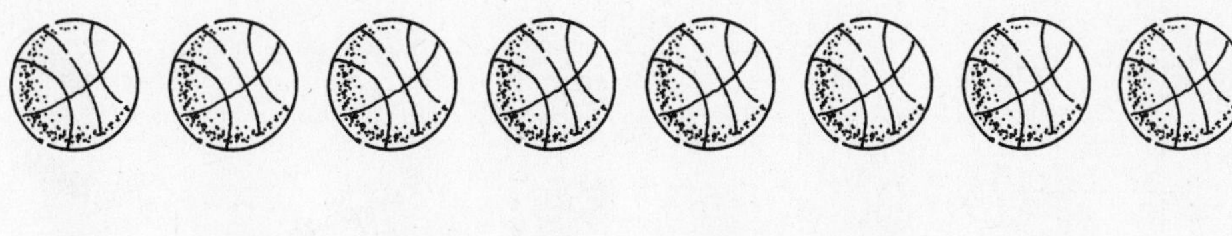

 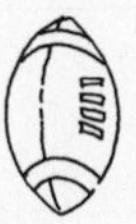     

3.

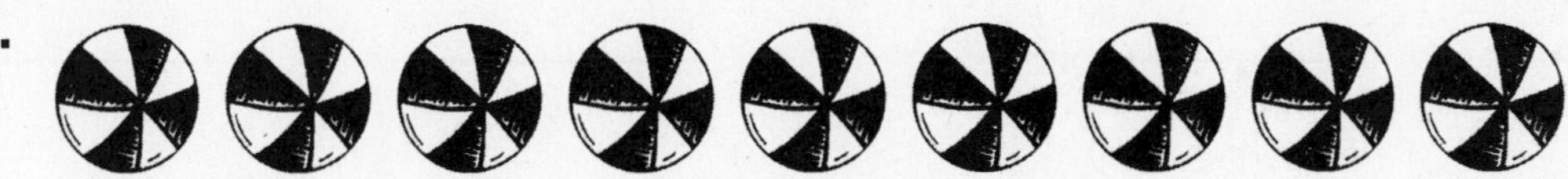

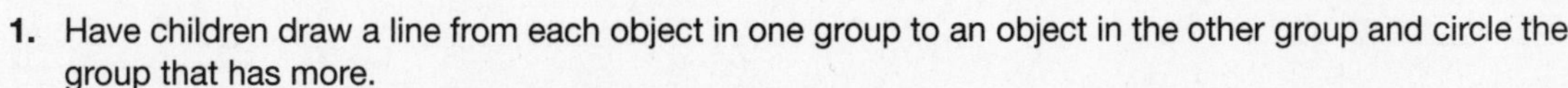

1. Have children draw a line from each object in one group to an object in the other group and circle the group that has more.
2. Have children count the objects and write the numbers for how many objects are in each group. Then have them circle the number which is more.
3. Do the same for the other two problems.

Name ______________________________

Comparing Numbers (continued)

How many? Circle the group with fewer objects.
Circle the number which is less.

4. 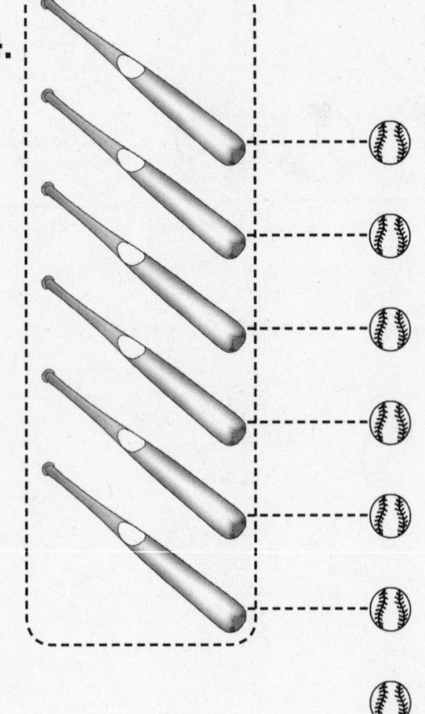

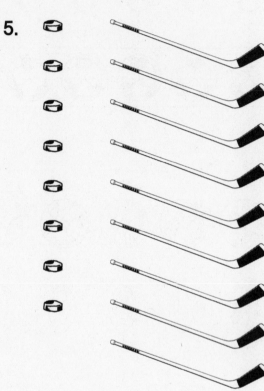

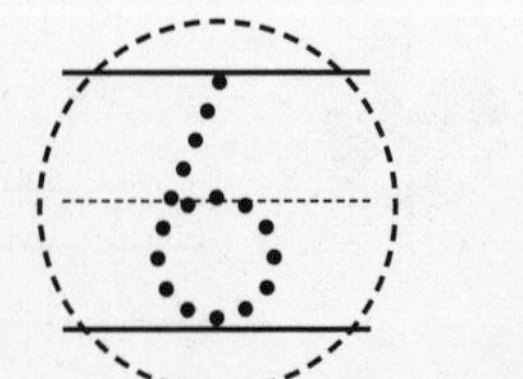

5.

______ ______

6. 

______

______

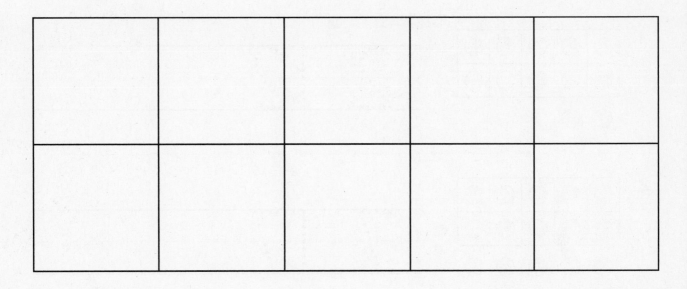

Name ____________________

11 to 19

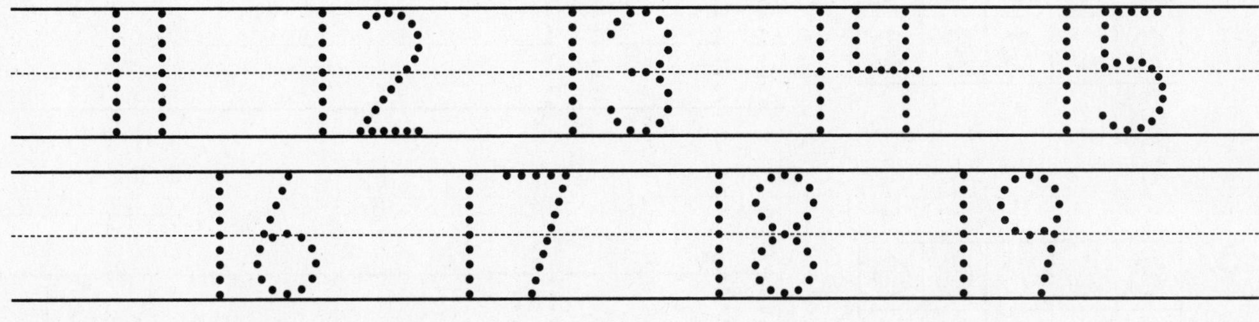

Materials: Two-color counters, 19 per child

1. Have children fill the tens grid with counters and count as they place the counters. Ask: ***How many?*** 10
2. Have children place one more counter on the page and say eleven. Have them write 11.
3. Have children place one more counter on the page and say twelve. Have them write 12.
4. Continue to 19.

Name ______________________

11 to 19 (continued)

How many?

1. 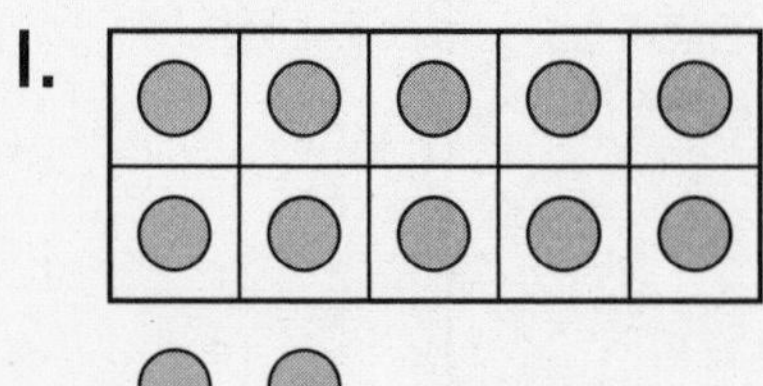

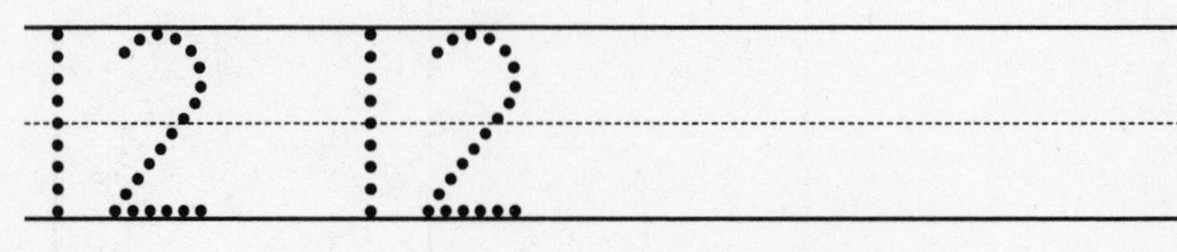

2. 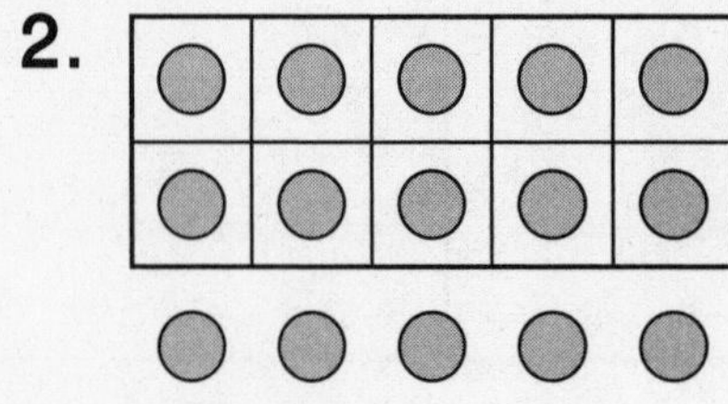

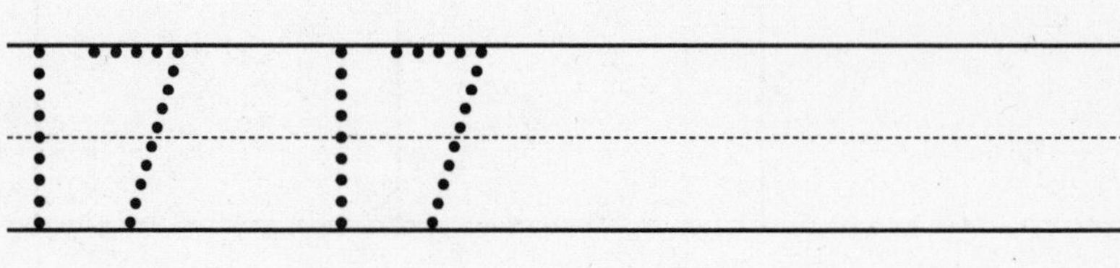

3. 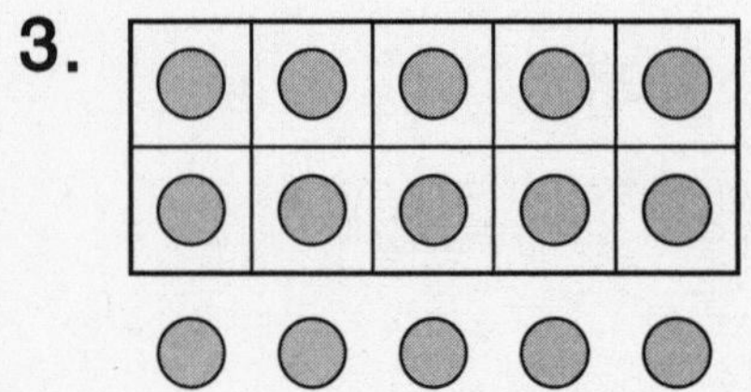

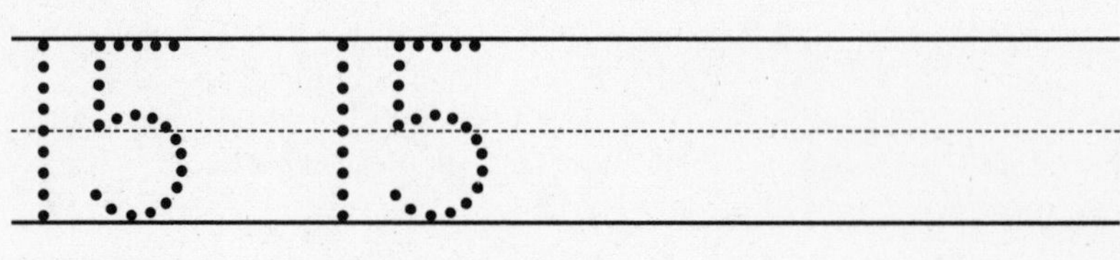

4. 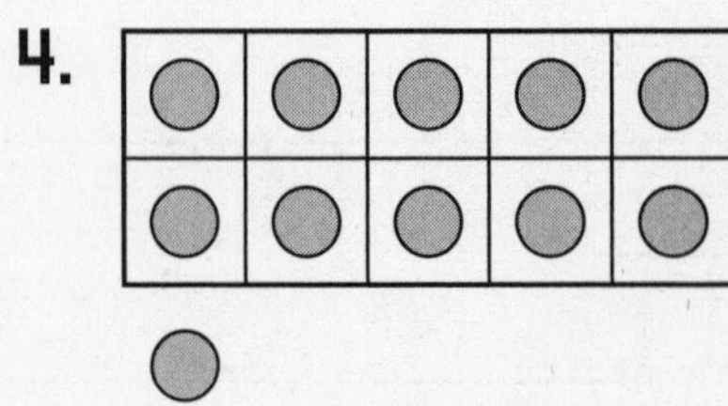

5. 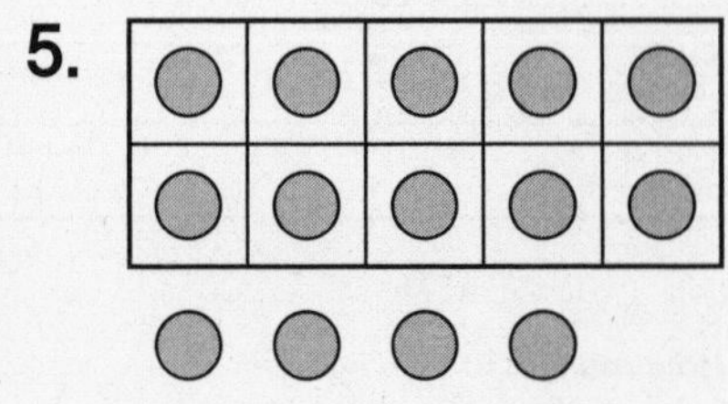

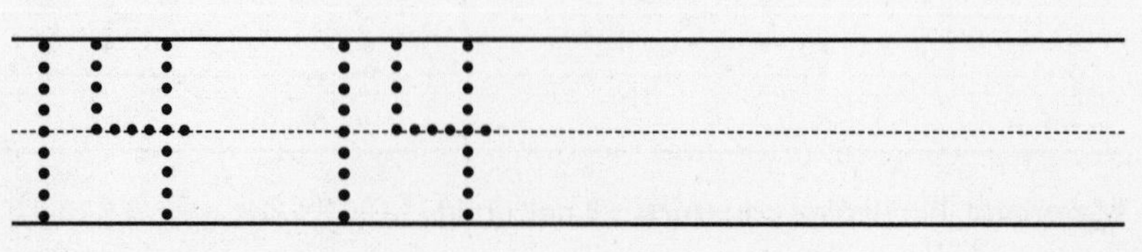

Name ________________________________

Numbers to 30

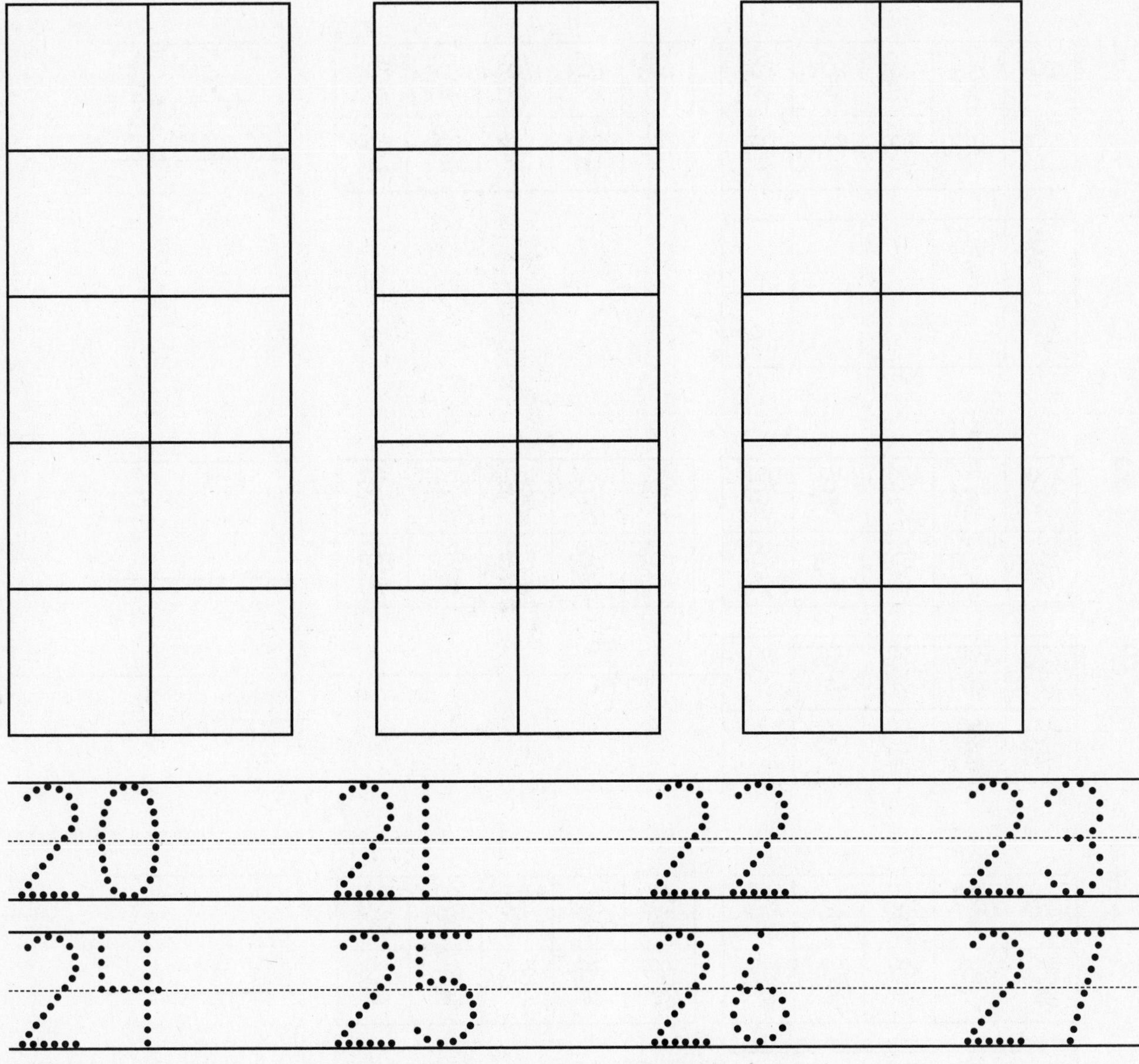

20 21 22 23
24 25 26 27
28 29 30

Materials: Crayons or markers

1. Have children color a circle in each section of the first tens grids and count as they color. Ask: ***How many?*** 10
2. Have children continue coloring and counting to 19. Ask: ***How many?*** 19
3. Have children color one more circle, and say twenty, and write 20.
4. Continue to 30.

Name ____________________

Numbers to 30 (continued)

How many?

1. 

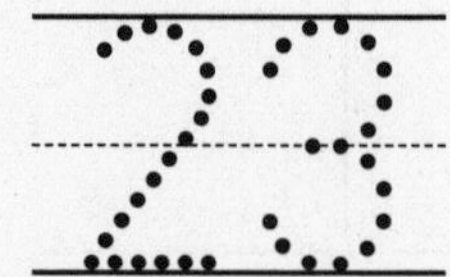

2. ______

3. ______

Name ______________________

Counting by 10's to 100

I.

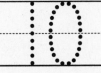

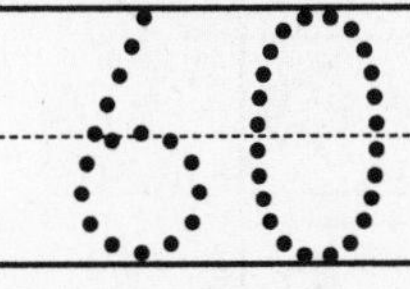

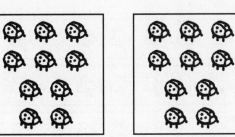

1. Count the groups of 10 lady bugs out loud, altogether as a class.
2. Have children say the numbers again, to themselves, and write the numbers.

Name ______________________

Counting by 10's to 100 (continued)

How many?

2. 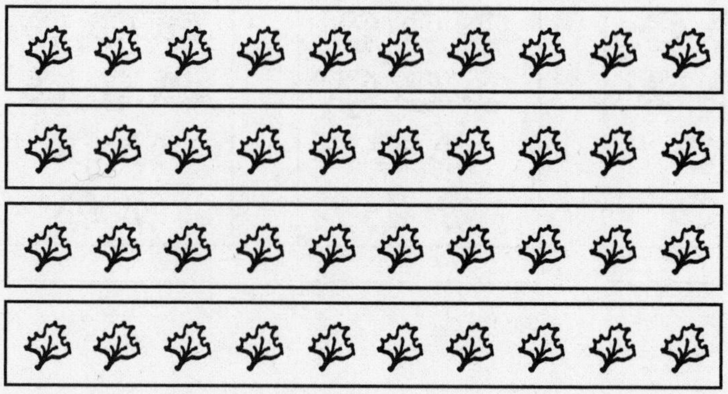 40

3. ______

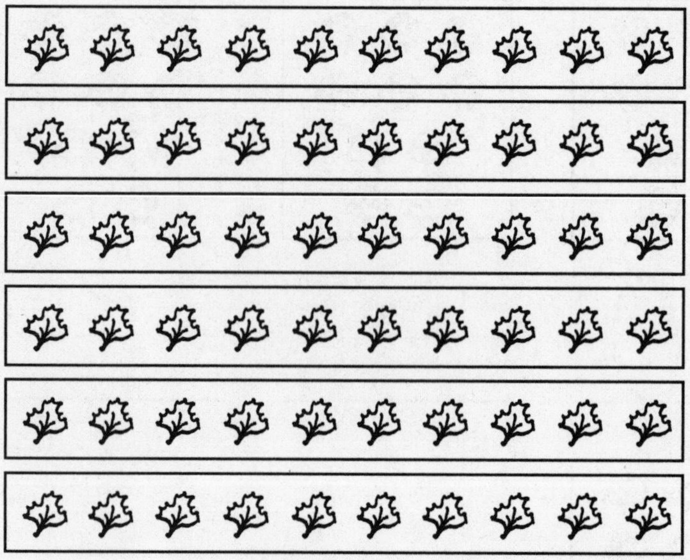

4. ______

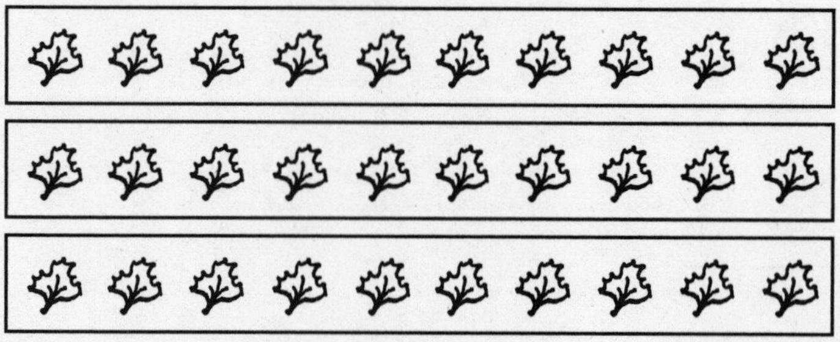

Name ______________________________

Counting to 100

1	2	3	4	5		7	8	9	10
11	12	13		15	16	17	18	19	20
21	22	23	24		26	27	28	29	
31	32	33	34	35	36		38	39	40
41		43	44	45	46	47	48	49	50
	52	53	54	55	56	57		59	60
61	62		64	65	66	67	68	69	
71	72	73	74	75		77	78	79	80
81	82	83		85	86	87	88	89	
91	92	93	94		96	97	98		100

1. Count to 100 as a class. Have children put a finger on each number as it is said.
2. Have children count to themselves and write the missing numbers.
3. Have children find 52. Have them count to 52 by saying 10, 20, 30, 40, 50, 51, 52.

Name ______________________________

Counting to 100 (continued)

How many?
Count by 10s and then by 1s.

1. 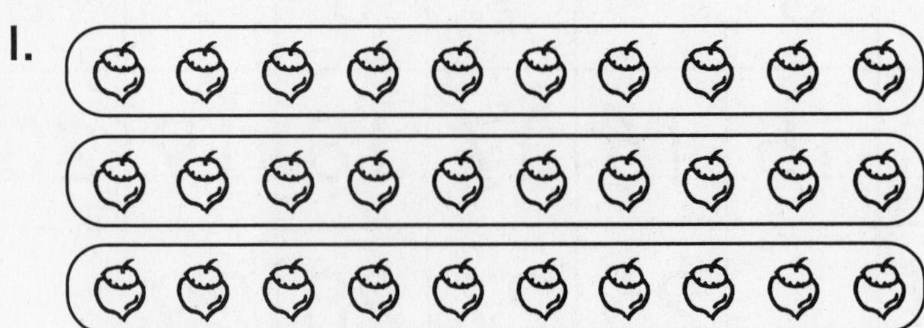

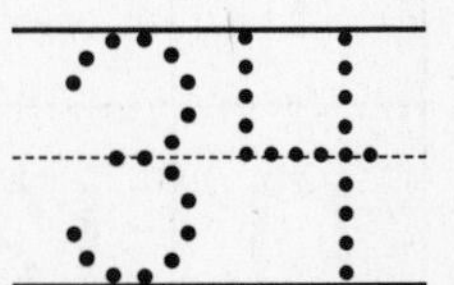

2. 

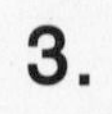

3. 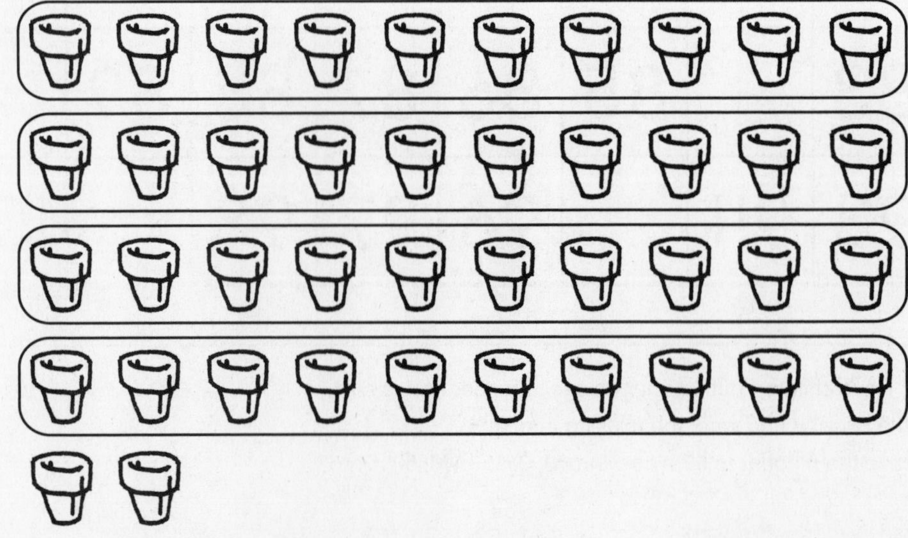

Name ______________________________

Numbers to 12

1 2 3 4
5 6 7 8
9 10

Materials: Two-color counters, 12 per child

1. Have children place one counter in the tens grid, say 1, and write the number.
2. Have children place one more counter in the grid, say 2, and write the number.
3. Continue to 11. Ask: ***Eleven is ten and how many more?*** 1
4. Do 12 similarly. Ask: ***Twelve is ten and how many more?*** 2

Name ______________________

Numbers to 12 (continued)

How many?

1.

2.

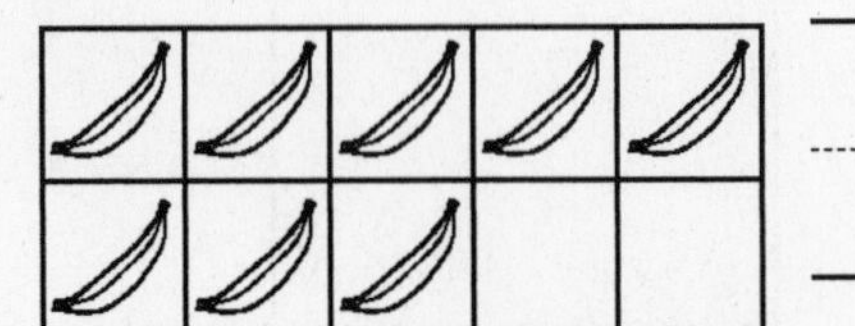

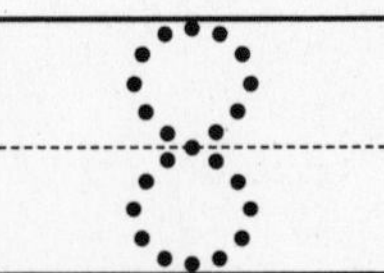

3.

4.

5.

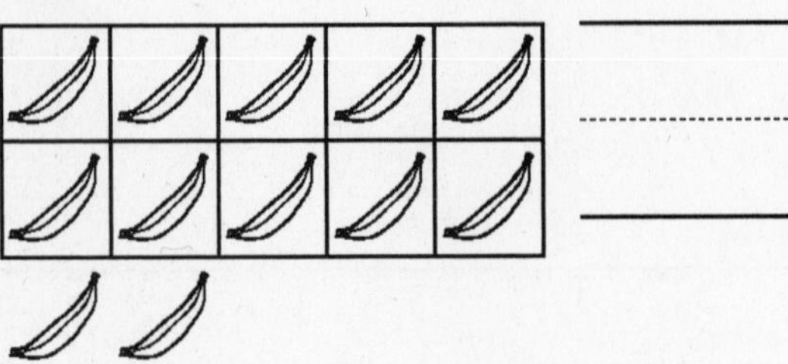

6.

7.

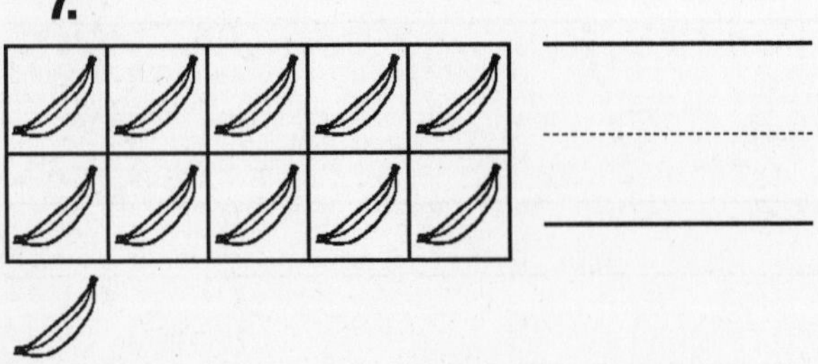

8.

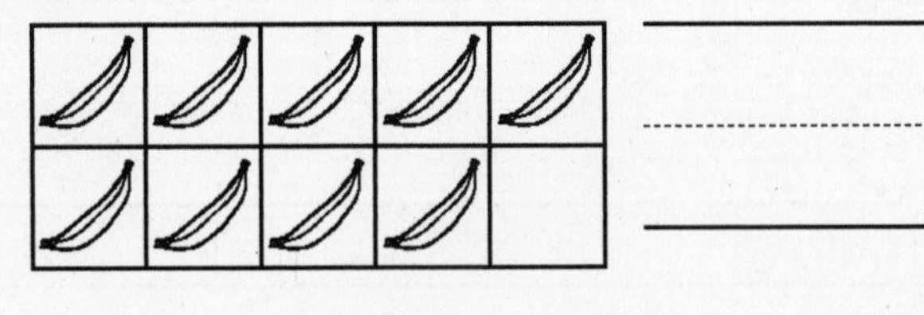

Reasoning

9. Draw 1 more.
Write how many.

Name ______________________________

Spatial Patterns for Numbers to 10

1\.

2\.

3\.

4\.

5\.

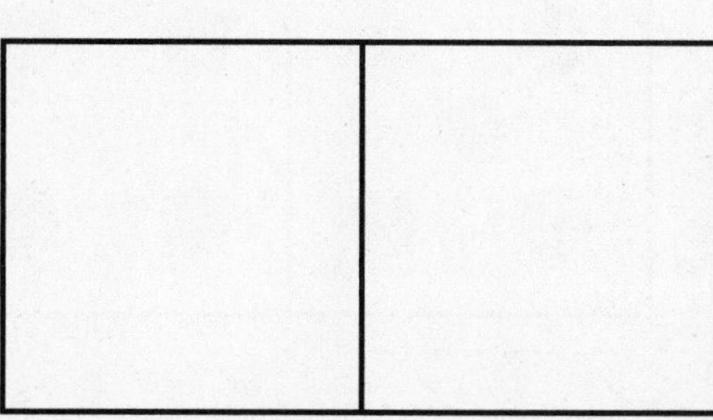

6\.

Materials: Two-color counters, 10 per child

1. Have children arrange 4 counters in different ways and notice the patterns.
2. Have children choose which pattern they like best, draw it in the box, and write the number.
3. Repeat for the other problems.

Name ______________________________

Spatial Patterns for Numbers to 10 (continued)

Write how many dots.

7.

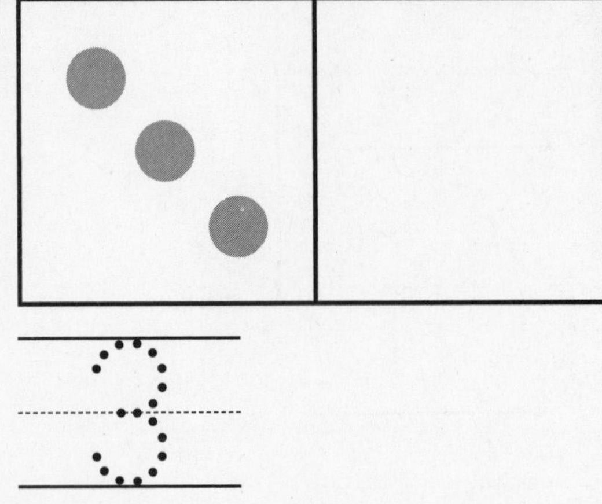

8.

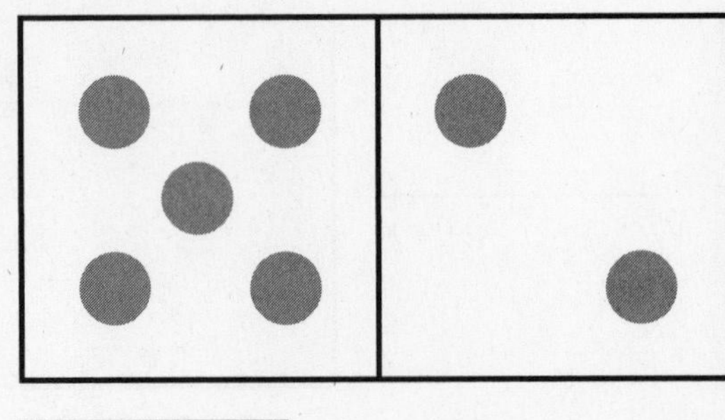

9.

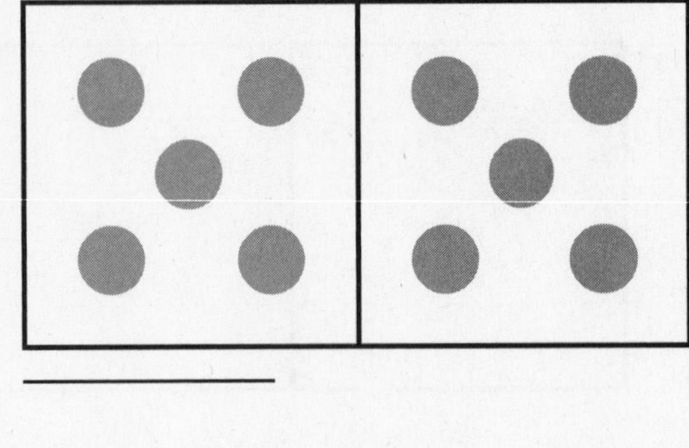

10.

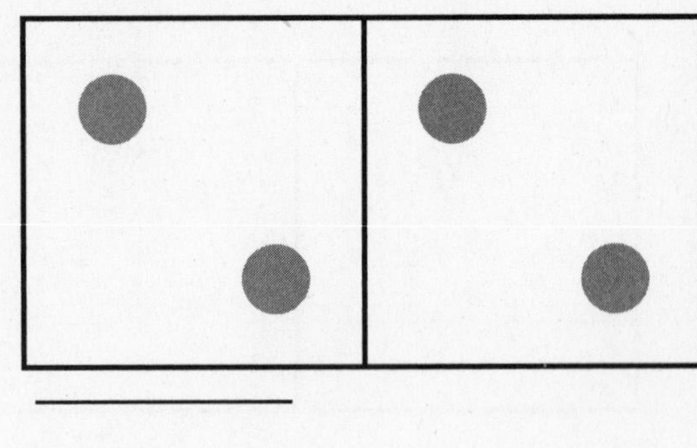

11.

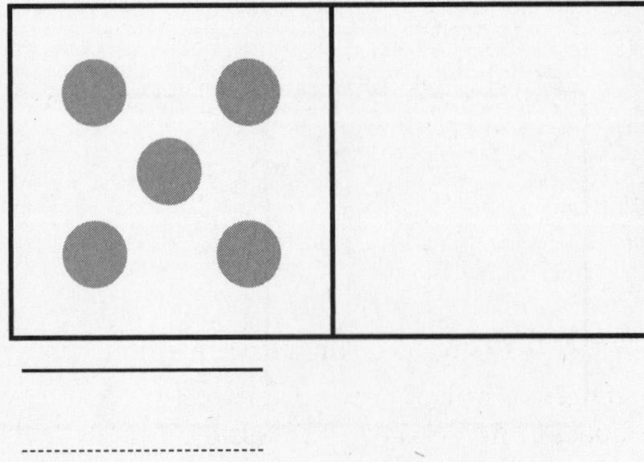

12.

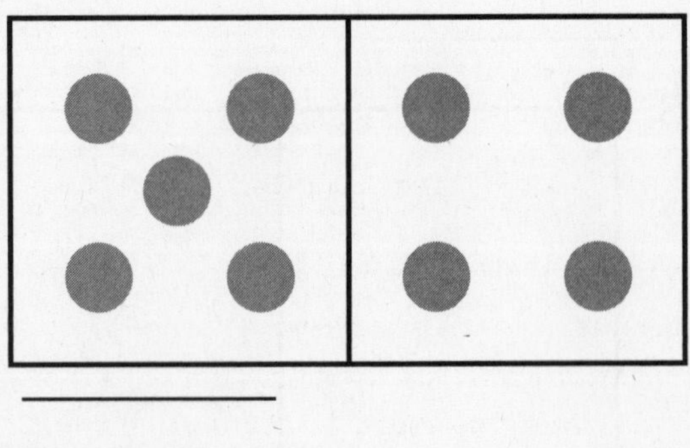

Name ______________________________

Comparing Numbers to 10

1. 3 is greater than / is less than 5

2. 7 is greater than / is less than 4

3. 6 is greater than / is less than 2

4. 5 is greater than / is less than 8

Materials: Two color counters, 19 per child

1. Have children show 3 red counters in the first square and 5 yellow counters in the second square.
2. Ask: ***Does the first square have more counters or fewer counters than the second square?*** Encourage children to line up the counters next to each other, outside the squares, if necessary.
3. Say: ***Since the first square with 3 counters has fewer than the second square with 5 counters, 3 is less than 5.*** Write "is less than" on the board or overhead and have children circle the phrase on their papers.
4. Repeat for Problem 2. Then say, ***Since the first square with 7 counters has more than the second square with 4 counters, 7 is greater than 4.*** Write "is greater than" on the board or overhead and have children circle the phrase on their papers.
5. Have children do the other problems similarly.

Name ______________________________

Comparing Numbers to 10 (continued)

Circle the number that is **less** than the other number.

5.  

4 or 3

6.  

2 or 5

7. 8 or 6

8. 7 or 10

Circle the answer.

9. 6 is greater than / is less than 5

10. 1 is greater than / is less than 4

11. 7 is greater than / is less than 3

12. 2 is greater than / is less than 5

13. 5 is greater than / is less than 7

14. 9 is greater than / is less than 8

15. 8 is greater than / is less than 10

16. 4 is greater than / is less than 6

Name ______________________

Ordering Numbers to 12

1. 2, 4, 7
least, between, greatest

2. ____, ____, ____
least, between, greatest

3. ____, ____, ____
least, between, greatest

4. ____, ____, ____
least, between, greatest

Materials: Snap cubes, 28 per child or pair

1. Have children show trains of 4, 7, and 2 snap cubes.
2. Ask: ***Which train has the least number of snap cubes?***
3. Ask: ***Which train has the greatest number?***
4. Ask: ***Which train has a number between the other two numbers?***
5. Have children arrange their trains in order from least to greatest and then write the numbers.
6. Repeat with trains that have 11, 8, and 9 cubes.
7. Have children write the numbers for the other two problems. Allow them to use cubes, if they need them.

Name ______________________________

Ordering Numbers to 12 (continued)

Complete.

5. 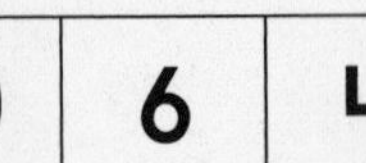

______, ______, ______
least between greatest

6.

5	11	9

______, ______, ______
least between greatest

7.

8	3	12

______, ______, ______
least between greatest

8.

7	10	9

______, ______, ______
least between greatest

9. **Number Sense** Tico bought 11 pencils. Kevin bought 7 pencils. Marco bought 10 pencils. Who bought the least number of pencils? ______

Name ______________________________

Ordering Numbers to 12 with a Number Line

1.

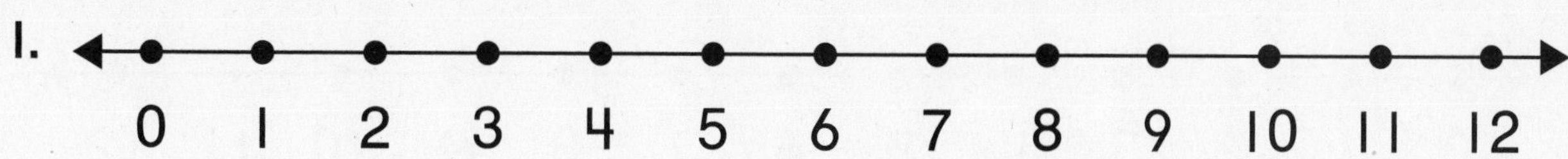

6 least ______ between 9 greatest

2.

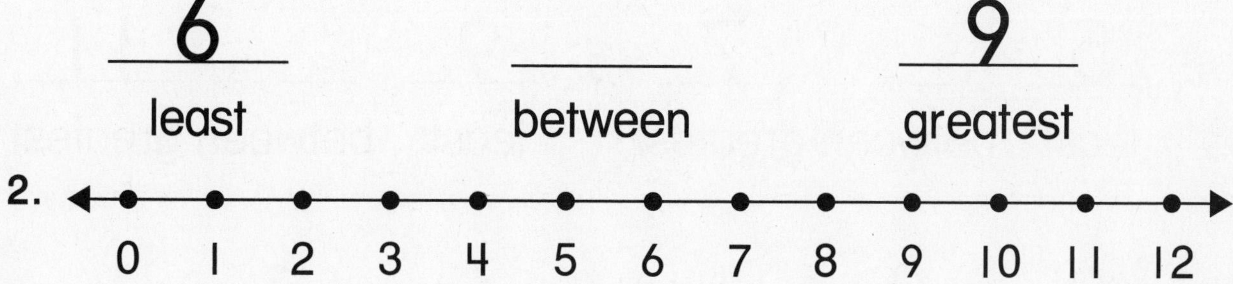

9 least 10 between ______ greatest

3.

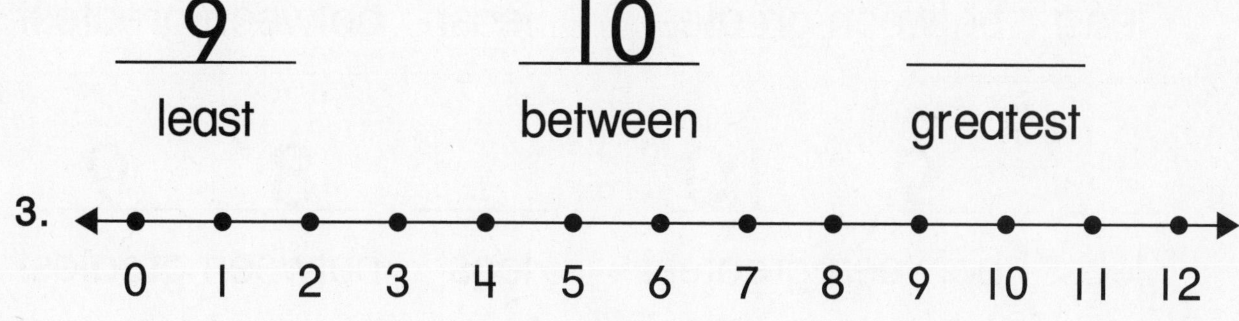

______ least 4 between 5 greatest

Materials: Crayons or markers

1. Have children circle the 6 and its dot on the number line.
2. Have them circle the 9 and its dot.
3. Ask: ***What number is between 6 and 9?*** 7 or 8 Have children write the number.
4. For Problem 2, have children circle the 9 and 10.
5. Ask: ***What number is after 10?*** Although 11 is the preferred answer, 12 is also correct. Have children write the number.
6. For Problem 3, have children circle 4 and 5. Ask: ***What number is before 4?*** 0 to 3 are acceptable. Have children write the number.

Name ______________________________

Ordering Numbers to 12 with a Number Line (continued)

Use the number line.
Write the missing number.

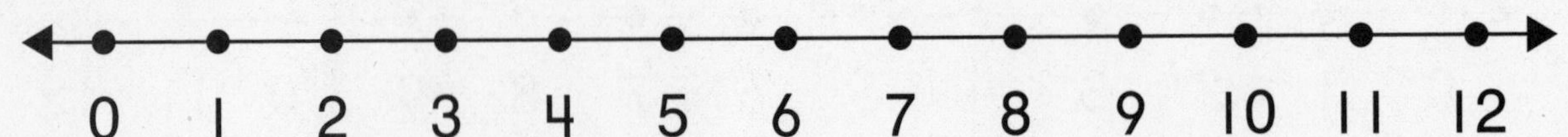

4. 5 ____ 7
least between greatest

5. 9 ____ 11
least between greatest

6. 2 3 ____
least between greatest

7. 6 7 ____
least between greatest

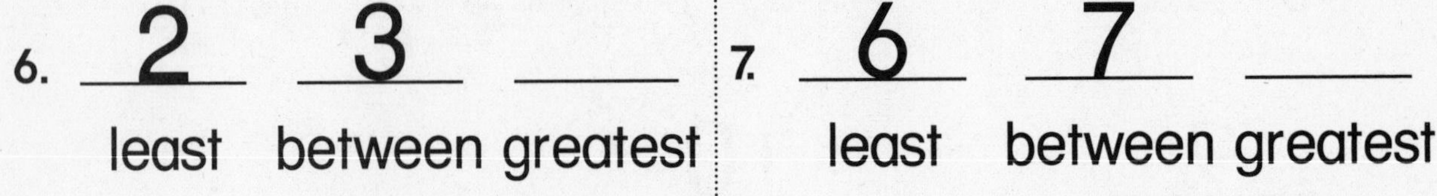

8. ____ 9 10
least between greatest

9. ____ 8 9
least between greatest

10. 3 4 ____
least between greatest

11. 10 11 ____
least between greatest

12. **Reasoning** Find the two numbers between 3 and 6.

3 ____ ____ 6
least between between greatest

Name ____________________

Making Numbers 11 to 20

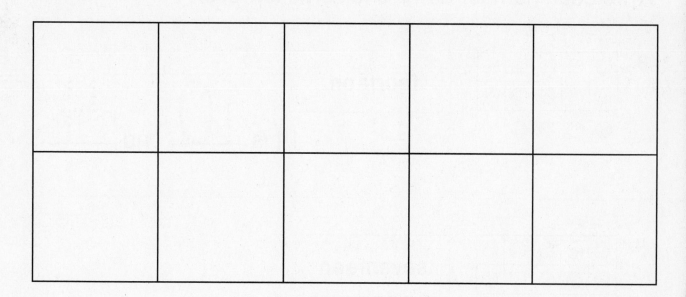

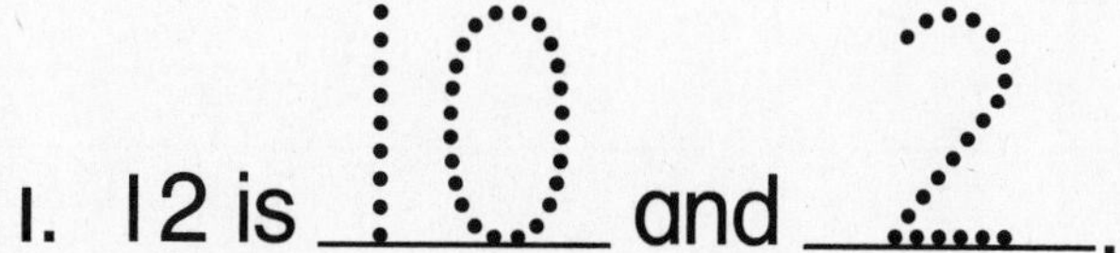

1. 12 is 10 and 2.

2. 19 is ______ and ______.

Materials: Two color counters, 19 per child

1. Have children fill the tens grid with counters and count as they place the counters. Ask: ***How many?*** 10
2. Have children place two more counters and say twelve. Ask: ***12 is 10 and how much more?*** (2) Have children write 10 and 2.
3. Have children place more counters and count to 19. Ask: ***19 is 10 and how much more?*** (9) Have children write 10 and 9.

Name ______________________________

Making Numbers 11 to 20 (continued)

Write each number as 10 and some left over.

3. 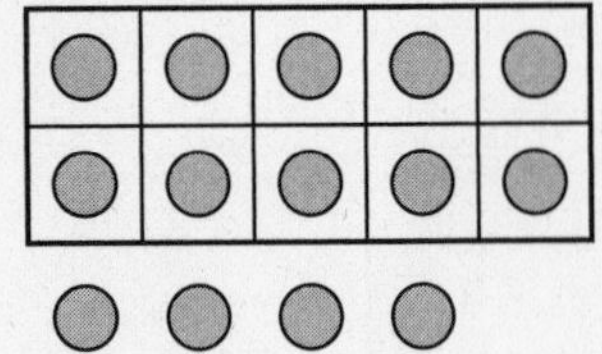

fourteen

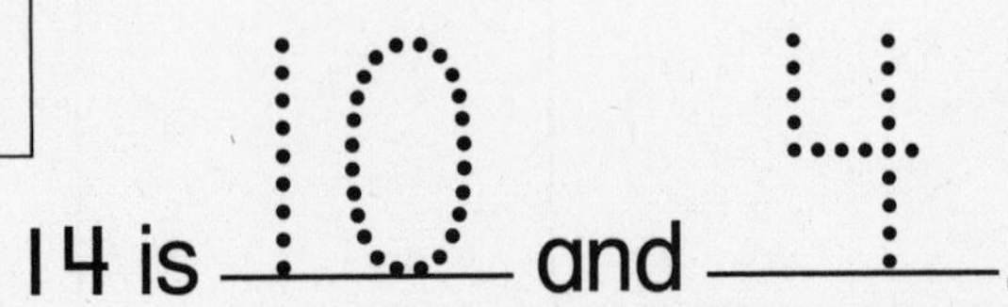

14 is ______ and ______.

4. 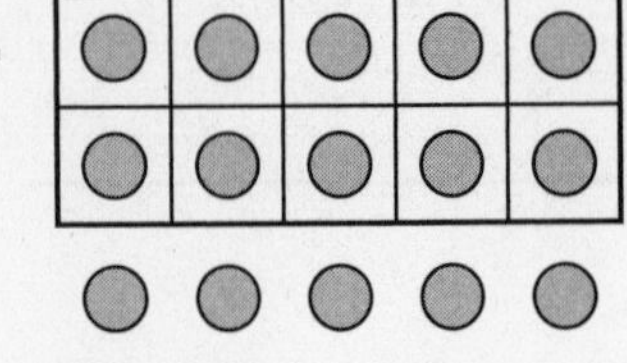

seventeen

17 is ______ and ______.

5. 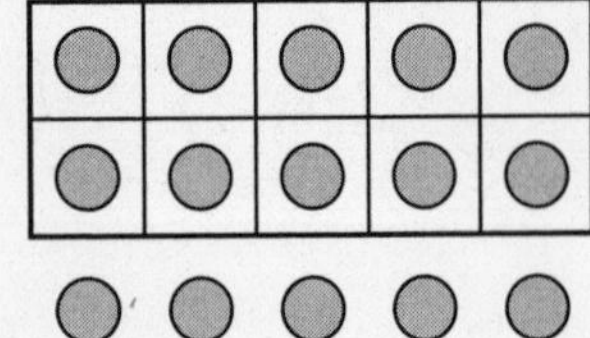

fifteen

15 is ______ and ______.

6. **Reasoning**

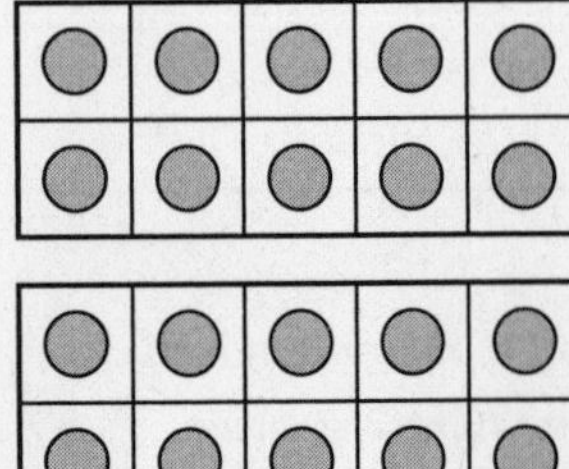

twenty

20 is 10 and ______.

Name ______________________________

Using Numbers 11 to 20

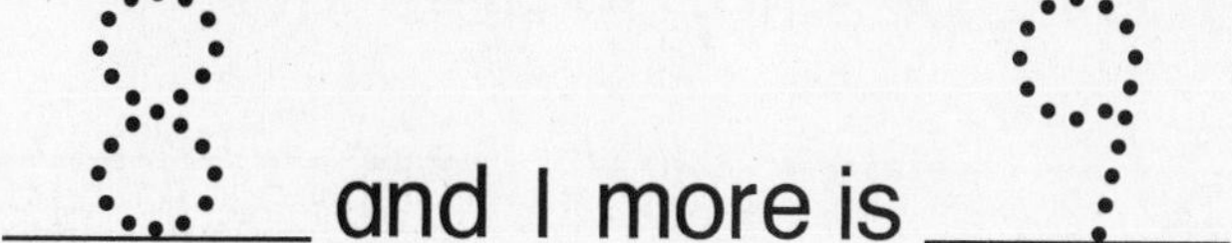

1. ______ and 1 more is ______.

2. ______ and 2 more is ______.

3. 1 fewer than ______ is ______.

4. 2 fewer than ______ is ______.

Write the numbers. Use cubes if you need to.

5.

6 and 1 more is ______. 6 and 2 more is ______.

1 fewer than 6 is ______. 1 fewer than 6 is ______.

Materials: Snap cubes, 10 of 1 color, 9 of a second color, and 2 of a third color per child or pair

1. Have children make a train of 8 cubes in one color and write 8.
2. Have children add a different colored cube to their train. Ask: ***How much is 8 and 1 more?*** Have children write 9.
3. Have children add another cube to their train. Ask: ***How much is 8 and 2 more?*** Have children write 10.
4. Have children show 17, using 10 cubes of one color and 7 cubes of another color and write 17.
5. Have children take away one cube. Ask: ***How much is 17 and one less?*** Have children write 16.
6. Have children take away another cube. Ask: ***How much is 17 and two less?*** Have children write 15.
7. For Problem 5, have children find one more, two more, 1 fewer, and 2 fewer than 6.

Name ______________________________

Using Numbers 11 to 20 (continued)

Write the numbers.
Use cubes if you need to.

6\.

18 and 1 more is 19. 18 and 2 more is 20.

7\.

1 fewer than 16 is ______. 2 fewer than 16 is ______.

8\. 9 and 1 more is ______. 9 and 2 more is ______.

9\. 1 fewer than 7 is ______. 2 fewer than 7 is ______.

10\. 10 and 1 more is ______. 10 and 2 more is ______.

11\. **Reasoning** 6 and 1 more is 7. Is 6 and 2 more the same as 7 and 1 more?

yes no

Name ______________________________

Using Skip Counting

1. 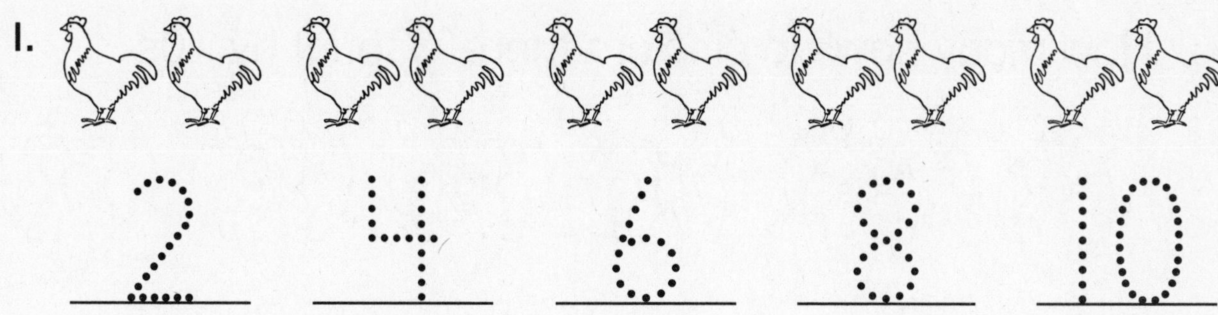

2. 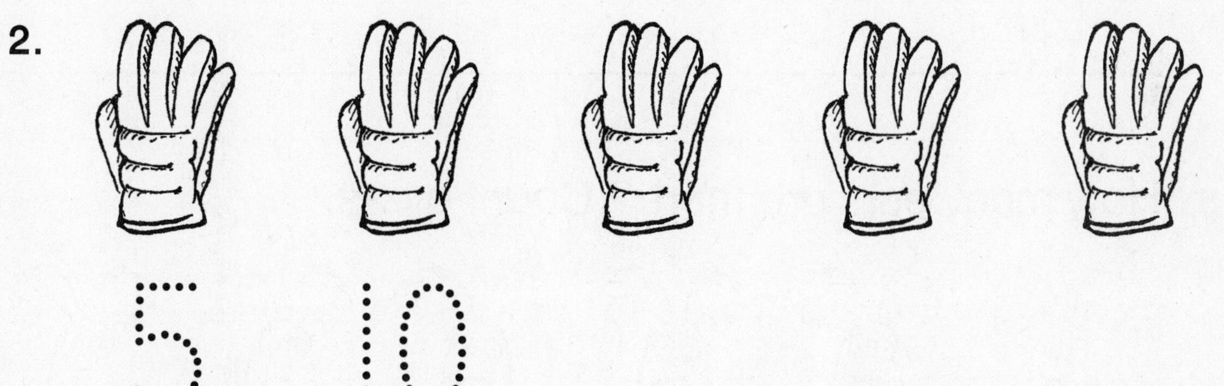

3. 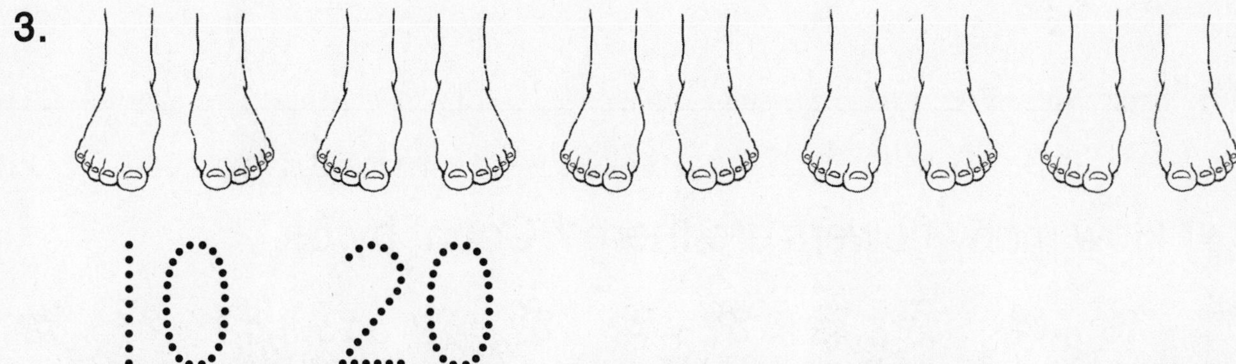

1. Say: ***How many roosters? Skip count by 2s to find out.*** Have children skip count and write the numbers.
2. Say: ***How many fingers? Skip count by 5s to find out.*** Have children skip count and write the numbers.
3. Say: ***How many toes? Skip count by 10s to find out.*** Have children skip count and write the numbers.

Name ______________________________

Using Skip Counting (continued)

Skip count.

4. How many bowling pins are there? Count by 10s.

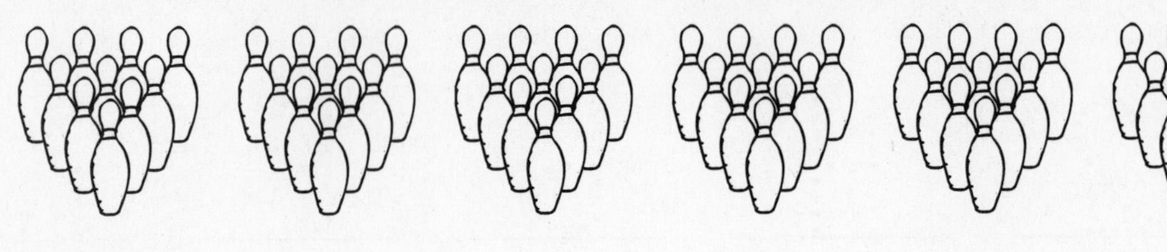

10 ______ ______ ______ ______ ______

5. How many ears are there? Count by 2s.

2 ______ ______ ______ ______ ______

6. How many flowers are there? Count by 5s.

5 ______ ______ ______ ______ ______

Name ______________________________

Odd and Even

1. 8

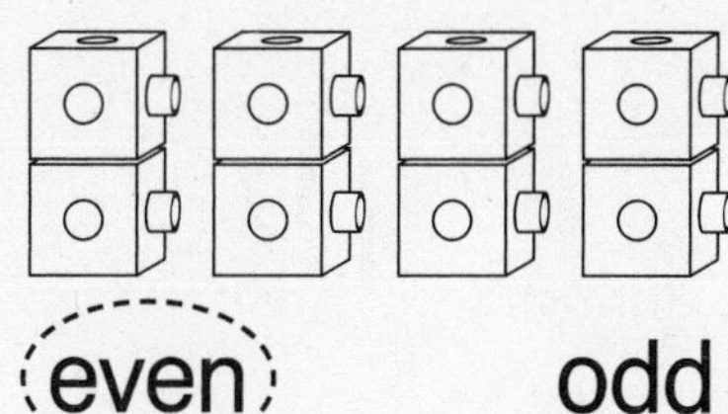

(even) odd

2. 15

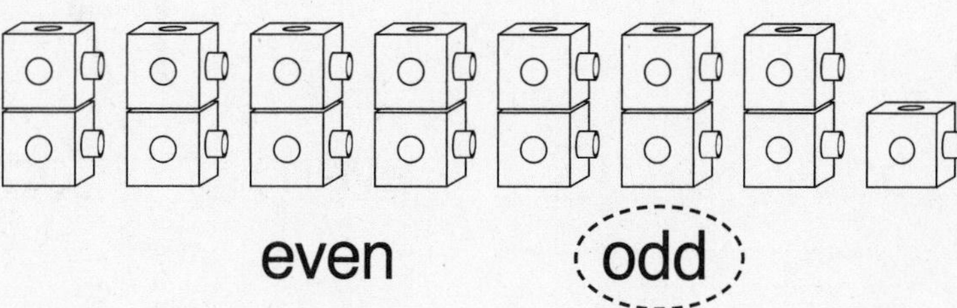

even (odd)

3. 3

even odd

4. 16

even odd

5. 6

even odd

6. 19

even odd

7. 20

even odd

8. 13

even odd

Materials: snap cubes, 20 per child

1. Have children count out 8 cubes and make pairs as shown. Say: ***Since you can make pairs out of 8 cubes with none left over, 8 is an even number.*** Have children circle even.
2. Have children count out 15 cubes and make pairs as shown. Say: ***Since there is one left over when you make pairs out of 15, 15 is an odd number.*** Have children circle odd.
3. Have children use cubes and pairs to do the other problems.

Name ______________________

Odd and Even (continued)

Circle **even** or **odd**.
Use cubes if you like.

9. 9
even odd

10. 14
even odd

11. 18
even odd

12. 17
even odd

13. 12
even odd

14. 11
even odd

15. 5
even odd

16. 4
even odd

Look at the pattern
What comes next?

17. 5, 7, 9, ______

18. 4, 6, 8, ______

19. 10, 12, 14, ______

20. 9, 11, 13, ______

Name ______________________

Counting from Any Number

1	2	3	4	5	6	7	8	9	10
11	12	13	14	15	16	17	18	19	20
21	22	23	24	25	26	27	28	29	30
31	32	33	34	35	36	37	38	39	40
41	42	43	44	45	46	47	48	49	50
51	52	53	54	55	56	57	58	59	60
61	62	63	64	65	66	67	68	69	70
71	72	73	74	75	76	77	78	79	80
81	82	83	84	85	86	87	88	89	90
91	92	93	94	95	96	97	98	99	100

1. 48, ____, ____, ____, ____　　**2.** 63, ____, ____, ____, ____

1. Have children point to the number 48 on the hundred chart. Ask: ***What number comes after 48?*** 49 ***What number comes after 49?*** 50; Continue to 52. Have children write the numbers.
2. Have children point to the number 63 on the hundred chart. Ask: ***What number comes before 63?*** 62 ***What number comes before 62?*** 61; Continue to 59. Have children write the numbers.

Name ______________________________

Counting from Any Number (continued)

Count by 1s.
Write the numbers.

3. 23, 24, ____, ____, ____

4. 74, ____, 76, ____, ____

5. 37, ____, 39, ____, ____

6. 19, ____, ____, ____, 23

7. 88, ____, ____, 91, ____

8. 94, ____, 96, ____, ____

Count back by 1s.
Write the numbers.

9. 43, 42, ____, ____, ____

10. 9, ____, ____, 6, ____

11. 80, ____, 78, ____, ____

12. 52, 51, ____, ____, ____

13. 60, ____, 58, ____, ____

14. 100, 99, ____, ____, ____

Reasoning Skip count by 2s.
Write the numbers.

15. 72, 74, 76, ____, ____

16. 30, 28, 26, ____, ____

Name ______________________________

Before, After, and Between

1. 52, 53, 54

2. 38, 39, ____

3. 97, 98, 99

4. ____, 20, 21

5. 13, ____, 15

6. 71, ____, 73

Materials: Snap cubes, 100 per pair or group

1. Have children show 52 with snap cubes, making five 10-trains and one 2-train. Have them add one more cube. Ask: ***What number comes after 52?*** Have them add one more cube and tell what number comes after 53. Have them write 54.
2. Repeat, starting with 38.
3. Have children show 99 with snap cubes. Have them take away one cube. Ask: ***What number comes before 99?*** Have them take away one more cube and tell what number comes before 98. Have them write 97.
4. Repeat, starting with 21.
5. Have children show 13 with snap cubes. Have them add one more cube. Ask: ***What number comes after 13? Does 15 come after 14?*** Say: ***So, 14 is between 13 and 15***.
6. Repeat, starting with 71.

Name ______________________________

Before, After, and Between (continued)

Write the number that comes just after.

7. 21, 22, 23

8. 43, 44, ____

9. 52, 53, ____

10. 28, 29, ____

Write the number that comes just before.

11. ____, 17, 18

12. ____, 84, 85

Write the number that comes between.

13. 26, 27, 28

14. 98, ____, 100

15. 48, ____, 50

16. 65, ____, 67

Reasoning Write the numbers that come just before and just after.

17. 85, 86, ____

18. ____, 31, ____

19. ____, 79, ____

20. ____, 60, ____

Name ______________________________

Counting with Tens and Ones

1. 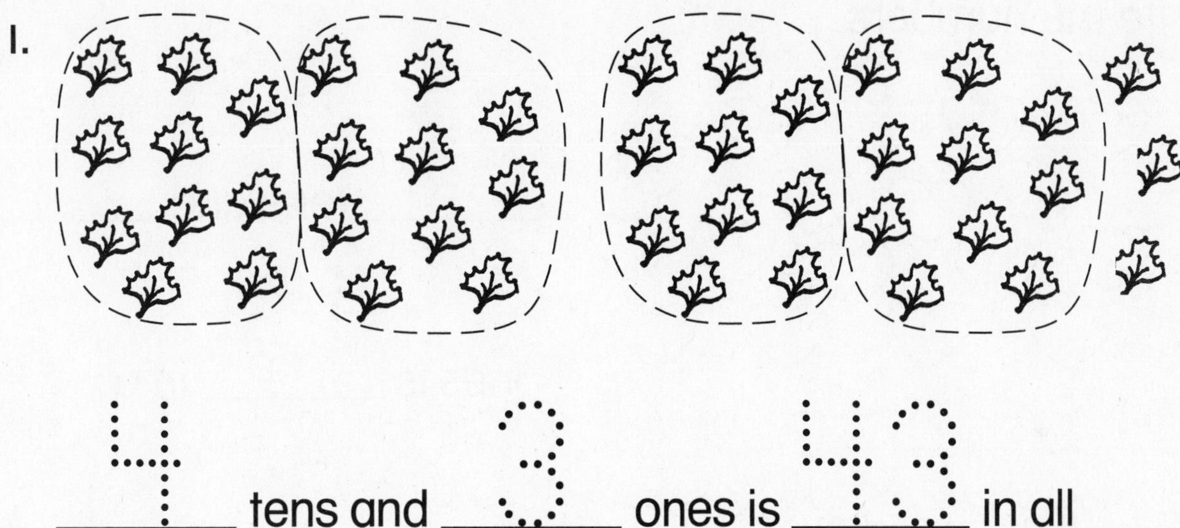

4 tens and 3 ones is 43 in all

2.

______ tens and ______ ones is ______ in all

1. Have children circle groups of ten leaves. Ask: ***How many tens?*** 4 ***How many ones are left?*** 3 ***How much is 4 tens and 3 ones in all?*** Have children write 4, 3, and 43.
2. Have children circle groups of ten ants. Ask: ***How many tens?*** 7 ***How many ones are left?*** 4 ***How much is 7 tens and 4 ones in all?*** Have children write 7, 4, and 74.

Name ______________________

Counting with Tens and Ones (continued)

Circle groups of ten. Count the tens and ones.
Write the numbers.

3. 

1 tens and 7 ones is 17 in all

4. 

_____ tens and _____ ones is _____ in all

5. 

_____ tens and _____ ones is _____ in all

6. **Reasoning** Alberto has trading cards in groups of 10. He has 4 groups of 10 and 8 left over. Write the numbers that tell how many in all.

_____ tens and _____ ones is _____ in all

Name ______________________________

Estimating with Groups of 10

1.

2.

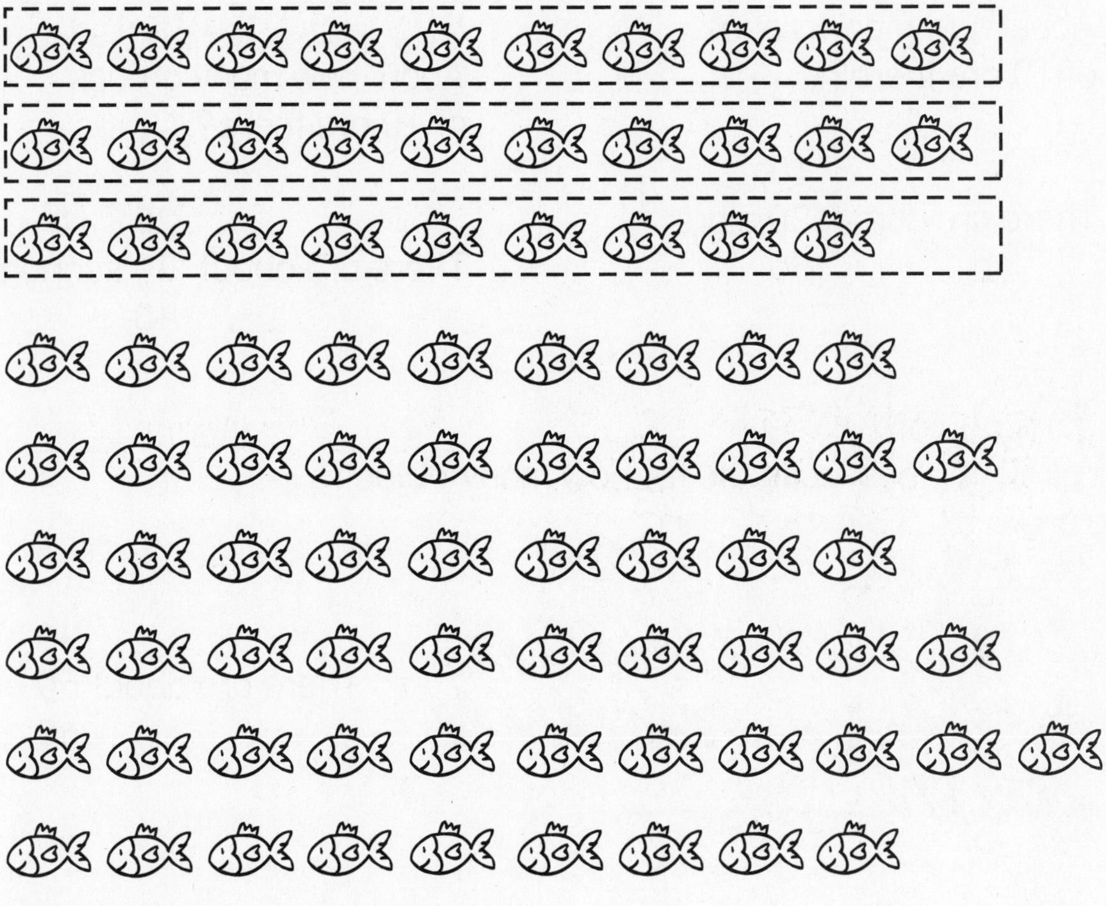

3. About how many groups of 10 fish are there? ________

4. About how many fish are there in all? ________

1. Have children count the fish in the first group. Ask: ***How many?***
2. Tell children to use the group of 10 in Number 1 to circle groups that have about 10 fish.
3. Ask: ***About how many groups of 10 are there?*** Have children write 9.
4. Ask: ***About how many fish are there in all?*** Have children write 90.

Name ____________________

Estimating with Groups of 10 (continued)

Use groups of 10 to estimate the total number of objects.

5. About how many groups of 10 are there? 2

There are about 10 / 20 / 30 stars.

6. About how many groups of 10 are there? ______

There are about 20 / 30 / 40 seahorses.

Circle a group of 10.
Then circle the best estimate for how many objects there are in all.

7. There are about 40 / 50 / 60.

8. There are about 30 / 40 / 50.

9. **Reasoning** If you estimate that there are about 10 frogs in a pond, what could the actual number of frogs be? Circle the **best** answer.

2 4 9

Name ______________________

Ordinal Numbers through Tenth

______	______	______	
1st first	2nd second	3rd third	
______	______	______	
4th fourth	5th fifth	6th sixth	
______	______	______	______
7th seventh	8th eighth	9th ninth	10th tenth

1. Choose 10 children with 10 different first initials and have them line up in the front of the class, facing the rest of the class.
2. Say: ***Some numbers help us tell the order in which people or things are arranged. These numbers are called ordinal numbers.*** Go to the first child and say the child's name and then, ***is first in line.*** Write *first* and *1st* on the board or overhead.
3. Have children who are seated write the child's initial on the first line of their worksheet.
4. Continue to tenth.
5. Have children who were standing write initials after they take a seat, as the class reviews the order.

Name ___________________________

Ordinal Numbers through Tenth (continued)

Write the word to show the order of the item.

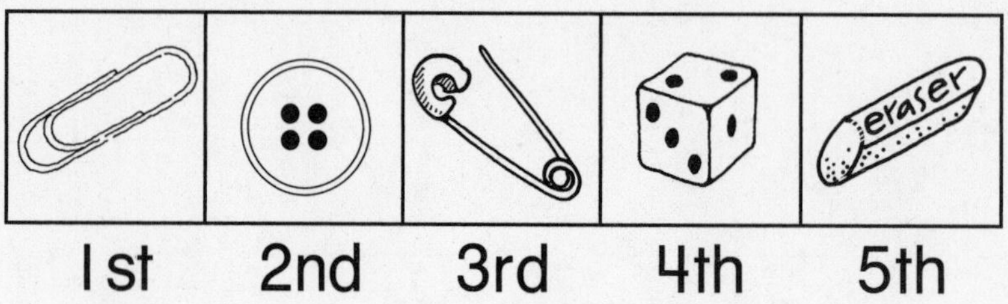

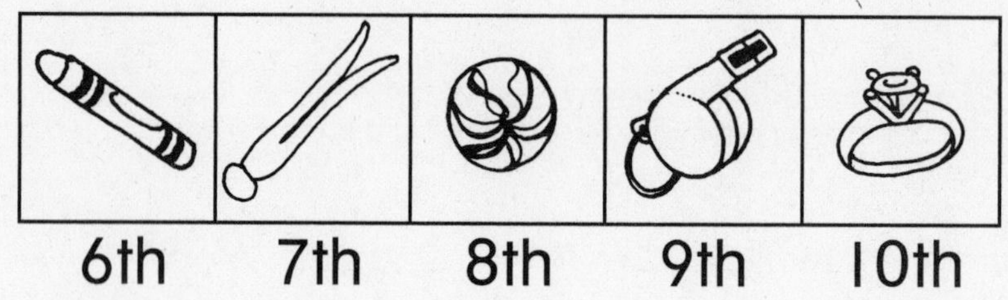

1. fourth / fifth / sixth

2. fifth / sixth / seventh

3. eighth / ninth / tenth

4. fifth / sixth / seventh

5. eighth / ninth / tenth

6. fifth / sixth / seventh

Name ______________________________

Tens

Circle groups of ten. Write how many.

1. ______ groups of ten = ______

2.

3.

______ groups of ten = ______

______ groups of ten = ______

1. Have children count groups of ten balloons and circle each group of ten.
2. Ask: ***How many groups of ten are there?*** Have children write 7. Ask: ***How much is 7 groups of ten?*** Have children write 70.
3. Have children count the other two groups of balloons similarly and write the number of groups and the total number of balloons.

Name ______________________________

Tens (continued)

Estimate how many. Then circle groups of ten and count.

4. 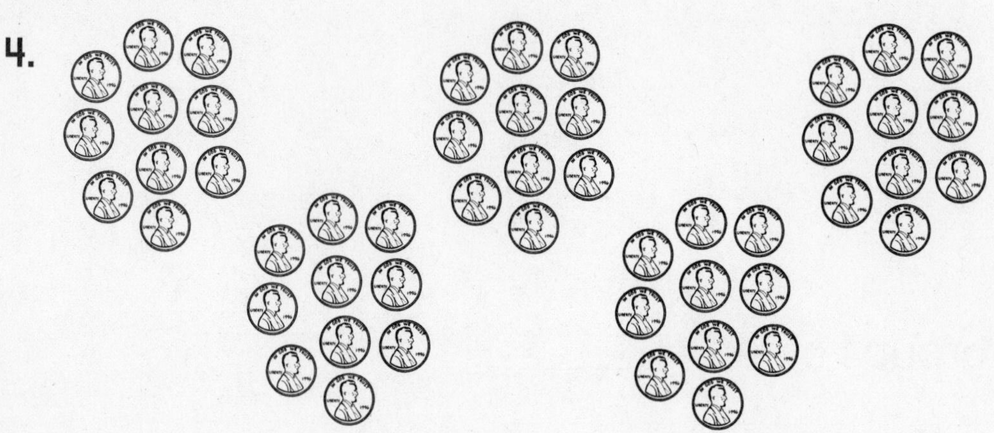

Estimate

Count

5. 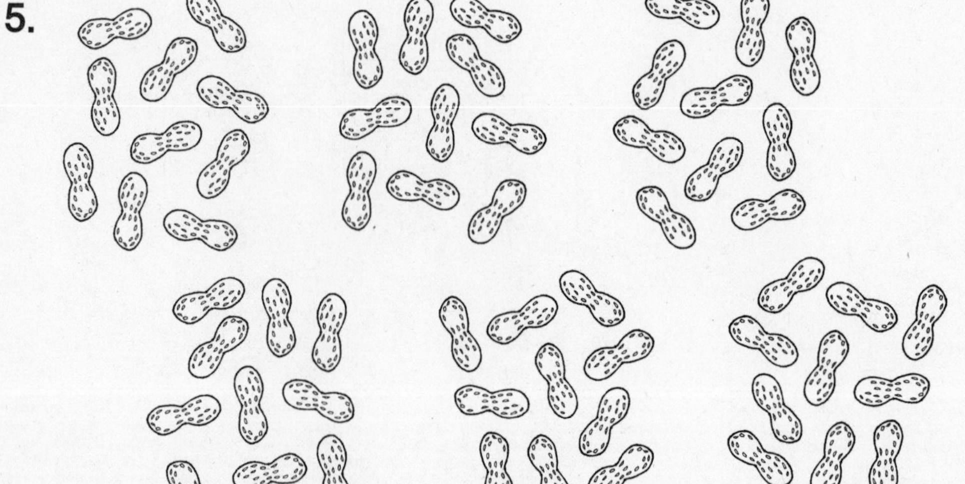

Estimate

Count

6. **Writing in Math** Are there more than 10 worms? Tell why you think as you do.

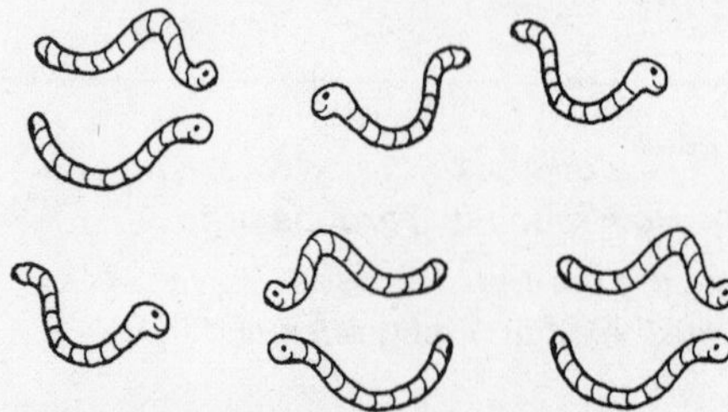

Name ______________________________

Tens and Ones

1.

tens	ones
4	9

40 + 9 = 49 

forty nine forty-nine

2.

tens	ones

_____ + _____ = _____ _____

thirty-seven

3. **Reasoning** 72 = _____ + 2

Materials: Place value blocks 49 ones and 4 tens per pair or group

1. Have children count out groups of 10 ones and trade each group of 10 ones for a tens block.
2. Ask: ***How many tens?*** Have children write 4 in the tens column of the Tens and Ones chart. ***How many ones left over?*** Have children write 9 in the ones column of the chart.
3. Ask: ***How much is 4 tens?*** Have children write 40 before the plus sign. ***How much is 9 ones?*** Have children write 9 after the plus sign. ***How many in all?*** Have children write 49 after the equal sign.
4. Have children count out 37 ones cubes and repeat the exercise.

Name ______________________

Tens and Ones (continued)

Complete each Tens and Ones chart and write how many.

4. 

tens	ones

______ + ______ = ______
sixty-five

5.

tens	ones

______ + ______ = ______
fifty-seven

6. 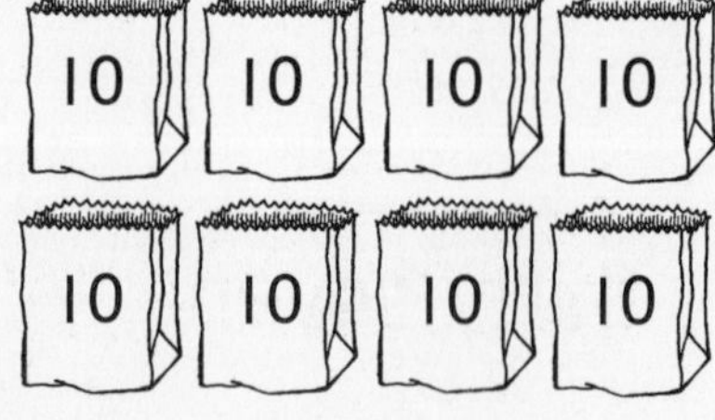

tens	ones

______ + ______ = ______
eighty

7. 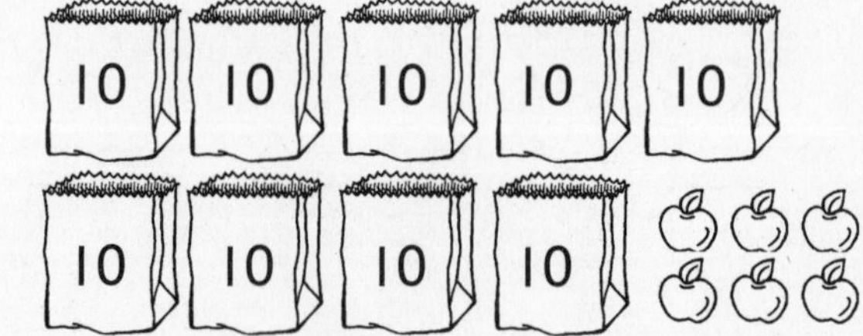

tens	ones

______ + ______ = ______
ninety-six

Name ______________________________

Number Patterns to 100

1	2	3	4	5	6	7	8	9	10
11	12	13	14	15	16	17	18	19	20
21	22	23	24	25	26	27	28	29	30
31	32	33	34	35	36	37	38	39	40
41	42	43	44	45	46	47	48	49	50
51	52	53	54	55	56	57	58	59	60
61	62	63	64	65	66	67	68	69	70
71	72	73	74	75	76	77	78	79	80
81	82	83	84	85	86	87	88	89	90
91	92	93	94	95	96	97	98	99	100

Materials: Crayons or markers

1. Have children circle the numbers with 7 ones in red.
2. Have children circle the numbers with 9 tens in blue.
3. Ask: ***What number has 7 ones and 9 tens?*** 97
4. Repeat with numbers with 2 ones in green and numbers with 5 tens in yellow.
5. Ask: ***What number has 2 ones and 5 tens?*** 52

Name ______________________________

Number Patterns to 100 (continued)

Use the hundred chart to fill in the blanks.

1. List the numbers with 8 tens.

80, ____, ____, ____, ____

____, ____, ____, ____, ____

2. List the numbers with 4 ones.

4, 14, ____, ____, ____

____, ____, ____, ____, ____

3. What number has 8 tens and 4 ones? ____

4. Write the missing numbers in the chart below.

41	42	43	44	45	46	47			50
51	52	53			56	57	58	59	60
		63	64	65	66	67	68	69	70
71		73	74	75	76	77		79	80
81	82	83	84	85	86	87	88		
91	92			95	96	97	98	99	100

Name ____________________

1 More or 1 Less, 10 More or Less

1. 27

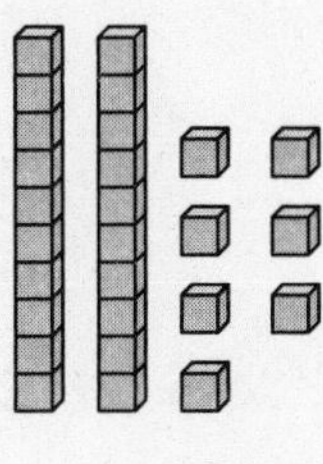

1 more is 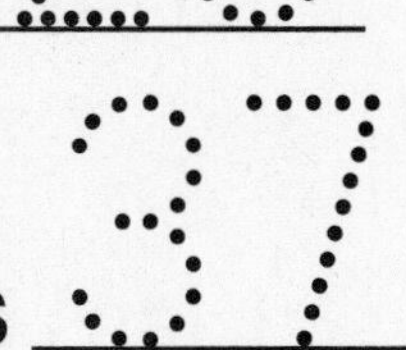

10 more is ______

1 less is ______

10 less is ______

2. 45

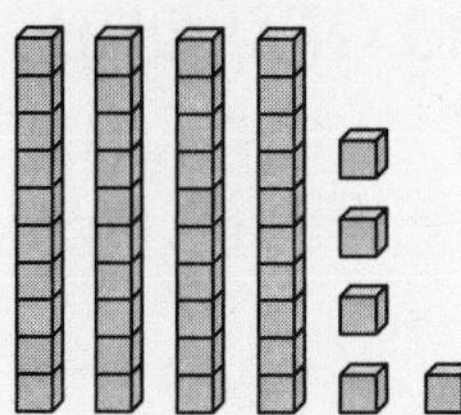

1 more is ______

10 more is ______

1 less is ______

10 less is ______

3. 39

1 more is ______

10 more is ______

1 less is ______

10 less is ______

4. 16

1 more is ______

10 more is ______

1 less is ______

10 less is ______

Materials: Place-value blocks, 5 tens and 10 ones per pair or group

1. Have one child show 27 with the place-value blocks. Have another child in each pair or group add one more cube. Ask: ***How much is 27 and 1 more?*** Have children write 28.
2. Have children take away one cube so each pair or group has 27 again. If children are in groups, have a third child add a ten block. Ask: ***How much is 27 and 10 more?*** Have children write 37.
3. Repeat, having children take away 1 one cube and then 1 ten block to do 1 less and 10 less.
4. Have children show each of the numbers in the other three exercises with the blocks.

Name ______________________

1 More or 1 Less, 10 More or Less (continued)

Write how many.
Use tens and ones if you like.

5. 36 1 more is 37

6. 56 1 less is 55

7. 29 10 more is ______

8. 60 10 less is ______

9. 73 10 more is ______

10. 41 1 less is ______

11. 24 1 less is ______

1 more is ______

10 less is ______

10 more is ______

12. 63 1 less is ______

1 more is ______

10 less is ______

10 more is ______

13. **Reasoning** Which digit in 75 changes when you find 10 more or 10 less? Why?

14. **Reasoning** Which digit in 32 changes when you find 1 more or 1 less? Why?

Name ______________________________

Using >, <, and = to Compare Numbers

5  3

is greater than

$5 > 3$

3  5

is less than

$3 < 5$

$4 = 4$

Circle >, <, or =.

1. 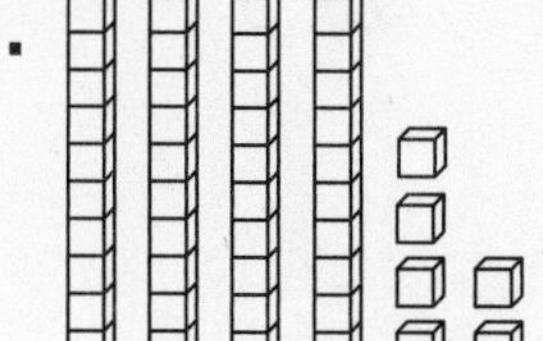

46 (> < =) 52

2. 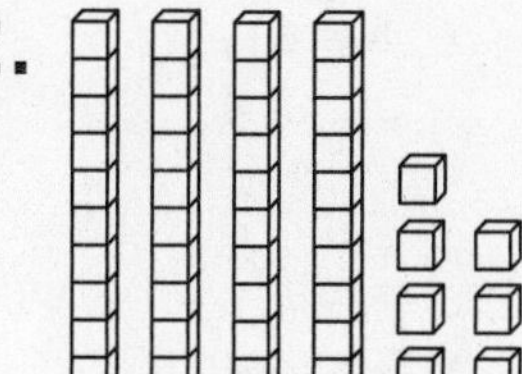

47 (> < =) 35

3. 26 (> < =) 28

4. 38 (> < =) 38

Materials: Place-value blocks, 10 tens, and 20 ones per child or pair

1. Ask: ***Is 5 greater than 3 or less than 3?*** Write > on the board or overhead. Say: ***This is a shorter way to write is greater than.*** Introduce < the same way. Explain that one way to tell them apart is to think of an alligator's mouth. The alligator always wants to eat the greater number.
2. Ask: ***Is 4 greater than or less than 4?*** After children say neither, explain that they are equal and show the symbol =.
3. Have children show 46 and 52 with place-value blocks. Ask: ***Is 46 greater than or less than 52?*** Have children circle the < sign.
4. Do the other problems similarly.

Name ______________________________

Using >, <, and = to Compare Numbers (continued)

Write >, <, or =.

5. 74 ◯ 56

6. 43 ◯ 43

7. 57 ◯ 49

8. 62 ◯ 26

9. 23 ◯ 32

10. 86 ◯ 89

11. 47 ◯ 47

12. 51 ◯ 15

13. 63 ◯ 57

14. 19 ◯ 19

15. 72 ◯ 78

16. 31 ◯ 21

17. 40 ◯ 50

18. 95 ◯ 85

Name ______________________________

Ordering Three Numbers

1.

17   25   12

______ < ______ < ______
least   greatest

2.

24	18	28

______ < ______ < ______
least   greatest

3.

43	60	58

______ < ______ < ______
least   greatest

Materials: Snap cubes, 60 per pair or group

1. Have children count out 3 groups of snap cubes, one with 17, one with 25, and one with 12. Each child should count out at least one group.
2. Have children make tens and ones out of the cubes they counted.
3. Ask: ***Which number is the least?*** Have children write 12 on the line above least. Ask: ***Which number is the greatest?*** Have children write 25 on the line above greatest. Ask: ***Which number is between 12 and 25?*** Have children write 17.
4. Ask: ***Which number has the greatest number of tens?*** 25 ***Was 25 the greatest number?*** Yes. Tell students: ***This will always be true. If one number has more tens than all the others, it is the greatest.***
5. Ask: ***Does one number have the fewest number of tens?*** No, 17 and 12 have the same number of tens. Tell students: ***When two or more numbers have the same number of tens, compare the number of ones. Which number has fewer ones, 17 or 12?*** 12 ***So, 12 is the least.***
6. Do the other problems similarly.

Math Diagnosis and Intervention System
Intervention Lesson **A28**

Name ____________________

Ordering Three Numbers (continued)

Write the numbers in order from **greatest** to **least**.

4. 40 26 14 — 40 > 26 > 14 (greatest, least)

5.  12 29 18 — ____ > ____ > ____ (greatest, least)

6. 55 36 27 — ____ > ____ > ____ (greatest, least)

7. 37 27 73 — ____ > ____ > ____ (greatest, least)

8. 71 80 75 — ____ > ____ > ____ (greatest, least)

9. 56 95 39 — ____ > ____ > ____ (greatest, least)

10. **Number Sense** Juan has 50 cards, Kim has 23 cards, and Jackie has 27 cards. Who has the least number of cards?

Name ______________________

Number Words to Twenty

One	1	Eleven	____
Two	2	Twelve	____
Three	____	Thirteen	____
Four	____	Fourteen	____
Five	____	Fifteen	____
Six	____	Sixteen	____
Seven	____	Seventeen	____
Eight	____	Eighteen	____
Nine	____	Nineteen	____
Ten	____	Twenty	____

Materials: Two-color counters, 20 per child

1. Have children show one counter. Say the word "one" as a class while children point to the word. Then have the children write the number in the blank beside the word.
2. Have children add one more counter. Say the word "two" as a class while children point to the word. Then have children write the number in the blank beside the word.
3. Repeat for each number to twenty.

Name ______________________

Number Words to Twenty (continued)

Match each word to the correct number.

1. twelve	9
2. eighteen	4
3. nine	12
4. fifteen	18
5. four	11
6. eight	15
7. nineteen	19
8. eleven	14
9. twenty	8
10. fourteen	20

Name ______________________________

Number Words

1. 51 = 50 + 1

fifty - one

2. 56 = 50 + ______

______ - ______

Number Words		
Ones	**Teens**	**Tens**
1 one	11 eleven	10 ten
2 two	12 twelve	20 twenty
3 three	13 thirteen	30 thirty
4 four	14 fourteen	40 forty
5 five	15 fifteen	50 fifty
6 six	16 sixteen	60 sixty
7 seven	17 seventeen	70 seventy
8 eight	18 eighteen	80 eighty
9 nine	19 nineteen	90 ninety

3. 58 = ______ + ______

______ - ______

4. 45 = ______ + ______

____

5. 74 = ______ + ______

______ - ______

6. 13 = ______ + ______

____

Materials: Index cards, 17 per child

1. Have children write the words for the ones from the table on index cards, with one number per card. Then have them do the same with twenty to ninety from the tens.
2. Ask: ***51 is 50 plus what?*** Have children find the index card with fifty and the one with one. Say: ***Put these two cards together with a hyphen and you have the word for 51.*** Write fifty-one (in words) on the board or overhead and have children write the words on paper.
3. Say: ***For 56, we put together the words for 50 and for 6.*** Have children find the words and complete item 2.
4. Have children use the cards to do the other items except Problem 6.
5. Say: ***The numbers 11 to 19 have special names. Most of them end in teen. You can find these numbers and their names in the table.*** Have children complete Problem 6.

Name ______________________________

Number Words (continued)

Write the number for each word.

7. two ______
8. thirty-six ______
9. sixteen ______
10. twenty-eight ______
11. seventy ______
12. eighty-one ______
13. eight ______
14. twelve ______
15. fifty-seven ______
16. fourteen ______

Write the word for each number.

17. 62 ______________________
18. 30 ______________________
19. 7 ______________________
20. 11 ______________________
21. 49 ______________________
22. 23 ______________________

Write the word for each number of objects.

23. ______________________

24. ______________________

Name ______________________

Ordinal Numbers

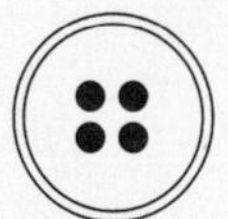				
first 1st	second 2nd	third 3rd	fourth 4th	fifth 5th
		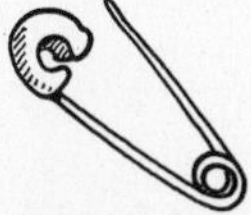		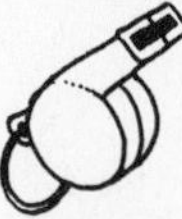
sixth 6th	seventh 7th	eighth 8th	ninth 9th	tenth 10th

eleventh 11th	twelfth 12th	thirteenth 13th	fourteenth 14th	fifteenth 15th
		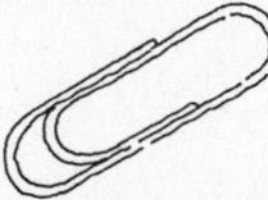		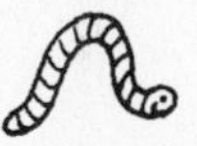
sixteenth 16th	seventeenth 17th	eighteenth 18th	nineteenth 19th	twentieth 20th

1.  

______________________ __________

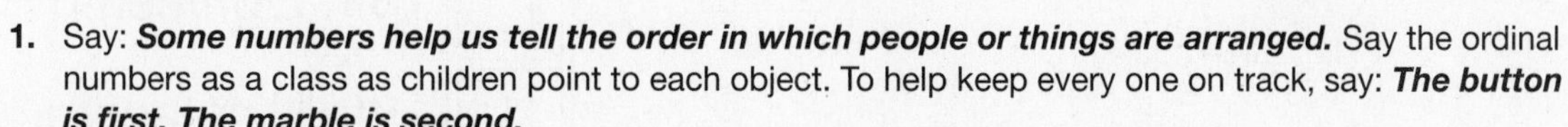

1. Say: ***Some numbers help us tell the order in which people or things are arranged.*** Say the ordinal numbers as a class as children point to each object. To help keep every one on track, say: ***The button is first. The marble is second.***
2. Ask: ***Where is the number cube?*** Have children write the word fourth and 4th.
3. Have children find the other objects and write the word and number forms of the ordinal numbers.

Name ______________________________

Ordinal Numbers (continued)

Draw a line to show each object's nook.

3. 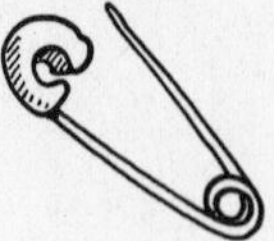

3rd nook

4. 

11th nook

5. 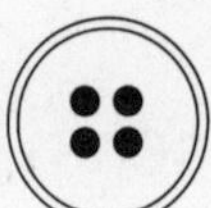

19th nook

6. 

16th nook

1st First
2nd Second
3rd Third
4th Fourth
5th Fifth
6th Sixth
7th Seventh
8th Eighth
9th Ninth
10th Tenth
11th Eleventh
12th Twelfth
13th Thirteenth
14th Fourteenth
15th Fifteenth
16th Sixteenth
17th Seventeenth
18th Eighteenth
19th Nineteenth
20th Twentieth

Name ______________________________

Numbers to 100 on the Number Line

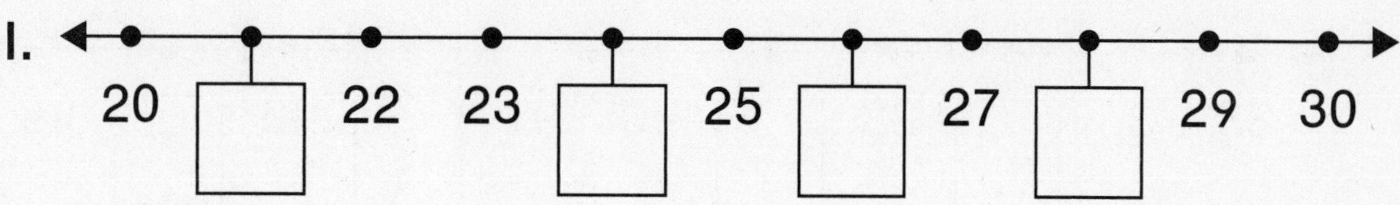

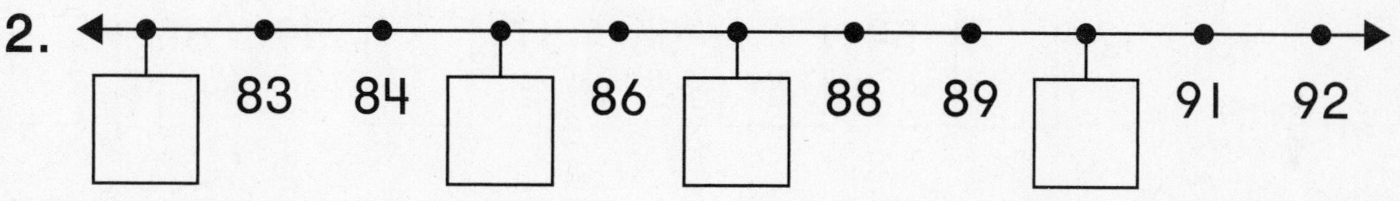

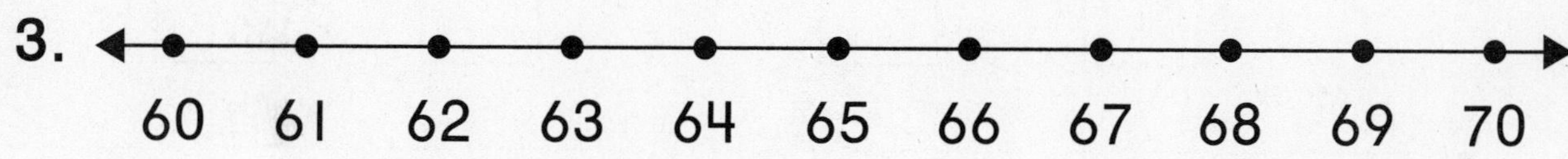

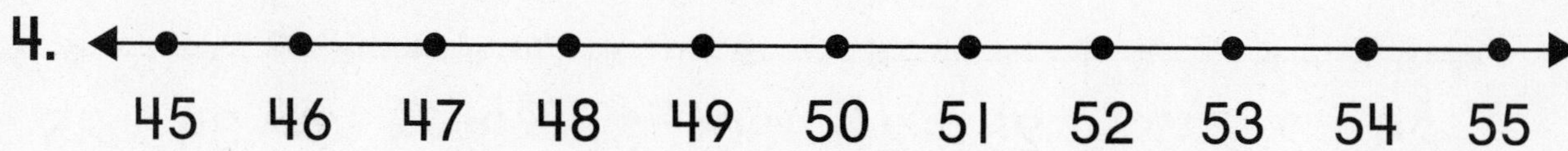

1. Say: ***Every number has its own place on the number line. The numbers go in order from least to greatest. What number comes after 20?*** Have children write 21 in the box.
2. ***What number comes between 23 and 25?*** Have children write 24 in the second box.
3. Have children complete the number lines for Problems 1 and 2. Ask questions like those above for children who have difficulty.
4. For Problem 3, have children find 64 on the number line and circle it and its point. Ask: ***What number is before 64? After?*** Have children circle 67 and its point. Ask: ***Is 67 greater than or less than 64?***
5. Have children circle a number that is greater than 53 on the last number line. Then have them circle one that is less than 46.

Name ______________________

Numbers to 100 on the Number Line (continued)

Write the missing numbers.

5.

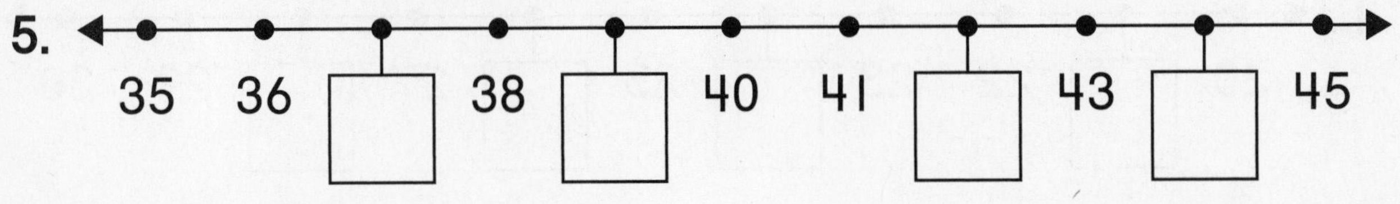

6.

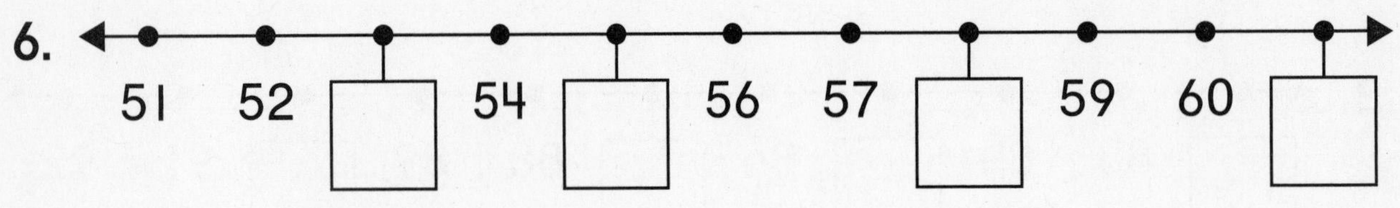

7.

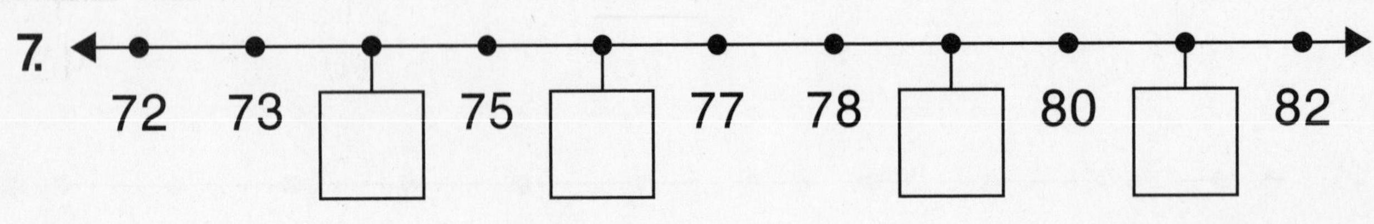

Circle the numbers on the number line.

8. 28, 33

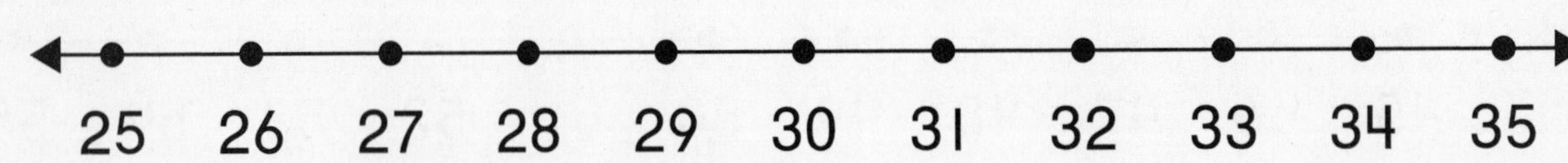

9. 91, 97

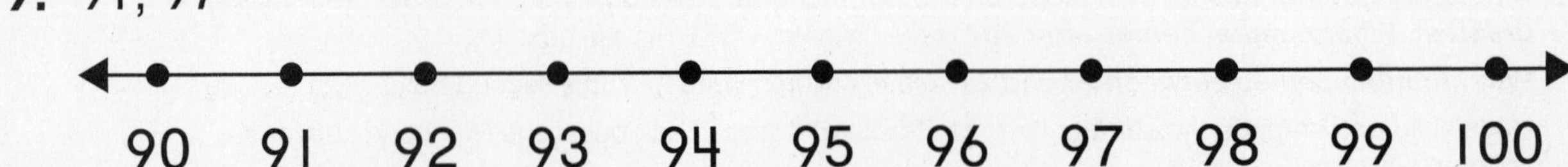

Name ______________________________

Number Line Estimation

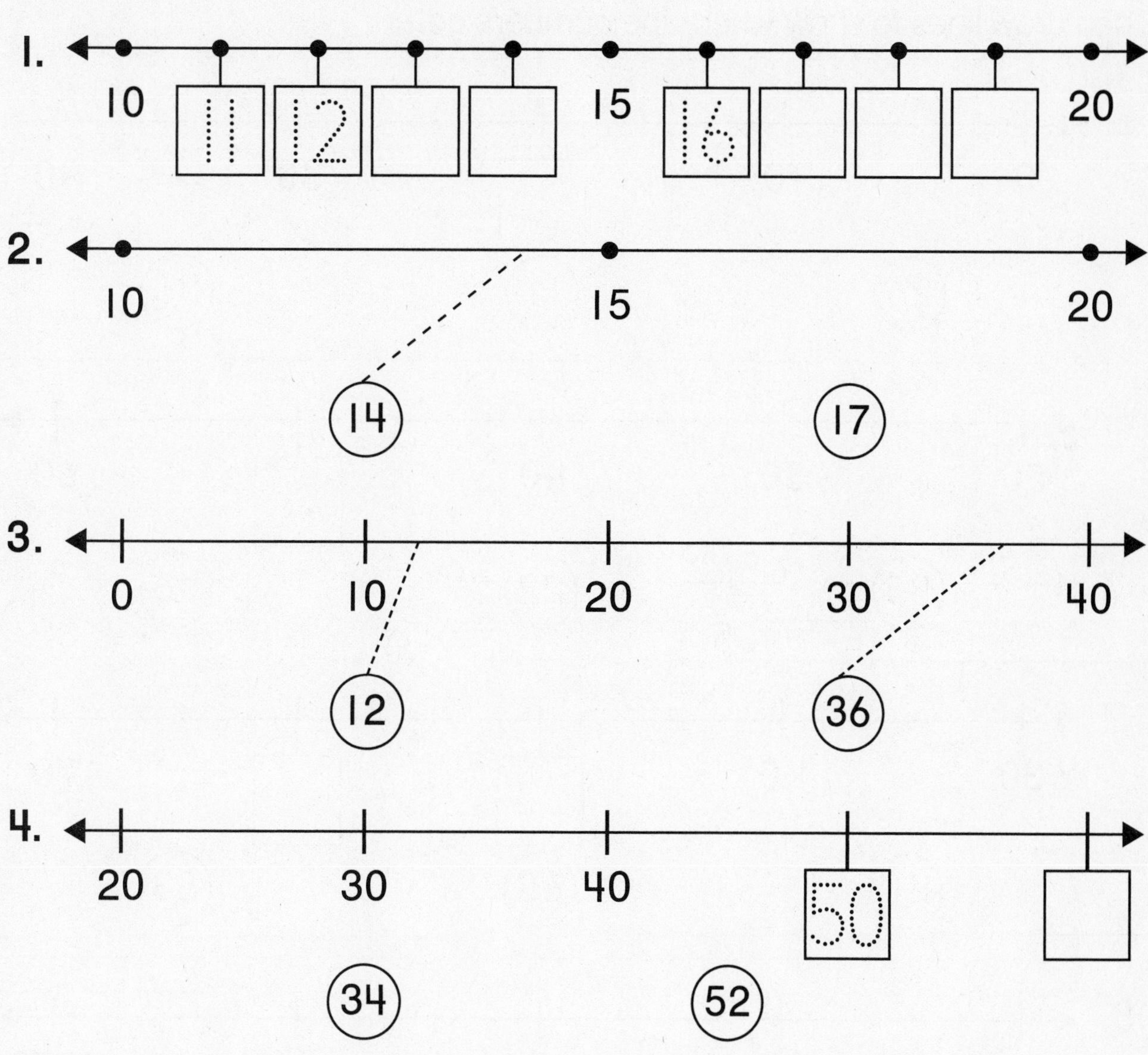

1. Say: ***Every number has its own place on the number line.*** Have children fill in the rest of the labels.
2. Have children estimate where 14 goes on the second number line and draw over the line from 14 to its place.
3. Have children estimate where 17 goes and draw a line from 17 to its place.
4. Ask: ***Is 12 between 0 and 10?*** No ***Is 12 between 10 and 20?*** Yes ***Is 12 closer to 10 or to 20?*** Have children estimate where 12 goes and draw over the line.
5. Repeat for 36.
6. Have children fill in the missing labels on the number line in Problem 4, by counting by tens.
7. In Problem 4, Ask: ***34 is between which two numbers?*** 30 and 40 ***Is 34 closer to 30 or 40?*** Have children estimate where 34 goes and draw a line from 34 to its position.
8. Repeat for 52.

Name ____________________________________

Number Line Estimation (continued)

Complete the number line.
Then draw lines to show where the numbers go.

5. 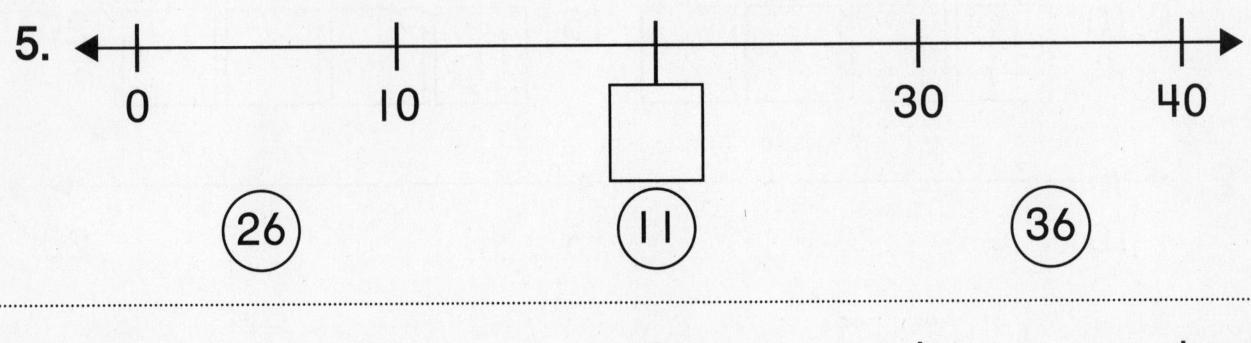

6. 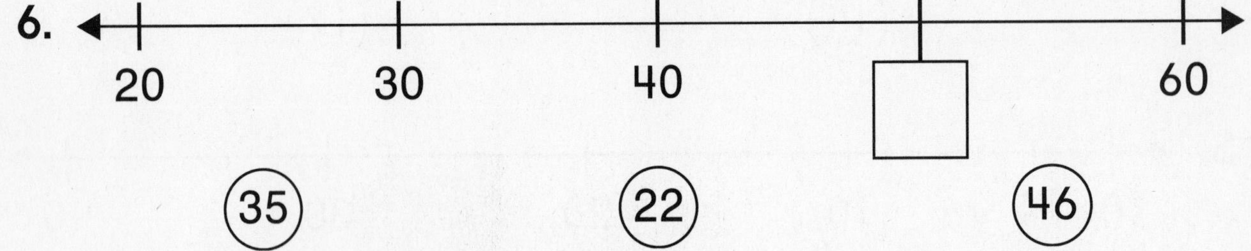

7. 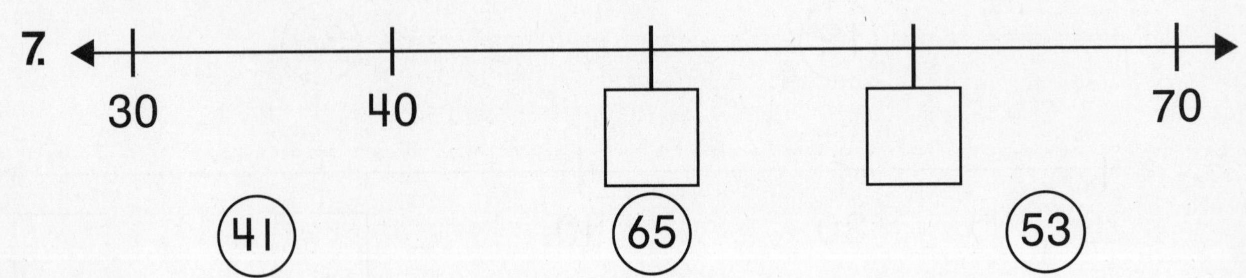

8. 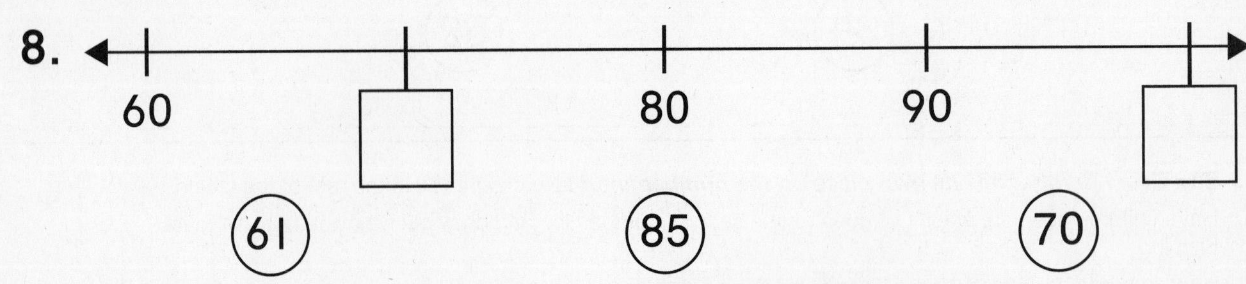

9. **Number Sense** Is the number 5 tens and 8 ones closer to 50 or 60? Explain.

Name ___________________________________

Halves

1. 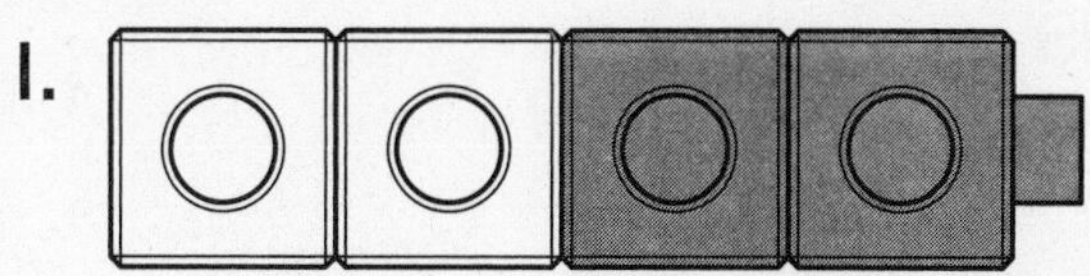

2. 

3. 

4. 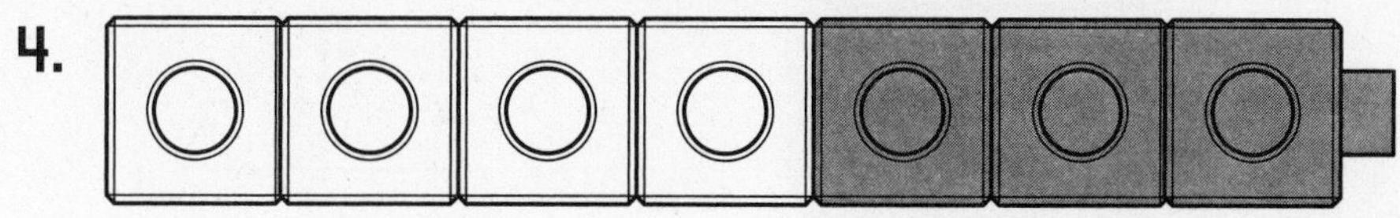

5. 

6. 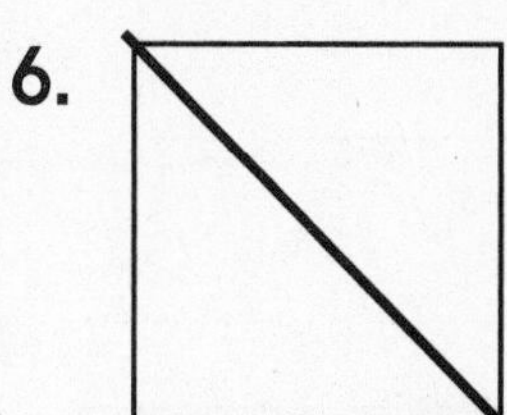

7. 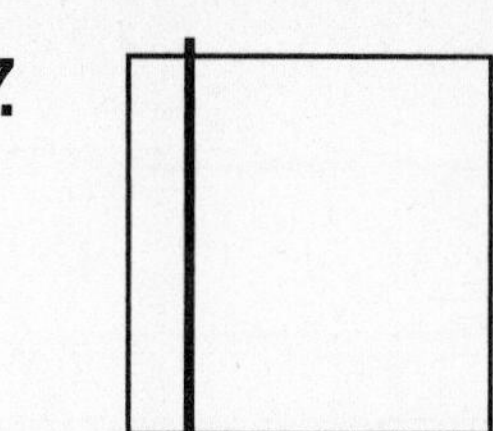

Materials: Snap cubes, 8 per child; crayons

1. Have children put 4 cubes together, 2 of one color and 2 of another. Say: ***Are the two parts equal? Since the parts are equal each part is a half.*** Have children circle the picture of the cubes which show halves.
2. Have children add one more cube to match one color. Say: ***Are the two parts equal? Since the parts are not equal, each part is not a half.***
3. Have children add a cube of the other color. Ask: ***Is each part a half?*** Have children circle the picture which shows halves.
4. Continue adding one cube at a time and asking whether or not each part is a half. Have children circle the pictures that show halves.
5. Have children choose which square shows halves. Have them color each half a different color. Have students put an X through the one that does not show halves.

Name ______________________________

Halves (continued)

Color halves.
Cross out ones that are not halves.

8.

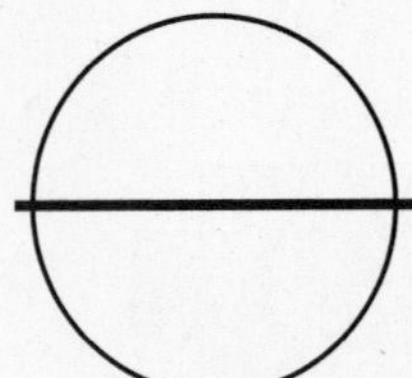

9.

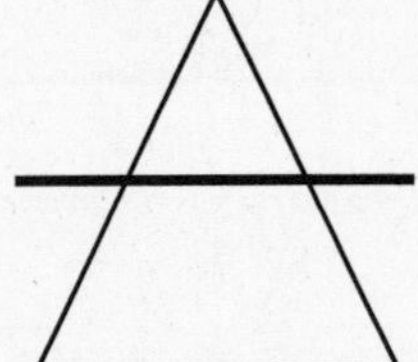
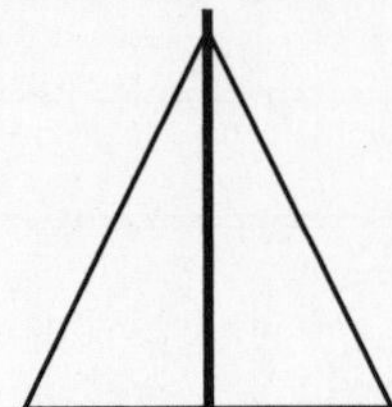

10.

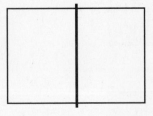

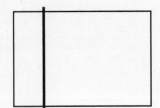

11.

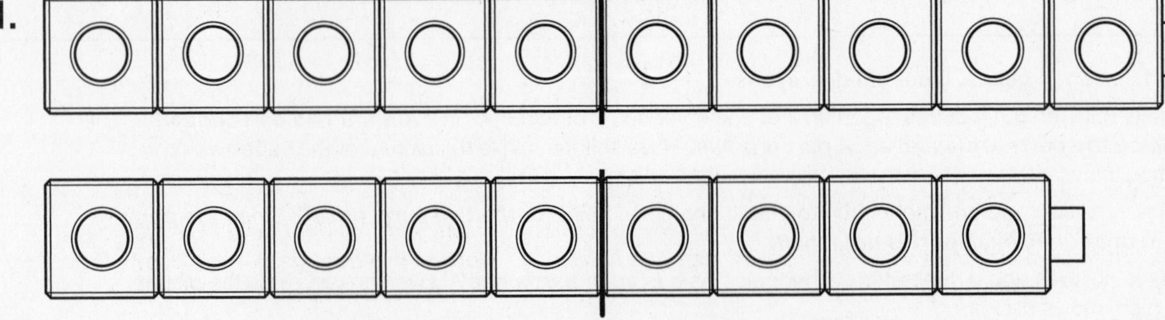

Name ______________________

Equal Parts

1. 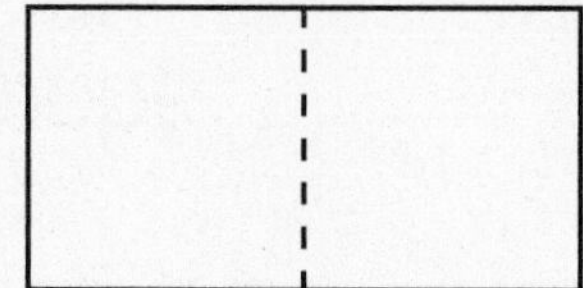 2 parts

2. 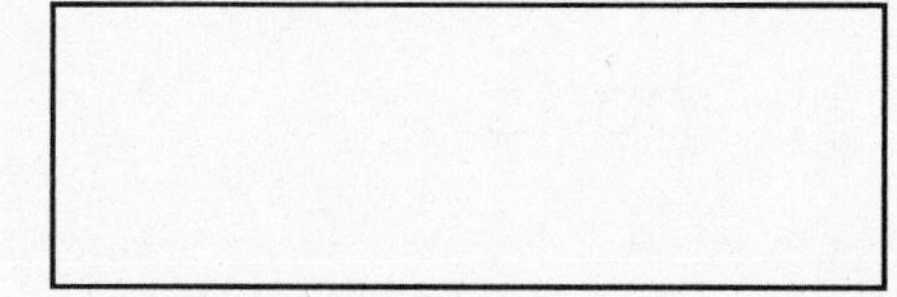 ____ parts

3. ____ parts

4. ____ parts

5.

Materials: Color Tiles, 6 per child in 4 colors

1. Have children cover the rectangle with color tiles using 2 different colors. Ask: ***Do the tiles divide the rectangle into equal parts?*** Draw a line to show the equal parts. ***How many equal parts are there?*** Have children write 2.
2. Do the second rectangle similarly, using 3 different colors.
3. Do the third rectangle similarly, using 4 different colors.
4. Have children use 2 colors to divide the fourth rectangle into 2 equal parts.
5. Have children divide the fifth rectangle into 4 parts that are not equal.

Name ______________________________

Equal Parts (continued)

Write the number of parts.
Circle **equal** or **not equal**.

6. 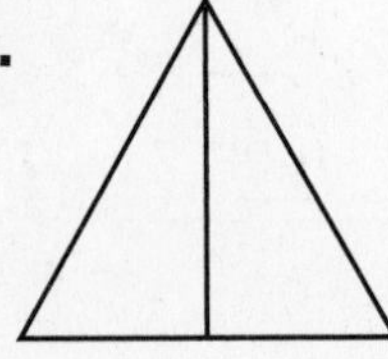

equal

not equal

_____ parts

7. 

equal

not equal

_____ parts

8. 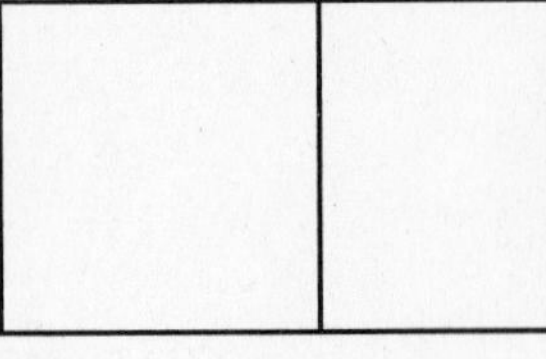

equal

not equal

_____ parts

9. 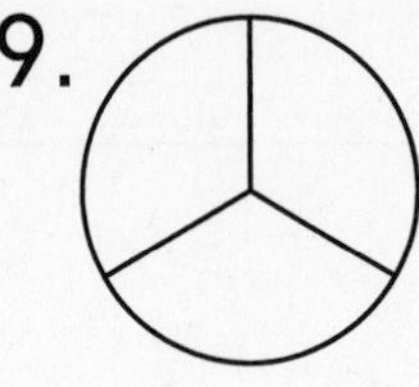

equal

not equal

_____ parts

Draw lines to show equal parts.

10. 4 parts

11. 2 parts

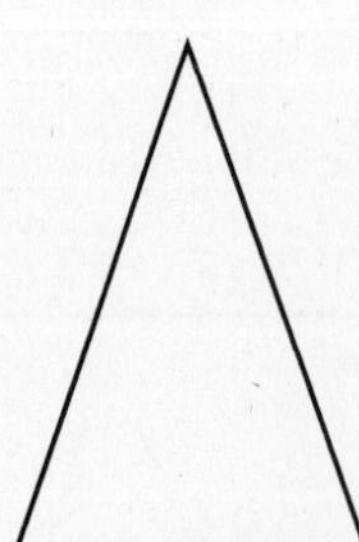

12. **Reasoning** Draw lines to show 3 different ways to make 2 equal parts.

Name ___________________________

Understanding Fractions to Fourths

1\.

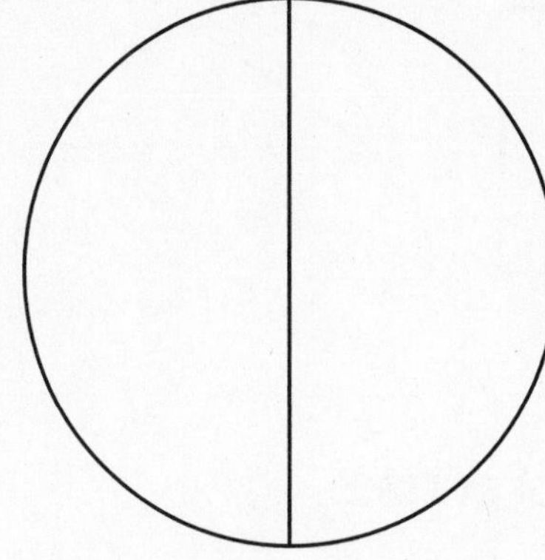

1 out of 2 equal parts

2\.

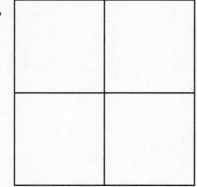

______ out of ______ equal parts

3\.

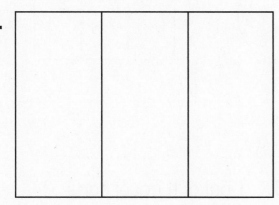

______ out of ______ equal parts

Materials: Crayons or markers

1. Have children color one of the equal parts in the first shape.
2. Ask: ***How many parts did you color?*** Have children write 1. Ask: ***How many equal parts in all?*** Have children write 2. Say: ***You colored 1 out of 2 equal parts or one half.***
3. Have children color 3 of the equal parts of the square. Then complete the problem similarly.
4. Have children color 1 of the equal parts of the rectangle. Then complete the problem similarly.

Name ______________________________

Understanding Fractions to Fourths (continued)

4. Circle each shape that shows 1 out of 2 equal parts.

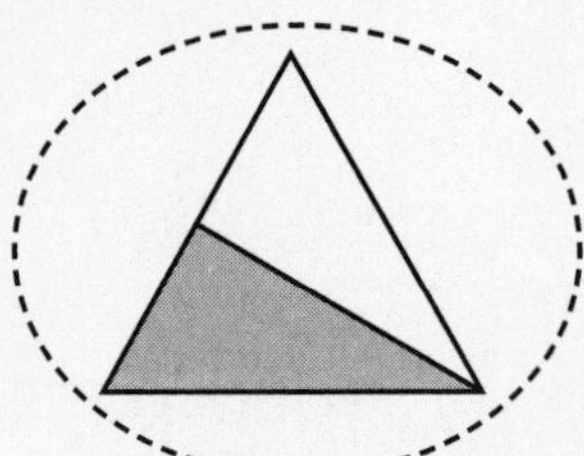 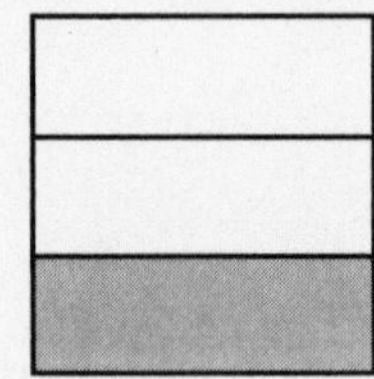 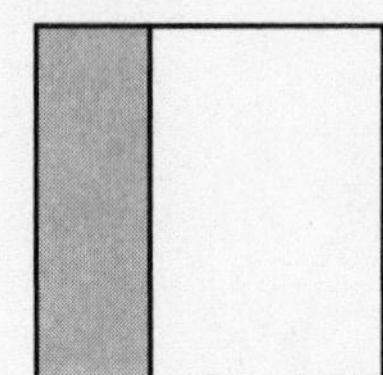 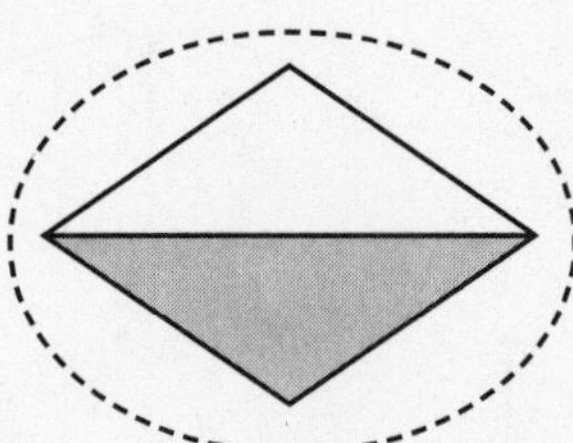

5. Circle each shape that shows 1 out of 3 equal parts.

 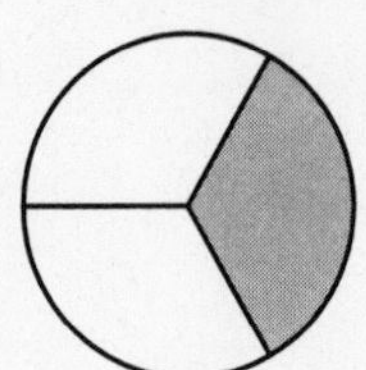 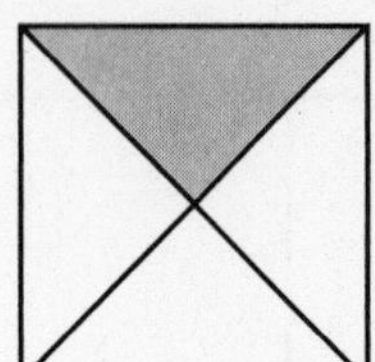 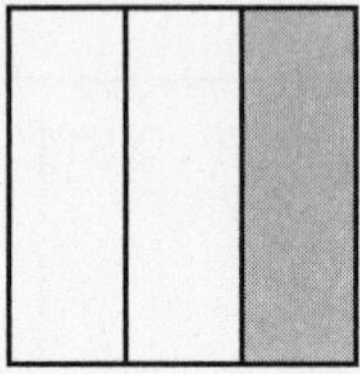

6. Circle each shape that shows 1 out of 4 equal parts.

 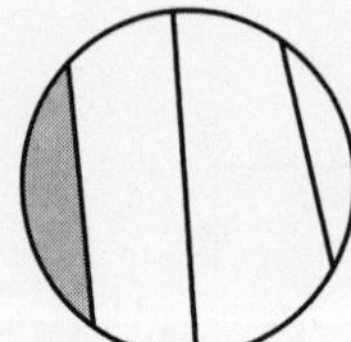 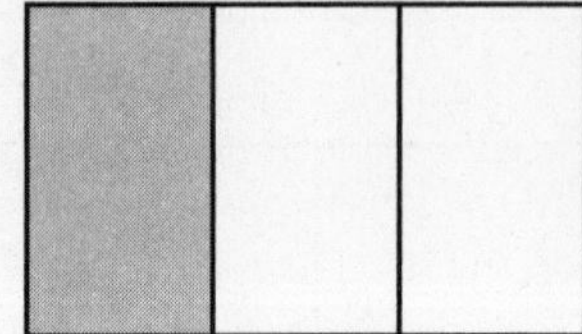

Color.

7. 1 out of 3 equal parts

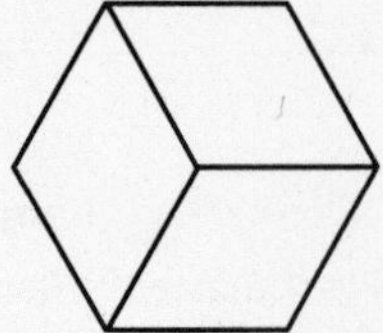

8. 1 out of 4 equal parts

Name ______________________

Fractions of a Set

1. 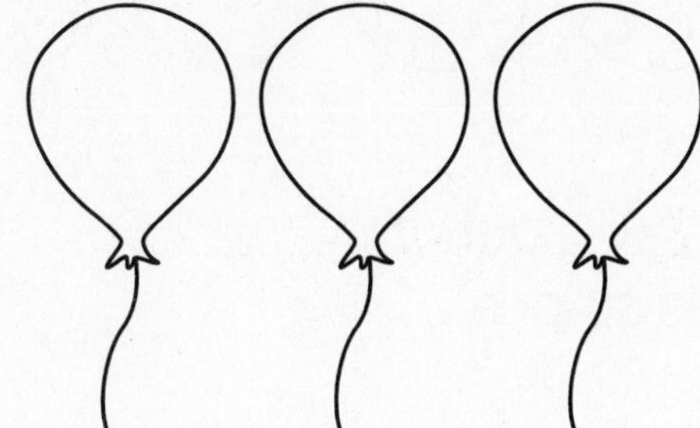

1 out of 3 is red

2. 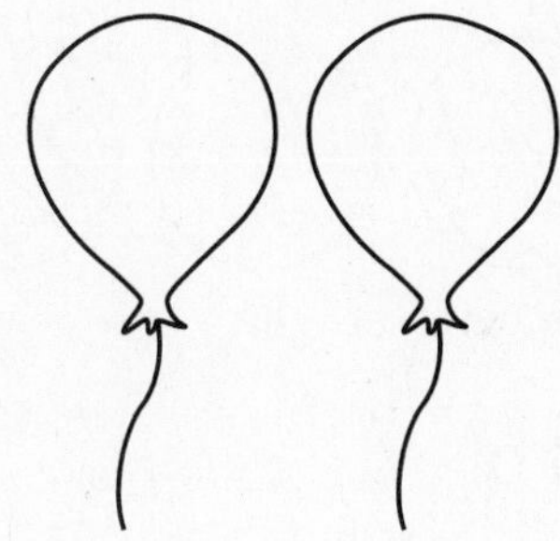

_____ out of _____ is blue

3. 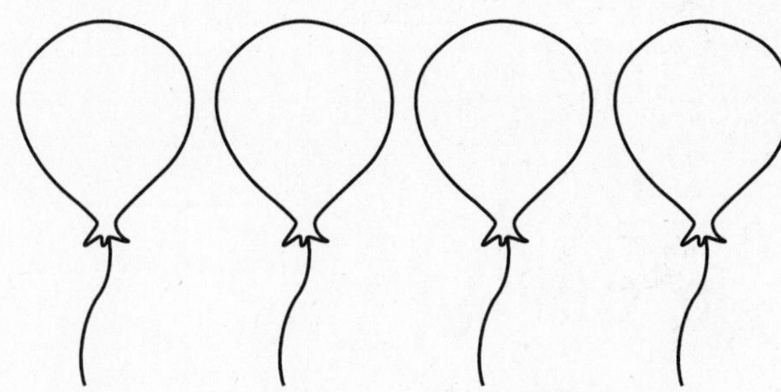

_____ out of _____ are yellow

4. 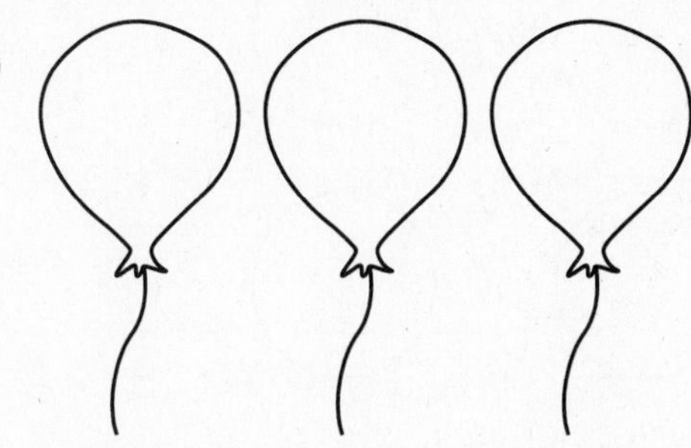

_____ out of _____ are orange

Materials: Crayons or markers

1. Have children color one balloon red. Ask: ***How many are red?*** Have children write 1. Ask: ***How many in all?*** Have children write 3. Say: ***One out of three is red.***
2. In Problem 2, have children color one balloon blue. Then complete the problem similarly.
3. In Problem 3, have children color 3 balloons yellow. Then complete the problem similarly.
4. In Problem 4, have children color 2 balloons orange. Then complete the problem similarly.

Name ______________________

Math Diagnosis and Intervention System
Intervention Lesson **A37**

Fractions of a Set (continued)

5. 

1 out of 2
has stripes

6. 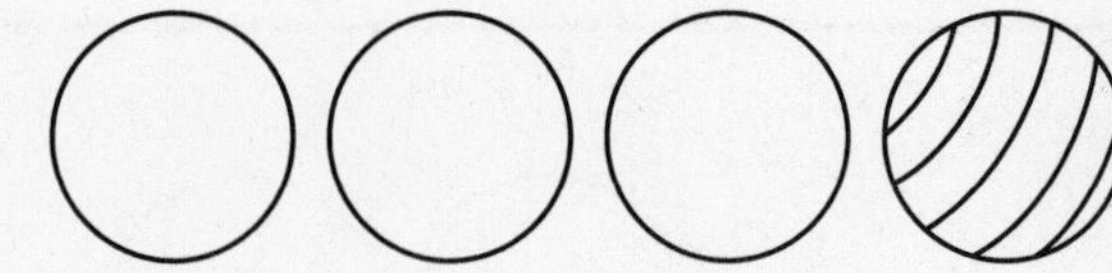

_____ out of _____
has stripes

7. 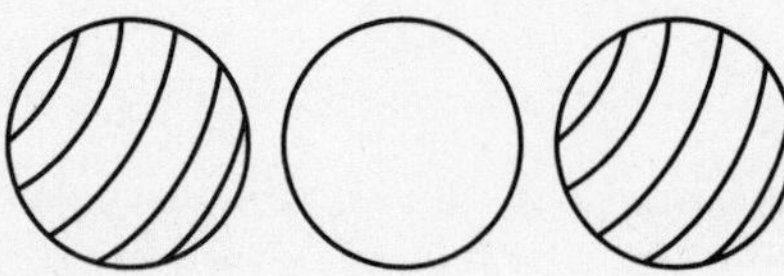

_____ out of _____
has stripes

8. 

_____ out of _____
has stripes

Color.

9. 1 out of 3

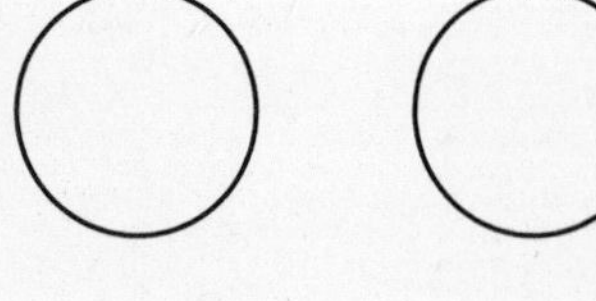

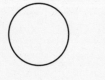

10. 3 out of 4

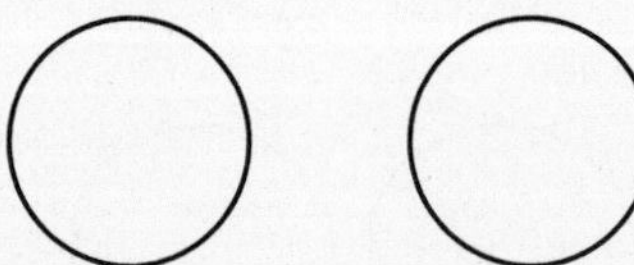

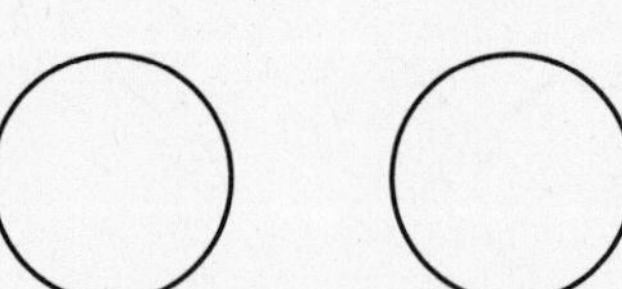

11. **Reasoning** If 1 out of 4 is striped,
then _____ out of _____ are not striped.

Name ______________________________

Writing Fractions for Part of a Region

1. 

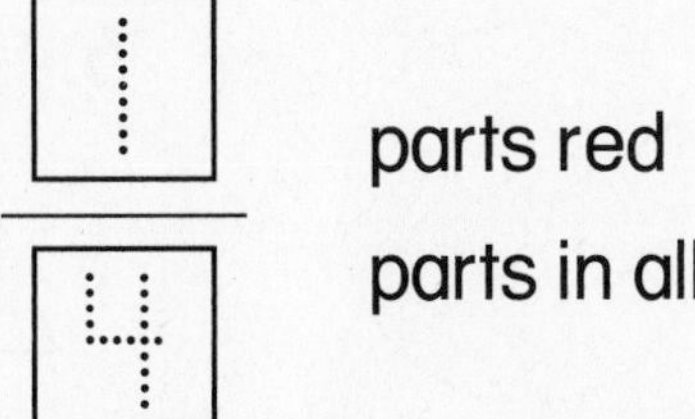

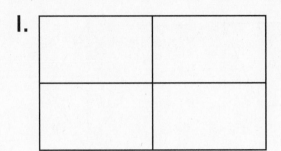

parts red
parts in all

one fourth

2. 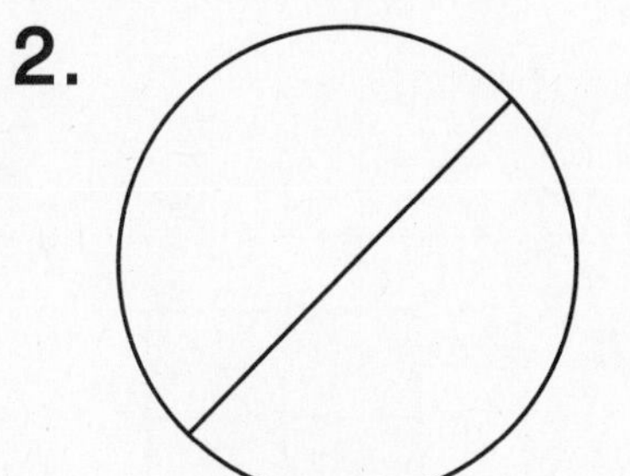

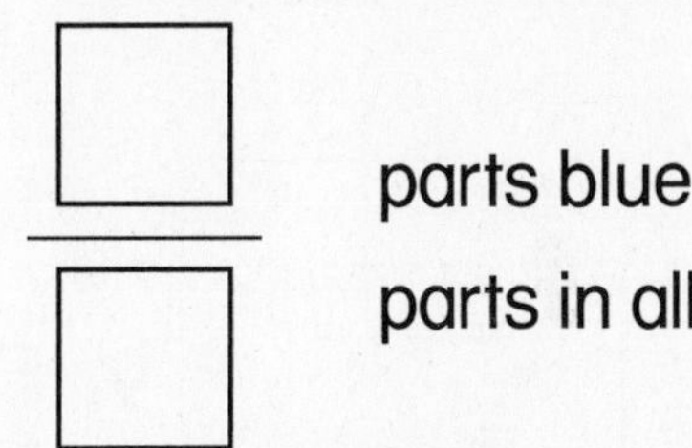

parts blue
parts in all

one half

3. 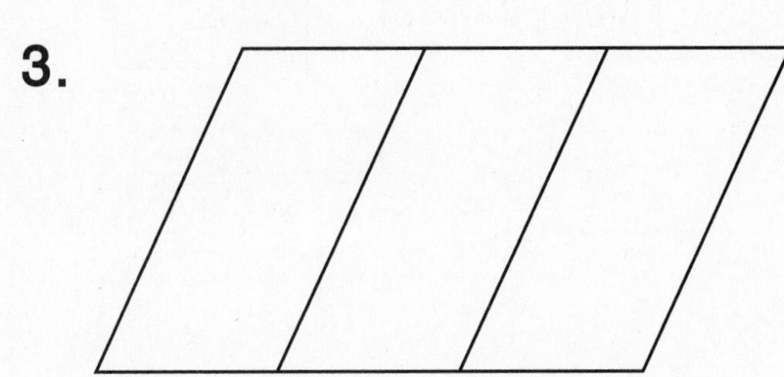

parts orange
parts in all

two thirds

4. **Reasoning** What part in Question 3 is not orange? ______

Materials: Crayons or markers

1. Ask: ***Is the rectangle divided into equal parts?*** Yes ***How many?*** Have children color 1 out of the 4 equal parts red.
2. Ask: ***How many parts are red?*** Have children write 1. ***How many equal parts in all?*** Have children write 4. Write $\frac{1}{4}$ on the board or overhead and say: ***This is the number one fourth. It tells us what part is shaded.***
3. Have children color one part of the circle blue. Ask: ***How many parts are blue?*** Have children write 1 above the fraction bar. ***How many equal parts in all?*** Have children write 2 below the fraction bar. Write $\frac{1}{2}$ on the board or overhead and introduce as with $\frac{1}{4}$.
4. Have children color 2 parts of the polygon orange. Ask questions like those above and have children write the fraction. Introduce $\frac{2}{3}$ similarly.
5. Ask the reasoning question and have children write the answer.

Writing Fractions for Part of a Region (continued)

Write the fraction that names the shaded part.

5. 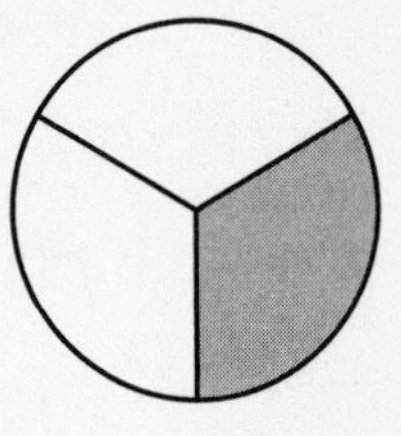

$\frac{1}{3}$

6. 

______

7. 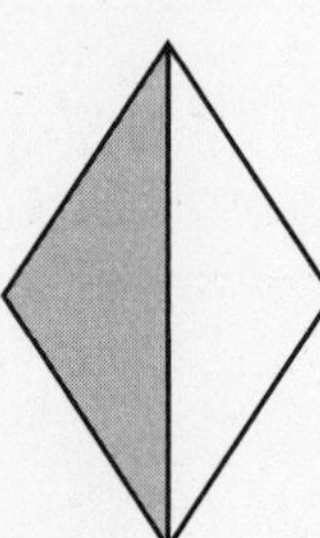

______

8. 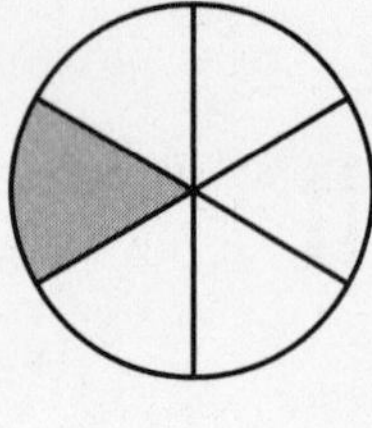

______

9. 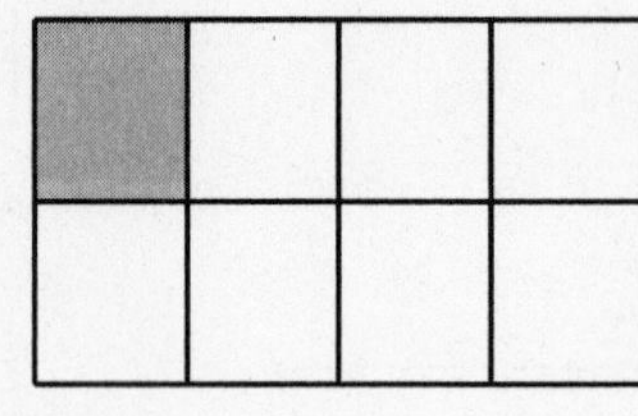

______

10. 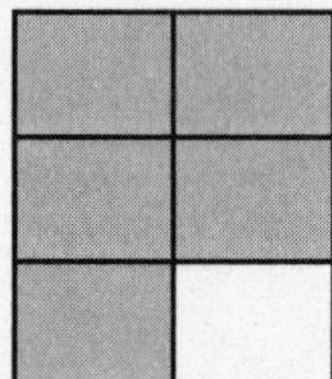

______

Color to show the fraction.

11. $\frac{1}{3}$ 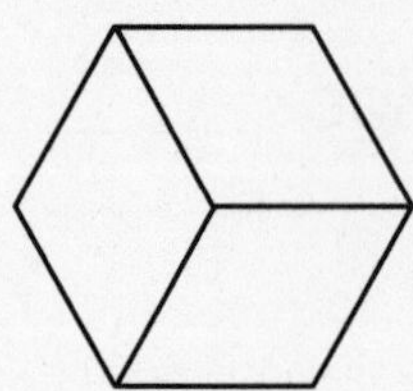

12. $\frac{1}{4}$ 

13. $\frac{5}{9}$ 

14. $\frac{3}{8}$ 

Name ______________________________

Writing Fractions for Part of a Set

1.

$\frac{1}{4}$ yellow / in all $\frac{\square}{\square}$ red / in all

2.

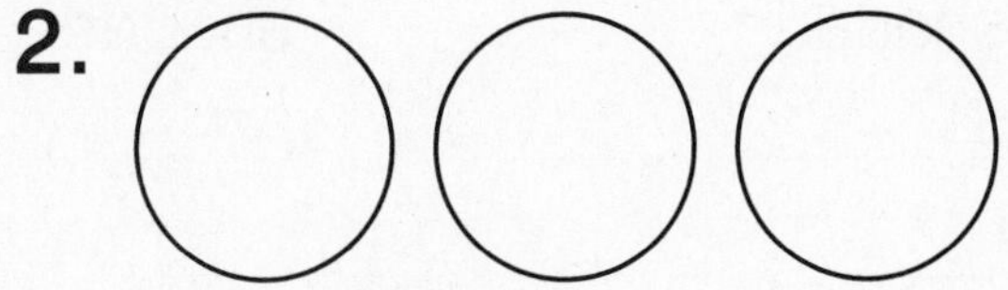

______ yellow   ______ red

3.

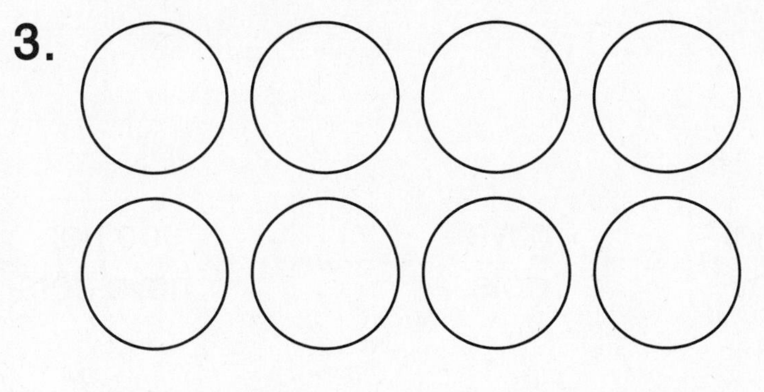

______ yellow   ______ red

Materials: Crayons or markers, 8 two-color counters per child or pair

1. Have children show 4 counters, 1 yellow and 3 red. Then have them color the circles to match the counters. Ask: ***How many are yellow?*** Have children write 1. ***How many in all?*** Have children write 4. ***What part is yellow?*** Say: ***One-fourth is yellow.***
2. Ask: ***What part is red?*** Have children write a fraction for the part that is red. Say: ***Three fourths are red.***
3. In Problem 2, have children show 1 yellow and 2 red counters and color the circles to match. Ask: ***What part is yellow?*** Have them write the fraction for the part that is yellow. Say: ***One third is yellow.*** Ask: ***What part is red?*** Have them write the fraction for the part that is red. Say: ***Two thirds are red.***
4. Repeat with 3 yellow and 5 red counters for item 3.

Name ____________________

Writing Fractions for Part of a Set (continued)

Write the fractions.

4. 

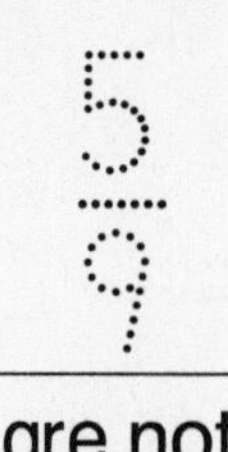

$\frac{4}{9}$ are shaded

$\frac{5}{9}$ are not shaded

5. 

____ are shaded

____ are not shaded

6. 

____ are happy

____ are not happy

7. 

____ have dots

____ do not have dots

Color to show each fraction.

8. $\frac{7}{8}$

9. $\frac{5}{12}$

Name ______________________________

Estimating Fractions

$\frac{1}{2}$ 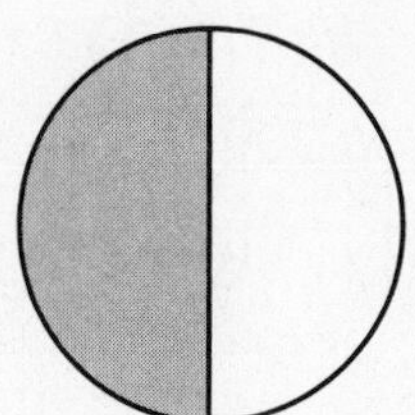

1. 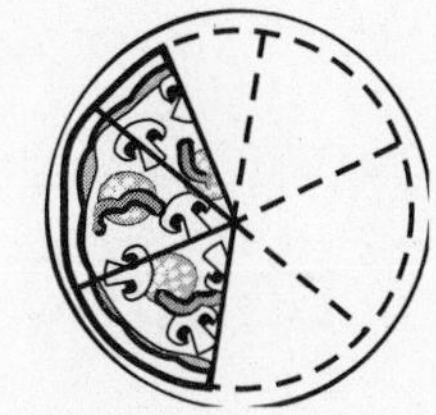 about 0  about $\frac{1}{2}$ about 1

2.  about 0 about $\frac{1}{2}$ about 1

3.  about 0 about $\frac{1}{2}$ about 1

4.  about 0 about $\frac{1}{2}$ about 1

1. Say: ***One half of the circle is shaded. Use it to estimate. About how much veggie pizza is left? Is the part left closer to the whole veggie pizza, half a pizza, or zero pizza?*** Have children circle about $\frac{1}{2}$.
2. Repeat for the other problems.

Name ______________________________

Estimating Fractions (continued)

How much is left? Circle the best estimate.

5. 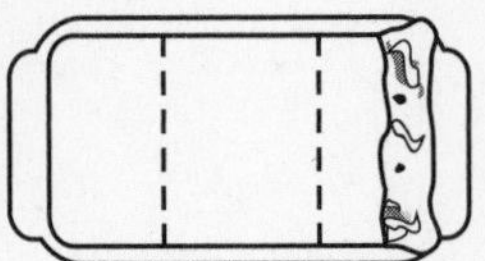
about 0
about $\frac{1}{2}$
about 1

6. 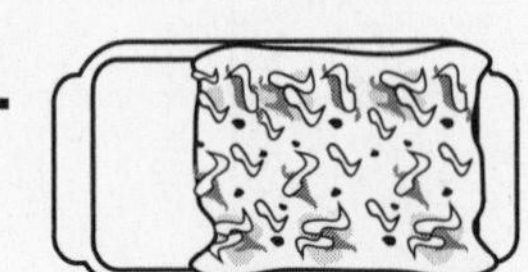
about 0
about $\frac{1}{2}$
about 1

7. 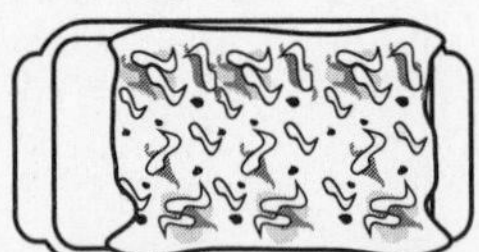
about 0
about $\frac{1}{2}$
about 1

8. 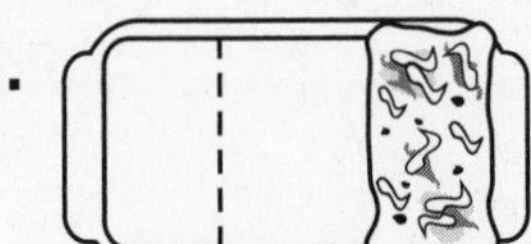
about 0
about $\frac{1}{2}$
about 1

9. 
about 0
about $\frac{1}{2}$
about 1

10. 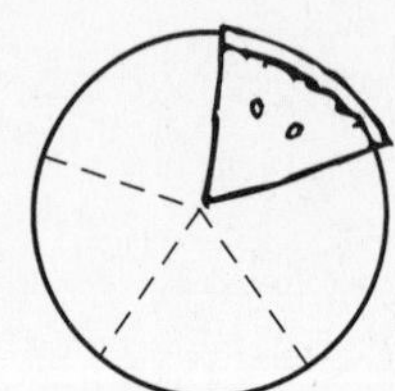
about 0
about $\frac{1}{2}$
about 1

Reasoning About how much water?
Circle the best estimate.

11. 
about 0
about $\frac{1}{2}$
about 1

12. 
about 0
about $\frac{1}{2}$
about 1

Name ______________________________

Understanding One as a Fraction

1. 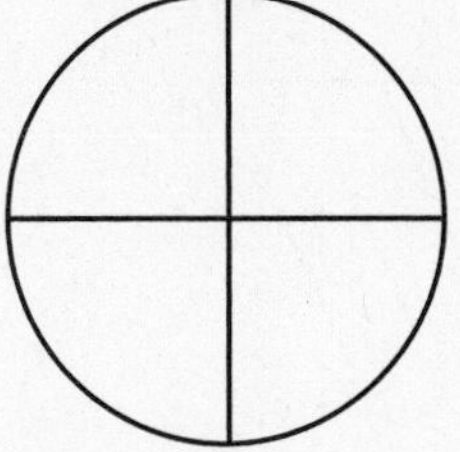

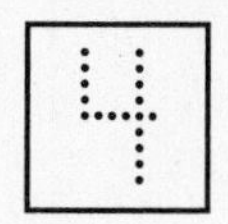

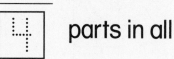

4 parts red

4 parts in all ______ = 1

2. 

☐ parts blue

☐ parts in all ______ = 1

3. 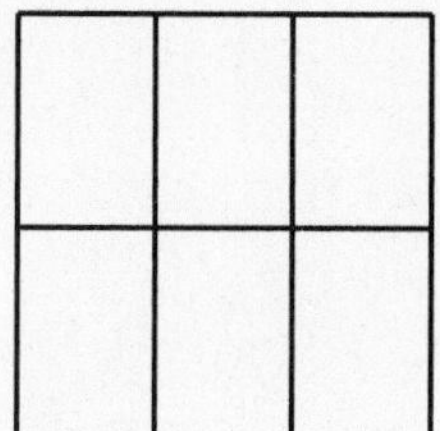

☐ parts orange

☐ parts in all ______ = 1

4. 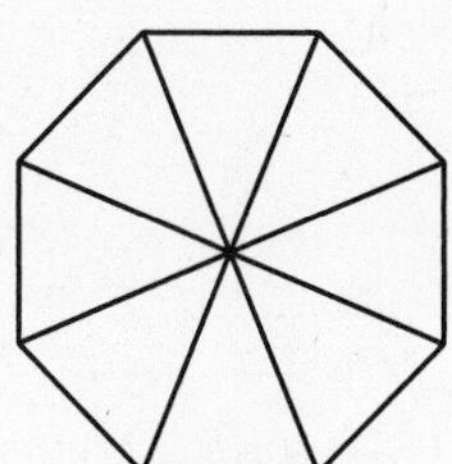

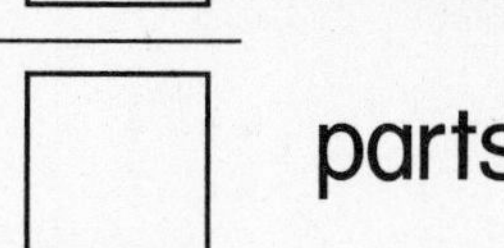

☐ parts orange

☐ parts in all ______ = 1

5. **Reasoning** $\frac{\square}{9} = 1$

Materials: Crayons or markers

1. Have children color all 4 parts of the circle red. Ask: ***How many parts are red?*** Have children write 4. ***How many parts in all?*** Have children write 4 again. ***What fraction of the circle is red?*** Say: ***Four fourths are red.***
2. Ask: ***Is the whole circle red?*** Say: ***So, four fourths equal one whole.*** Have children write $\frac{4}{4}$.
3. Have children color all 3 parts of the square blue. Ask questions like those above.
4. Have children finish the other problems, coloring all 6 parts of the square orange and all 8 parts of the octagon yellow.

Name ____________________

Understanding One as a Fraction (continued)

Color each shape. Write a fraction equal to 1.

6. 

$\frac{2}{2} = 1$

7. 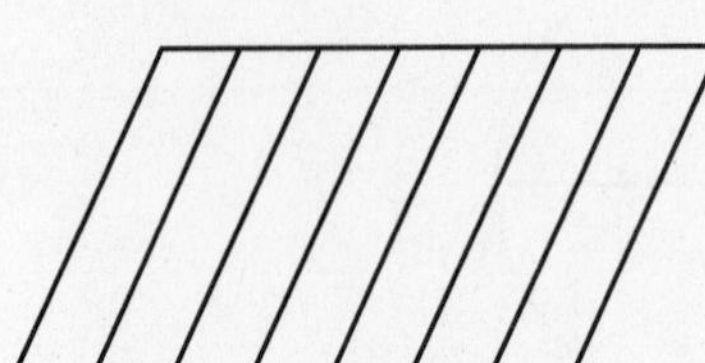

_____ = 1

8. 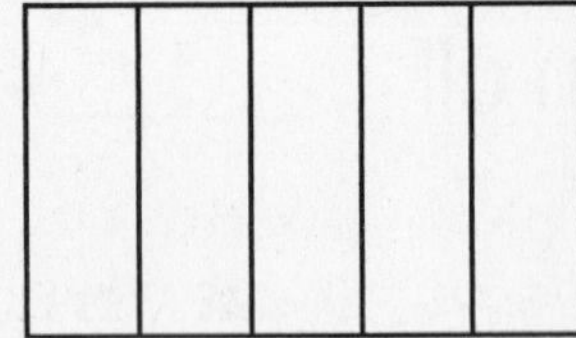

_____ = 1

9. 

_____ = 1

10. 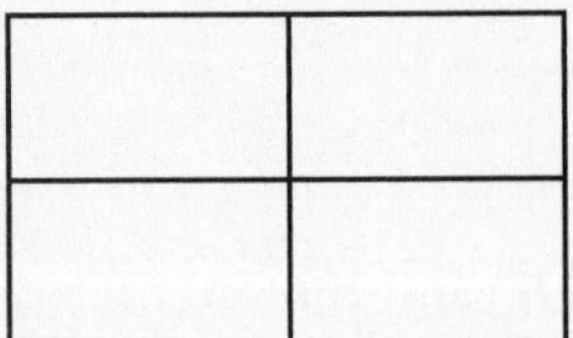

_____ = 1

11. 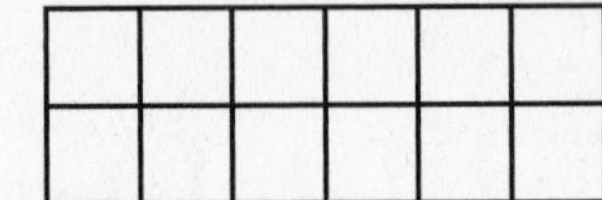

_____ = 1

12. **Reasoning** Color the whole group.

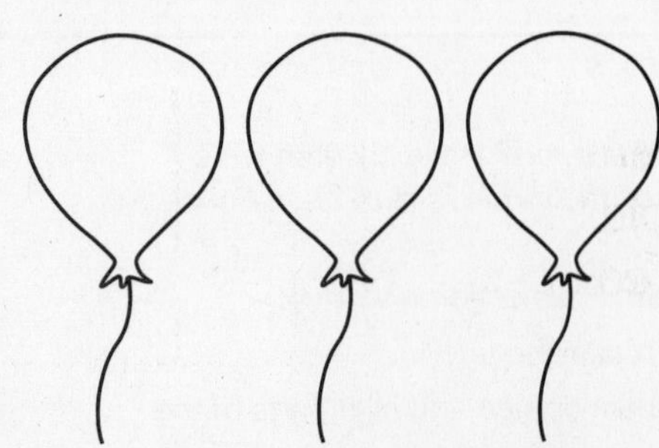

_____ = 1

Name ______________________________

Equal Parts of a Whole

Materials rectangular sheets of paper, 3 for each student; crayons or markers

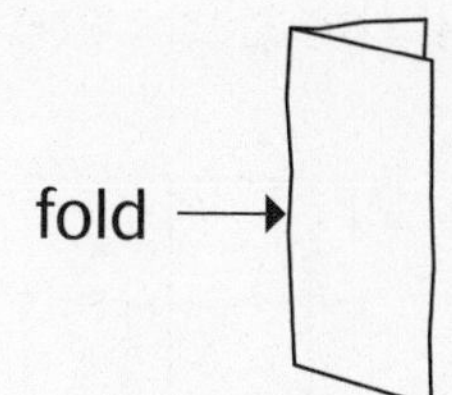

1. Fold a sheet of paper so the two shorter edges are on top of each other, as shown at the right.

2. Open up the piece of paper. Draw a line down the fold. Color each part a different color.

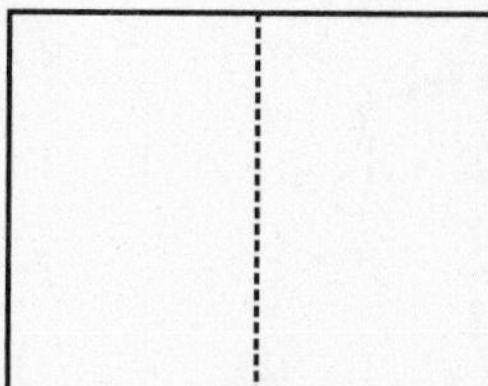

The table below shows special names for the equal parts. All parts must be **equal** before you can use these special names.

3. Are the parts you colored equal in size? ______

4. How many equal parts are there? ______

5. What is the name for the parts you colored?

____

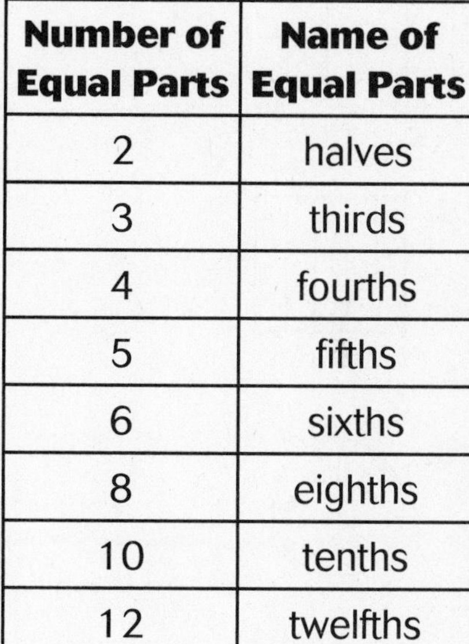

Number of Equal Parts	Name of Equal Parts
2	halves
3	thirds
4	fourths
5	fifths
6	sixths
8	eighths
10	tenths
12	twelfths

6. Fold another sheet of paper like above. Then fold it again so that it makes a long slender rectangle as shown below.

7. Open up the piece of paper. Draw lines down the folds. Color each part a different color.

8. Are the parts you colored equal in size? ______

9. How many equal parts are there? ______

10. What is the name for the parts you colored?

____

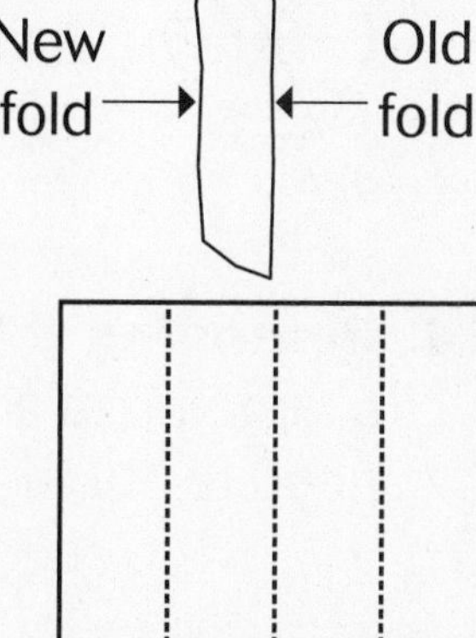

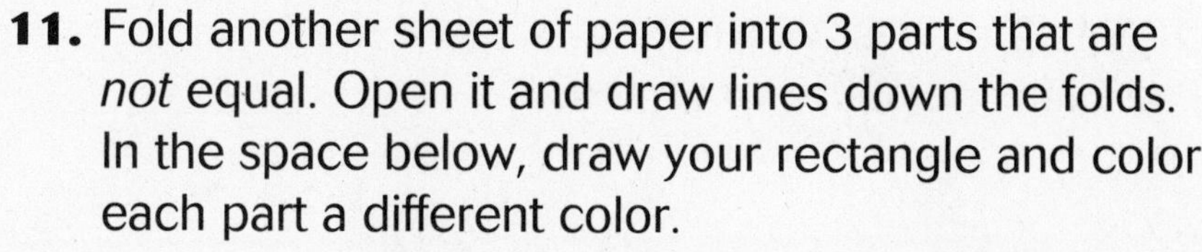

11. Fold another sheet of paper into 3 parts that are *not* equal. Open it and draw lines down the folds. In the space below, draw your rectangle and color each part a different color.

Name ______________________

Equal Parts of a Whole (continued)

Tell if each shows parts that are equal or parts that are not equal. If the parts are equal, name them.

12. 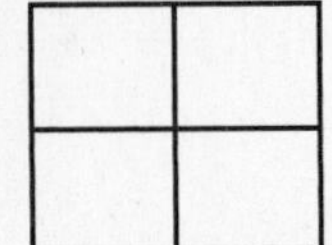 ______________ ______________

13.  ______________ ______________

14.  ______________ ______________

15. 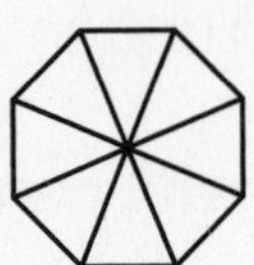 ______________ ______________

16.  ______________ ______________

17.  ______________ ______________

18.  ______________ ______________

19.  ______________ ______________

20. 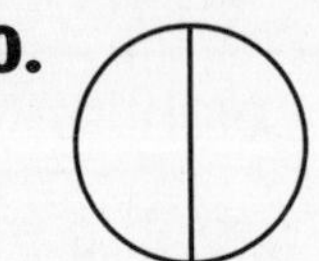 ______________ ______________

21. 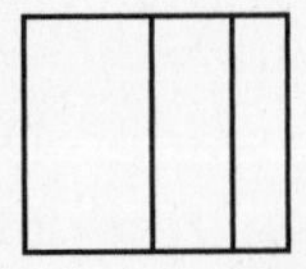 ______________ ______________

22. 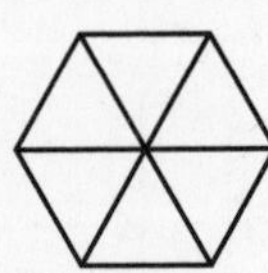 ______________ ______________

23. 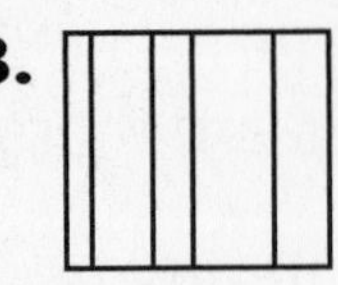 ______________ ______________

24. Reasoning If 5 children want to equally share a large pizza and each gets 2 pieces, will they need to cut the pizza into fifths, eighths, or tenths? ______________

Name ______________________________

Parts of a Region

Materials crayons or markers

1. In the circle at the right, color 2 of the equal parts blue and 4 of the equal parts red.

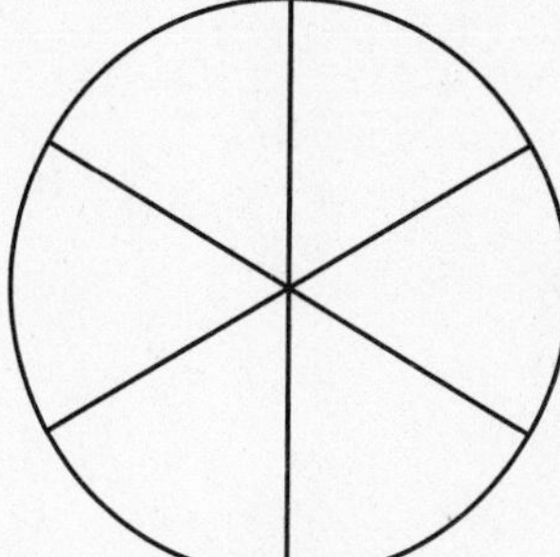

Write fractions to name the parts by answering 2 to 6.

2. How many total equal parts does the circle have? ______

3. How many of the equal parts of the circle are blue? ______

4. What fraction of the circle is blue?

$$\frac{\square}{\square} = \frac{\text{number of equal parts that are blue}}{\text{total number of equal parts}} = \frac{\text{(numerator)}}{\text{(denominator)}}$$

Two sixths of the circle is blue.

5. How many of the equal parts of the circle are red? ______

6. What fraction of the circle is red?

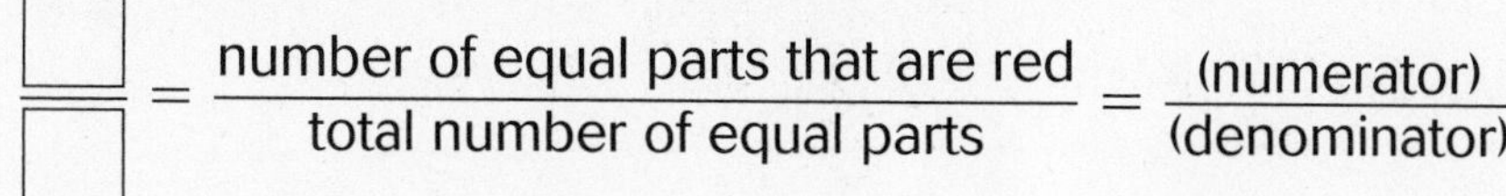

$$\frac{\square}{\square} = \frac{\text{number of equal parts that are red}}{\text{total number of equal parts}} = \frac{\text{(numerator)}}{\text{(denominator)}}$$

Four sixths of the circle is red.

Show the fraction $\frac{3}{8}$ by answering 7 to 9.

7. Color $\frac{3}{8}$ of the rectangle at the right.

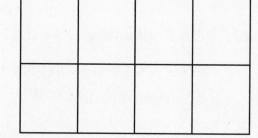

8. How many equal parts does the rectangle have? ______

9. How many parts did you color? ______

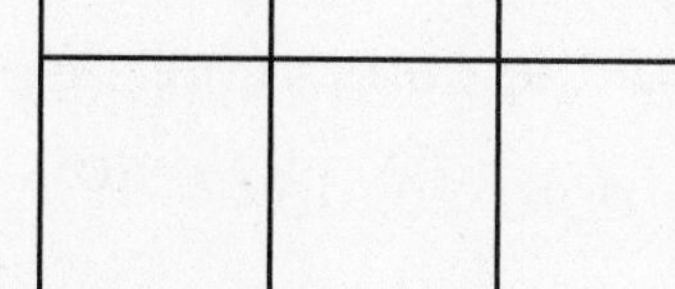

Parts of a Region (continued)

Write the fraction for the shaded part of each region.

10. 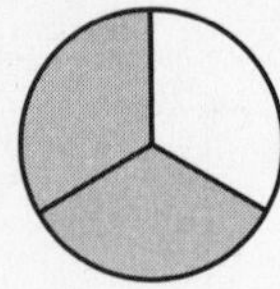 ______

11. 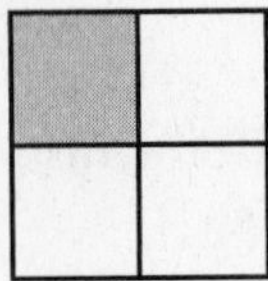 ______

12. 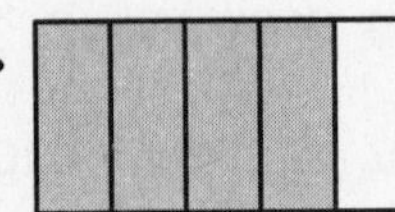 ______

13.  ______

14. 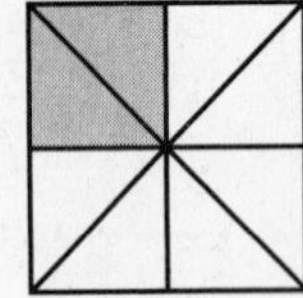 ______

15. 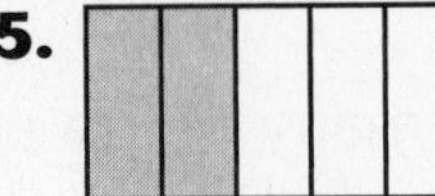 ______

16. 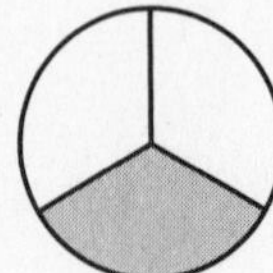 ______

17. 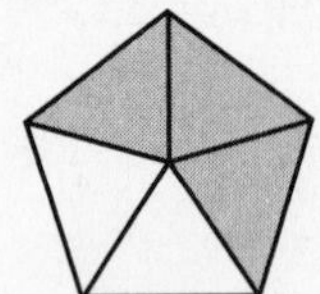 ______

18. 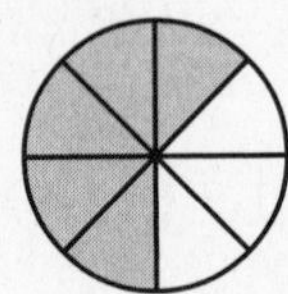 ______

Color to show each fraction.

19. $\frac{3}{4}$

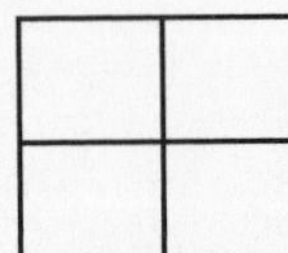

20. $\frac{5}{6}$

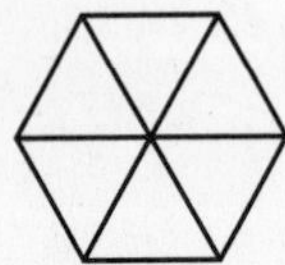

21. $\frac{7}{10}$

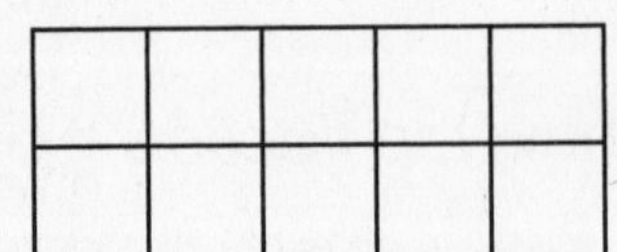

22. Math Reasoning Draw a picture to show $\frac{1}{3}$. Then divide each of the parts in half. What fraction of the parts does the $\frac{1}{3}$ represent now? ______

23. Ben divided a pie into 8 equal pieces and ate 3 of them. How much of the pie remains? ______

Name ______________________________

Parts of a Set

Materials two-color counters, 20 for each pair; crayons or markers

1. Show 4 red counters and 6 yellow counters.

Write a fraction for the part that is red and the part that is yellow by answering 2 to 6.

2. How many counters are there in all? _______

3. How many of the counters are red? _______

4. What fraction of the group of counters is red?

$$\frac{\square}{\square} = \frac{\text{number of counters that are red}}{\text{total number of counters}} = \frac{\text{(numerator)}}{\text{(denominator)}}$$

Four tenths of the group of counters is red

5. How many of the counters are yellow? _______

6. What fraction of the counters are yellow?

$$\frac{\square}{\square} = \frac{\text{number of counters that are yellow}}{\text{total number of counters}} = \frac{\text{(numerator)}}{\text{(denominator)}}$$

Six tenths of the group of counters is yellow.

Show a group of counters with $\frac{5}{6}$ red by answering 7 to 9.

7. How many counters do you need in all? _______

8. How many of the counters need to be red? _______

9. Show the counters and color below to match.

Name ______________________

Parts of a Set (continued)

Write the fraction for the shaded parts of each set.

10. ______

11. ______

12. ______

13. ______

14. ______

15. ______

Draw a set of shapes and shade them to show each fraction.

16. $\frac{5}{9}$

17. $\frac{6}{10}$

18. Reasoning If Sally has 5 yellow marbles and 7 blue marbles. What fraction of her marbles are yellow? Draw a picture to justify your answer.

Name ______________________

Fractions and Length

Materials fraction strips; crayons or markers

Fractions can be used to describe parts of lengths.

1. Use fraction strips to make what is shown below.

1					
$\frac{1}{6}$	$\frac{1}{6}$	$\frac{1}{6}$	$\frac{1}{6}$	$\frac{1}{6}$	$\frac{1}{6}$

2. How many sixth strips does it take to be the same length as 1 whole? ______

3. Use fraction strips to make what is shown below.

1					
$\frac{1}{6}$	$\frac{1}{6}$	$\frac{1}{6}$	$\frac{1}{6}$		

4. What fraction of the length of the 1 strip do the other strips show?

$$\frac{\square}{\square} = \frac{\text{number of parts shown}}{\text{total number of parts to make 1 whole}} = \frac{\text{(numerator)}}{\text{(denominator)}}$$

5. Show the model below.

1							
$\frac{1}{8}$	$\frac{1}{8}$	$\frac{1}{8}$	$\frac{1}{8}$	$\frac{1}{8}$	$\frac{1}{8}$	$\frac{1}{8}$	$\frac{1}{8}$

6. How many eighth strips does it take to be the same length as 1 whole? ______

7. Show $\frac{5}{8}$ with fractions strips. Color strips above to show $\frac{5}{8}$.

Name ______________________________

Fractions and Length (continued)

Write the fraction for the shaded part of each length.

8.

1			
$\frac{1}{4}$	$\frac{1}{4}$	$\frac{1}{4}$	$\frac{1}{4}$

______

9.

1					
$\frac{1}{6}$	$\frac{1}{6}$	$\frac{1}{6}$	$\frac{1}{6}$	$\frac{1}{6}$	$\frac{1}{6}$

______

10.

1				
$\frac{1}{5}$	$\frac{1}{5}$	$\frac{1}{5}$	$\frac{1}{5}$	$\frac{1}{5}$

______

11.

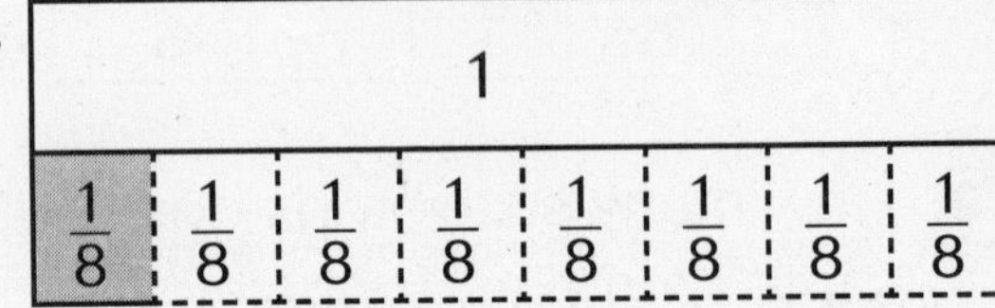

______

12.

1		
$\frac{1}{3}$	$\frac{1}{3}$	$\frac{1}{3}$

______

13.

1									
$\frac{1}{10}$	$\frac{1}{10}$	$\frac{1}{10}$	$\frac{1}{10}$	$\frac{1}{10}$	$\frac{1}{10}$	$\frac{1}{10}$	$\frac{1}{10}$	$\frac{1}{10}$	$\frac{1}{10}$

______

Color to show each fraction.

14. $\frac{1}{2}$

1	
$\frac{1}{2}$	$\frac{1}{2}$

15. $\frac{4}{5}$

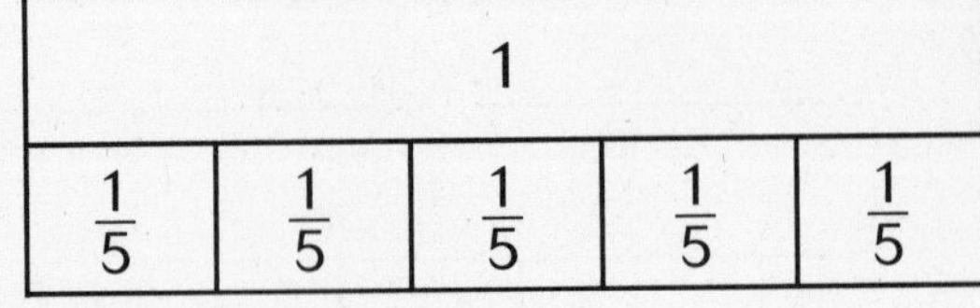

16. $\frac{1}{3}$

1		
$\frac{1}{3}$	$\frac{1}{3}$	$\frac{1}{3}$

17. $\frac{7}{8}$

1							
$\frac{1}{8}$	$\frac{1}{8}$	$\frac{1}{8}$	$\frac{1}{8}$	$\frac{1}{8}$	$\frac{1}{8}$	$\frac{1}{8}$	$\frac{1}{8}$

Name ______________________

Fractions on the Number Line

Each fraction names a point on a number line. Name the missing fractions on the number line below by answering 1 to 3.

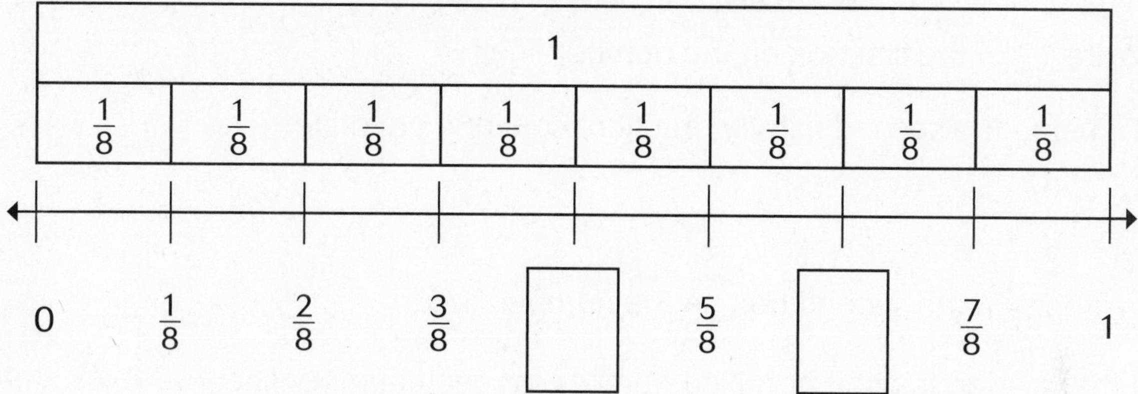

1. How many equal lengths is the distance between 0 and 1 divided into? ______

Since, the distance between 0 and 1 is divided into 8 equal lengths, each length is $\frac{1}{8}$ of the whole length.

2. To name the first missing fraction, count by eighths. $\frac{1}{8}, \frac{2}{8}, \frac{3}{8},$ ______

Write $\frac{4}{8}$ in the first box above.

3. To name the next missing fraction, keep counting. $\frac{4}{8}, \frac{5}{8},$ ______

Write $\frac{6}{8}$ in the second box above.

Name the missing numbers on the number line below by answering 4 to 6.

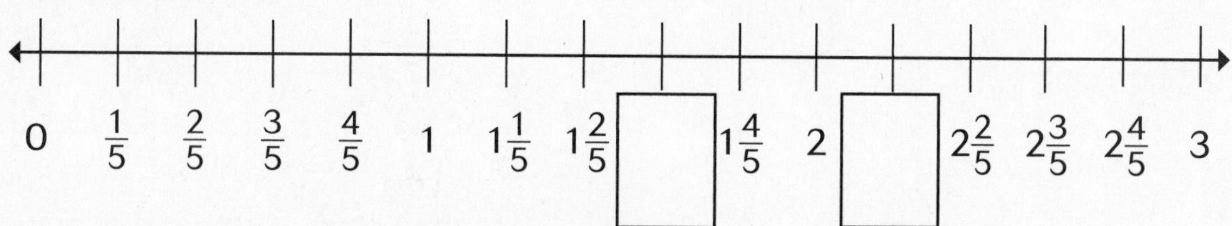

4. How many equal parts is the distance between 0 and 1 divided into? ______

Since, the distance between 0 and 1 is divided into 5 equal lengths, each length is $\frac{1}{5}$ of the whole length.

Name ____________________

Fractions on the Number Line (continued)

5. To name the first missing fraction, count by fifths.

$\frac{1}{5}, \frac{2}{5}, \frac{3}{5}, \frac{4}{5}, 1, 1\frac{1}{5}, 1\frac{2}{5},$ ______

Write $1\frac{3}{5}$ in the first box on the number line.

6. To name the second missing fraction, continue counting.

$1\frac{3}{5}, 1\frac{4}{5}, 2,$ ______

Write $2\frac{1}{5}$ in the second box on the number line.

Write the missing fraction or mixed number for each number line.

7.

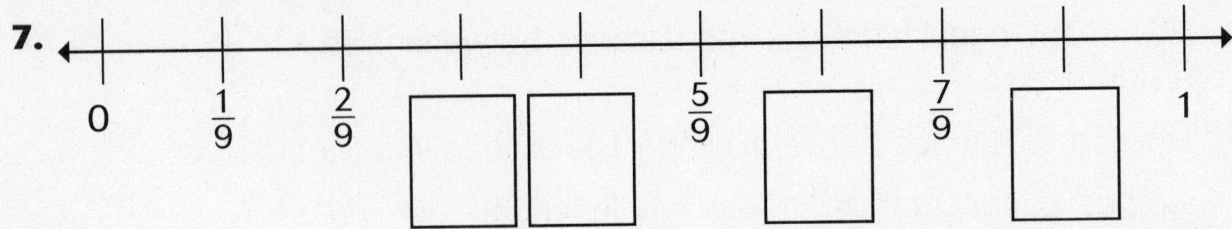

8.

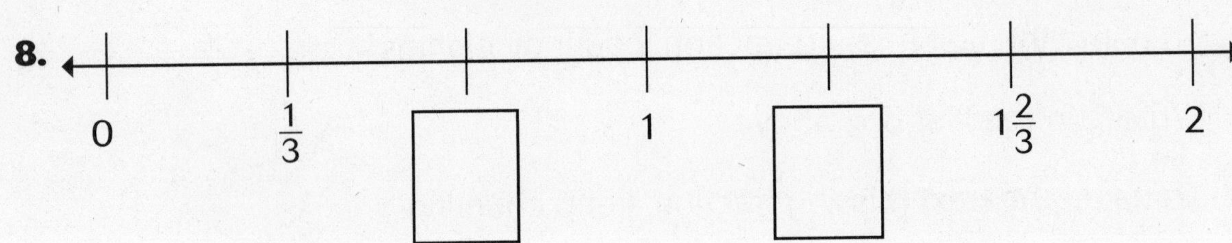

9. The number line shows how far Glen, Ned, and Lois ran in a one-mile race. Write a fraction that shows how far Ned and Lois ran.

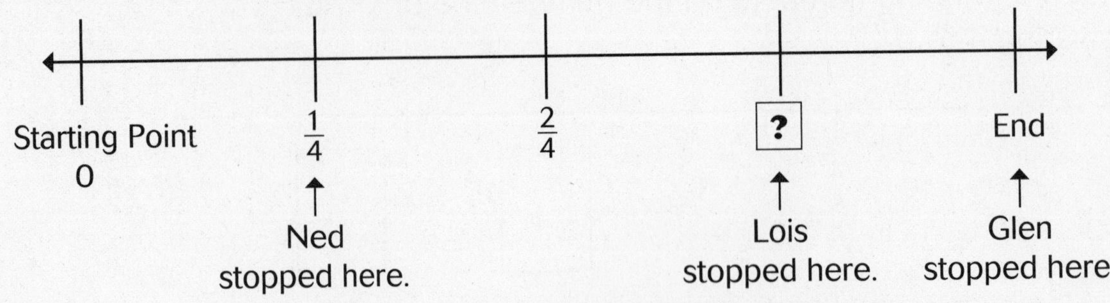

Ned ______ Lois ______

Name ______________________________

Using Models to Compare Fractions

Materials fraction strips

Use >, <, or = to compare $\frac{4}{5}$ and $\frac{2}{3}$ by answering 1 to 3.

1. Show 1, $\frac{4}{5}$, and $\frac{2}{3}$ with fraction strips.

1				
$\frac{1}{5}$	$\frac{1}{5}$	$\frac{1}{5}$	$\frac{1}{5}$	
$\frac{1}{3}$	$\frac{1}{3}$			

2. Compare. Which is greater in total length, $\frac{4}{5}$ or $\frac{2}{3}$? ________

3. Since $\frac{4}{5}$ is longer than $\frac{2}{3}$, $\frac{4}{5}$ is **greater than** $\frac{2}{3}$. Write >, <, or =.

$\frac{4}{5}$ ◯ $\frac{2}{3}$

Compare $\frac{1}{10}$ and $\frac{1}{4}$ by answering 4 to 6.

4. Show 1, $\frac{1}{10}$, and $\frac{1}{4}$ with fraction strips.

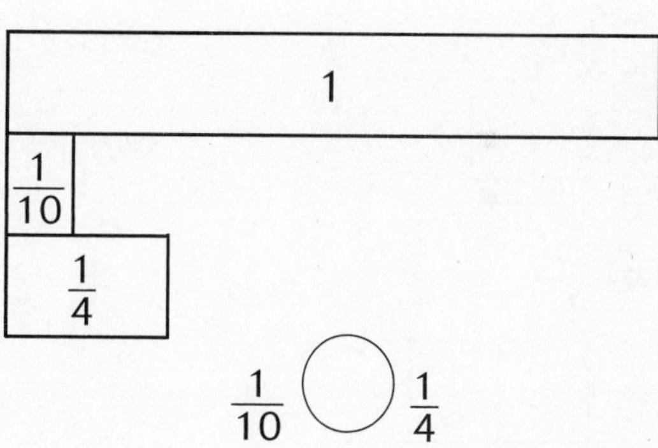

5. Compare. Which is greater in total length, $\frac{1}{10}$ or $\frac{1}{4}$? ________

6. Since $\frac{1}{10}$ is shorter than $\frac{1}{4}$, $\frac{1}{10}$ is **less than** $\frac{1}{4}$. Write >, <, or =.

$\frac{1}{10}$ ◯ $\frac{1}{4}$

Compare $\frac{2}{5}$ and $\frac{4}{10}$ by answering 7 to 9.

7. Show 1, $\frac{2}{5}$, and $\frac{4}{10}$ with fraction strips.

1			
$\frac{1}{5}$		$\frac{1}{5}$	
$\frac{1}{10}$	$\frac{1}{10}$	$\frac{1}{10}$	$\frac{1}{10}$

8. Compare. Which is greater in total length, $\frac{2}{5}$ or $\frac{4}{10}$?

____

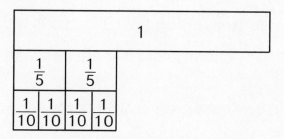

9. Since $\frac{2}{5}$ and $\frac{4}{10}$ are the same length, $\frac{2}{5}$ is **equal to** $\frac{4}{10}$. Write >, <, or =.

$\frac{2}{5}$ ◯ $\frac{4}{10}$

Name ____________________

Using Models to Compare Fractions (continued)

Compare. Write <, >, or =.

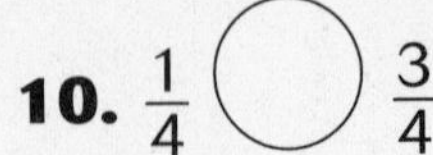

10. $\frac{1}{4}$ ◯ $\frac{3}{4}$

$\frac{1}{4}$
$\frac{1}{4}$ | $\frac{1}{4}$ | $\frac{1}{4}$

11. $\frac{3}{4}$ ◯ $\frac{2}{8}$

$\frac{1}{4}$ | $\frac{1}{4}$ | $\frac{1}{4}$
$\frac{1}{8}$ | $\frac{1}{8}$

12. $\frac{2}{3}$ ◯ $\frac{4}{6}$

$\frac{1}{3}$ | $\frac{1}{3}$
$\frac{1}{6}$ | $\frac{1}{6}$ | $\frac{1}{6}$ | $\frac{1}{6}$

13. $\frac{1}{5}$ ◯ $\frac{5}{10}$

$\frac{1}{5}$
$\frac{1}{10}$ | $\frac{1}{10}$ | $\frac{1}{10}$ | $\frac{1}{10}$ | $\frac{1}{10}$

14. $\frac{1}{2}$ ◯ $\frac{1}{5}$

$\frac{1}{2}$
$\frac{1}{5}$

15. $\frac{7}{8}$ ◯ $\frac{3}{4}$

$\frac{1}{8}$ | $\frac{1}{8}$ | $\frac{1}{8}$ | $\frac{1}{8}$ | $\frac{1}{8}$ | $\frac{1}{8}$ | $\frac{1}{8}$
$\frac{1}{4}$ | $\frac{1}{4}$ | $\frac{1}{4}$

16. $\frac{2}{6}$ ◯ $\frac{1}{2}$

$\frac{1}{6}$ | $\frac{1}{6}$
$\frac{1}{2}$

17. $\frac{3}{5}$ ◯ $\frac{1}{4}$

$\frac{1}{5}$ | $\frac{1}{5}$ | $\frac{1}{5}$
$\frac{1}{4}$

18. **Reasoning** Give 3 fractions with different denominators that are less than $\frac{4}{6}$. ____________________

19. **Reasoning** Two students are writing stories. Eric's story is $\frac{2}{3}$ of a page. Alba's story is $\frac{4}{6}$ of a page. Whose story is longer? ____________________

Name ______________________________

Using Models to Find Equivalent Fractions

Materials fraction strips

Find a fraction equivalent to $\frac{3}{4}$ by answering 1 to 3.

1. Show a 1 and $\frac{3}{4}$ with fraction strips.

1		
$\frac{1}{4}$	$\frac{1}{4}$	$\frac{1}{4}$

2. How many $\frac{1}{8}$ strips does it take to equal $\frac{3}{4}$? ______

$\frac{3}{4} = \frac{\square}{8}$

3. So, $\frac{3}{4}$ is equal to six $\frac{1}{8}$ strips.

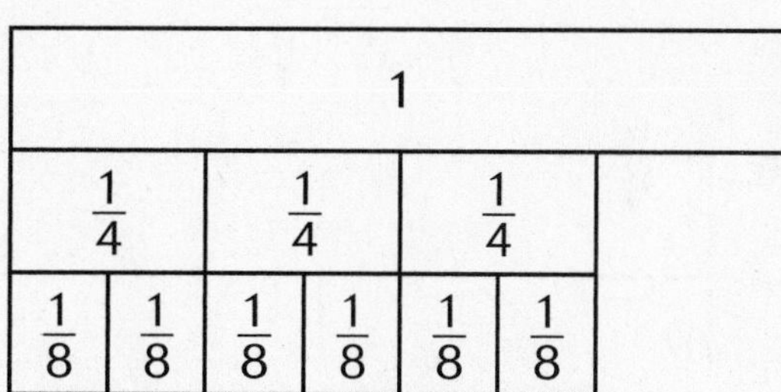

Find the missing number in $\frac{1}{2} = \frac{?}{10}$, by answering 4 to 7.

The denominators of the fractions tell which fraction strips to use.

4. Show 1 and $\frac{1}{2}$ with fraction strips.

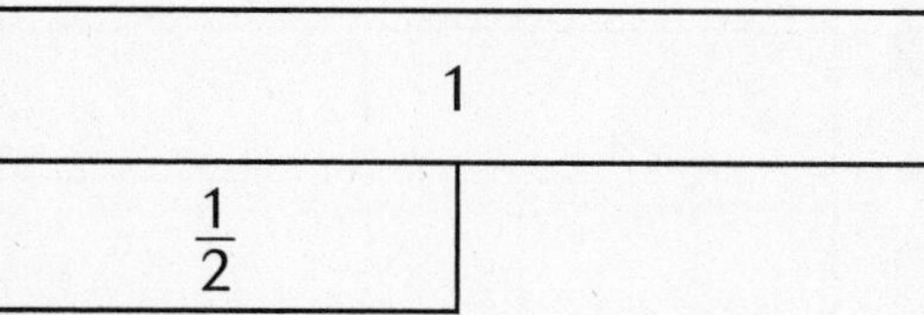

5. What is the denominator of the second fraction? ______

6. Since the denominator of the second fraction is 10, find the number of $\frac{1}{10}$ strips equal to $\frac{1}{2}$. ______

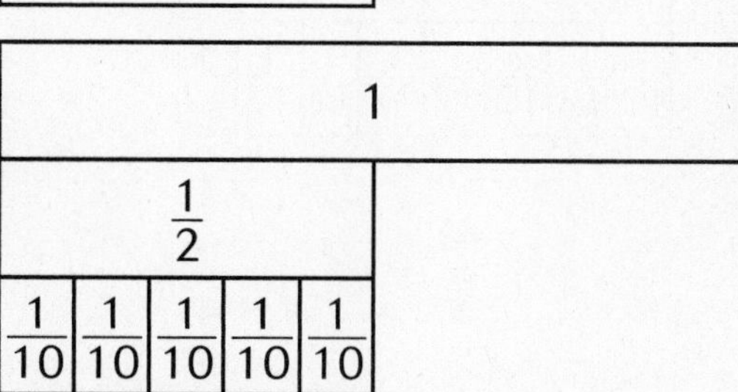

7. So, $\frac{1}{2}$ is equal to five $\frac{1}{10}$ strips.

$\frac{1}{2} = \frac{\square}{10}$

Using Models to Find Equivalent Fractions (continued)

Complete each number sentence.

8.

$\frac{1}{4} = \frac{\_\_\_}{8}$

9.

$\frac{2}{3} = \frac{\_\_\_}{6}$

10.

$\frac{1}{2} = \frac{\_\_\_}{8}$

11.

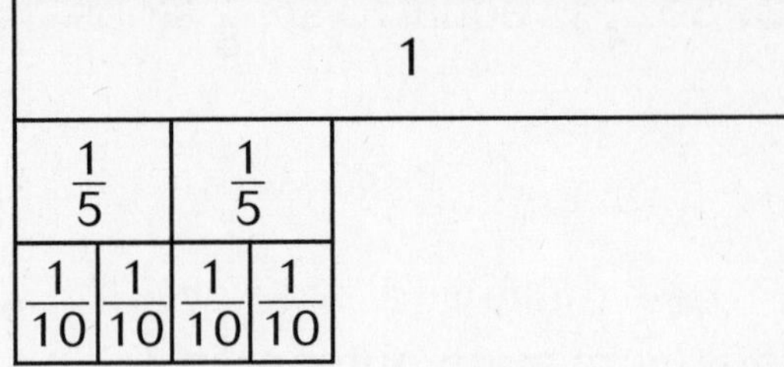

$\frac{2}{5} = \frac{\_\_\_}{10}$

12.

$\frac{2}{3} = \frac{\_\_\_}{12}$

13.

$\frac{2}{4} = \frac{\_\_\_}{6}$

14. Reasoning On Tuesday, $\frac{2}{3}$ of the class time was spent on math projects. How many *sixths* of the class time was spent on math projects? ______

Name ______________________________

Equivalent Fractions

Materials crayons or markers

1					
$\frac{1}{3}$		$\frac{1}{3}$		$\frac{1}{3}$	
$\frac{1}{6}$	$\frac{1}{6}$	$\frac{1}{6}$	$\frac{1}{6}$	$\frac{1}{6}$	$\frac{1}{6}$

1. Show $\frac{2}{3}$ by coloring 2 of the $\frac{1}{3}$ strips.

2. Color as many $\frac{1}{6}$ strips as it takes to cover the same region as the $\frac{2}{3}$.

How many $\frac{1}{6}$ strips did you color? _____

3. So, $\frac{2}{3}$ is equivalent to four $\frac{1}{6}$ strips. $\frac{2}{3} = \frac{\square}{6}$

You can use multiplication to find a fraction equivalent to $\frac{2}{3}$. To do this, multiply the numerator and the denominator by the same number.

4. What number is the denominator of $\frac{2}{3}$ multiplied by to get 6?

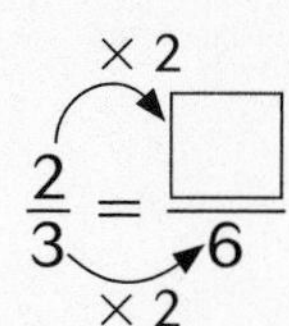

_____

5. Since the denominator was multiplied by 2, the numerator must also be multiplied by 2. Put the product of 2 × 2 in the numerator of the second fraction above.

Multiply the numerator and denominator of each fraction by the same number to find a fraction equivalent to each.

6. × 3 $\frac{2}{3} = \frac{\square}{9}$ × 3

7.

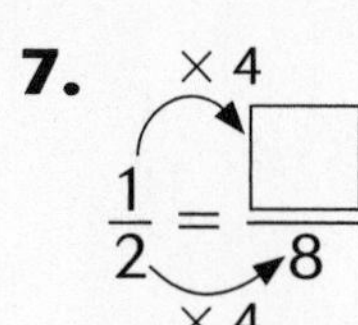

8. Show $\frac{9}{12}$ by coloring 9 of the $\frac{1}{12}$ strips.

1											
$\frac{1}{4}$			$\frac{1}{4}$			$\frac{1}{4}$			$\frac{1}{4}$		
$\frac{1}{12}$	$\frac{1}{12}$	$\frac{1}{12}$	$\frac{1}{12}$	$\frac{1}{12}$	$\frac{1}{12}$	$\frac{1}{12}$	$\frac{1}{12}$	$\frac{1}{12}$	$\frac{1}{12}$	$\frac{1}{12}$	$\frac{1}{12}$

9. Color as many $\frac{1}{4}$ strips as it takes to cover the same region as $\frac{9}{12}$.

How many $\frac{1}{4}$ strips did you color? _____

Name ______________________________

Equivalent Fractions (continued)

10. So, $\frac{9}{12}$ is equivalent to three $\frac{1}{4}$ strips. $\frac{9}{12} = \frac{\square}{4}$

You can use division to find a fraction equivalent to $\frac{9}{12}$. To do this, divide the numerator and the denominator by the same number.

11. What number is the denominator of $\frac{9}{12}$ divided by to get 4? ______

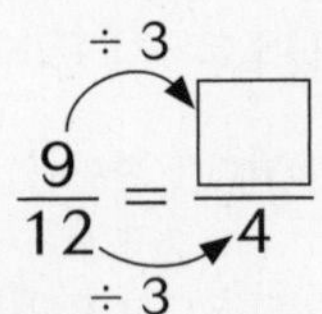

12. Since the denominator was divided by 3, the numerator must also be divided by 3. Put the quotient of 9 ÷ 3 in the numerator of the second fraction above.

Divide the numerator and denominator of each fraction by the same number to find a fraction equivalent to each.

13. $\frac{8}{10} = \frac{\square}{5}$ (÷ 2)

14. $\frac{10}{15} = \frac{\square}{3}$ (÷ 5)

If the numerator and denominator cannot be divided by anything else, then the fraction is in simplest form.

15. Is $\frac{5}{12}$ in simplest form? ______

16. Is $\frac{6}{8}$ in simplest form? ______

Find each equivalent fraction.

17. $\frac{1}{5} = \frac{\square}{15}$

18. $\frac{8}{10} = \frac{\square}{5}$

19. $\frac{2}{8} = \frac{\square}{4}$

20. $\frac{7}{10} = \frac{\square}{20}$

21. $\frac{6}{14} = \frac{\square}{7}$

22. $\frac{8}{11} = \frac{\square}{22}$

Write each fraction in simplest form.

23. $\frac{6}{8}$ ______

24. $\frac{8}{12}$ ______

25. $\frac{7}{35}$ ______

26. $\frac{16}{24}$ ______

27. Reasoning Explain why $\frac{4}{6}$ is not in simplest form.

Name ______________________

Comparing Fractions on the Number Line

Materials 21 index cards for each pair; crayons or markers, 13 craft sticks for each pair; 1 yard of yarn for each pair

1. Write numbers on index cards, one number on each card. One partner writes the following numbers.

$0, \frac{1}{3}, \frac{2}{3}, 1, 1\frac{1}{3}, 1\frac{2}{3}, 2, 2\frac{1}{3}, 2\frac{2}{3}, 3, 3\frac{1}{3}, 3\frac{2}{3}$, and 4

The other partner writes the following numbers.

$\frac{1}{3}, \frac{2}{3}, 1\frac{1}{3}, 1\frac{2}{3}, 2\frac{1}{3}, 2\frac{2}{3}, 3\frac{1}{3}$, and $3\frac{2}{3}$

2. Create a number line, like the one shown below, with the yarn, craft sticks, and the first set of index cards.

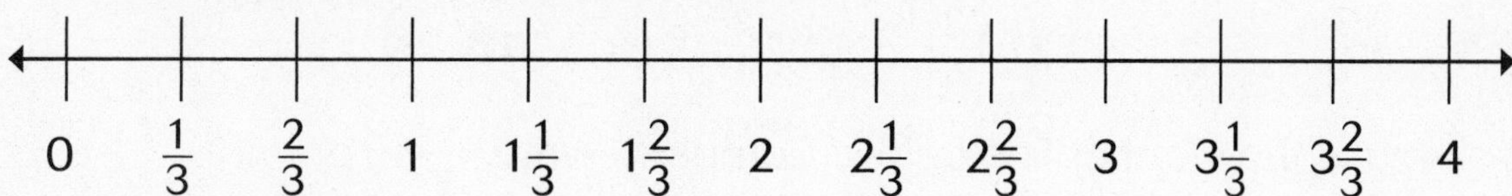

3. Shuffle the other set of cards. Both you and your partner draw a card.

4. Match the numbers on the cards you drew with numbers on the number line you created.

Which number is farther to the right? ______________

On the number line, fractions increase in value from left to right. So the fraction farther to the right is greater.

5. Write a comparison of your two numbers, such as $2\frac{2}{3} < 3\frac{1}{3}$. ______________

Set the first two cards aside. Continue drawing cards and writing comparisons until all the cards are gone.

6. ______________ **7.** ______________

8. ______________ **9.** ______________

Name ____________________

Comparing Fractions on the Number Line (continued)

For 10–18, use the number line below. Compare. Write <, >, or =.

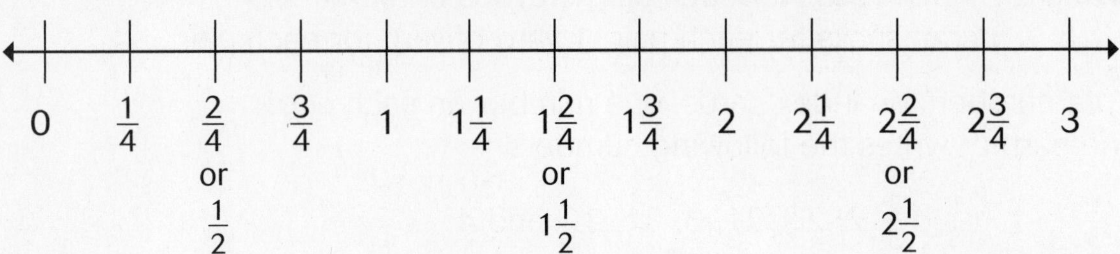

10. $\frac{3}{4}$ ◯ $\frac{1}{4}$ **11.** $1\frac{1}{4}$ ◯ $2\frac{1}{2}$ **12.** $1\frac{1}{2}$ ◯ $1\frac{3}{4}$

13. $1\frac{1}{4}$ ◯ $\frac{1}{4}$ **14.** $2\frac{3}{4}$ ◯ $2\frac{1}{4}$ **15.** $1\frac{1}{2}$ ◯ $1\frac{1}{2}$

16. $\frac{1}{4}$ ◯ $\frac{1}{2}$ **17.** $1\frac{3}{4}$ ◯ $1\frac{3}{4}$ **18.** $\frac{3}{4}$ ◯ $\frac{1}{2}$

For 19–24, use the number line below. Compare. Write <, >, or =.

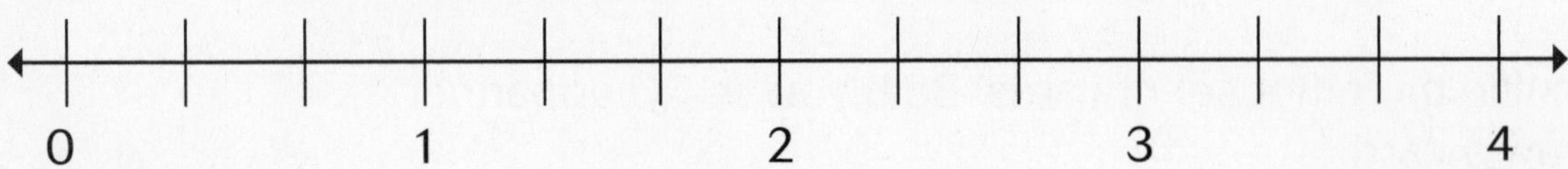

19. $\frac{2}{3}$ ◯ $\frac{1}{3}$ **20.** $2\frac{1}{3}$ ◯ $1\frac{2}{3}$ **21.** $1\frac{1}{3}$ ◯ $2\frac{1}{3}$

22. $\frac{3}{3}$ ◯ 1 **23.** $2\frac{2}{3}$ ◯ $2\frac{1}{3}$ **24.** $\frac{2}{3}$ ◯ $1\frac{1}{3}$

25. Reasoning Why is $2\frac{1}{8}$ greater than $1\frac{7}{8}$, even though $\frac{1}{8}$ is less than $\frac{7}{8}$?

26. Reasoning Explain how you can use the number line above to compare $6\frac{1}{3}$ and $6\frac{2}{3}$.

Name ______________________________

Comparing Fractions

Materials fraction strips

Compare $\frac{3}{10}$ and $\frac{7}{8}$ by answering 1 to 3.

Compare each fraction to $\frac{1}{2}$. Write $>$ or $<$.

1. $\frac{3}{10}$ ◯ $\frac{1}{2}$

$\frac{1}{2}$		
$\frac{1}{10}$	$\frac{1}{10}$	$\frac{1}{10}$

2. $\frac{7}{8}$ ◯ $\frac{1}{2}$

$\frac{1}{2}$						
$\frac{1}{8}$	$\frac{1}{8}$	$\frac{1}{8}$	$\frac{1}{8}$	$\frac{1}{8}$	$\frac{1}{8}$	$\frac{1}{8}$

3. Since $\frac{3}{10} < \frac{1}{2}$ and $\frac{7}{8} > \frac{1}{2}$, then $\frac{3}{10}$ ◯ $\frac{7}{8}$.

You can compare two fractions with the same denominator just by comparing the numerators.

Use equivalent fractions to compare $\frac{1}{4}$ and $\frac{5}{12}$ by answering 4 to 6.

4. $\frac{1}{4}$ is the same as how many twelfths? ______

5. Since $\frac{1}{4} = \frac{3}{12}$, you can now compare $\frac{3}{12}$ and $\frac{5}{12}$.

Which fraction has the greater numerator? ________

6. Compare. Write $>$ or $<$. $\frac{3}{12}$ ◯ $\frac{5}{12}$

So, $\frac{1}{4}$ ◯ $\frac{5}{12}$.

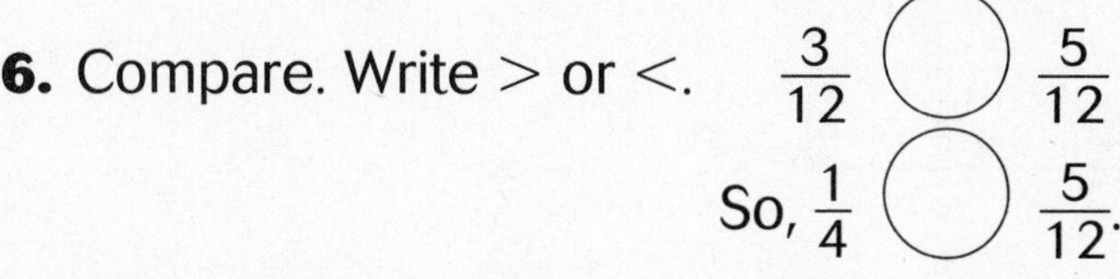

7. Use fraction strips to compare $\frac{1}{8}$ and $\frac{1}{4}$. Write $>$ or $<$.

$\frac{1}{8}$ ◯ $\frac{1}{4}$

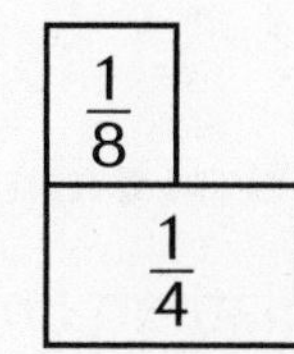

8. Which fraction has the greater denominator $\frac{1}{8}$ or $\frac{1}{4}$? ________

When both fractions have the same numerator, the fraction with the greater denominator is **less than** the other fraction.

Name ______________________________

Comparing Fractions (continued)

Compare. Write >, <, or = for each.

9. $\frac{1}{4}$ ◯ $\frac{3}{4}$

$\frac{1}{4}$

$\frac{1}{4}$ $\frac{1}{4}$ $\frac{1}{4}$

10. $\frac{5}{10}$ ◯ $\frac{3}{10}$

$\frac{1}{10}$ $\frac{1}{10}$ $\frac{1}{10}$ $\frac{1}{10}$ $\frac{1}{10}$

$\frac{1}{10}$ $\frac{1}{10}$ $\frac{1}{10}$

11. $\frac{1}{5}$ ◯ $\frac{5}{8}$

$\frac{1}{5}$

$\frac{1}{8}$ $\frac{1}{8}$ $\frac{1}{8}$ $\frac{1}{8}$ $\frac{1}{8}$

12. $\frac{7}{10}$ ◯ $\frac{9}{10}$

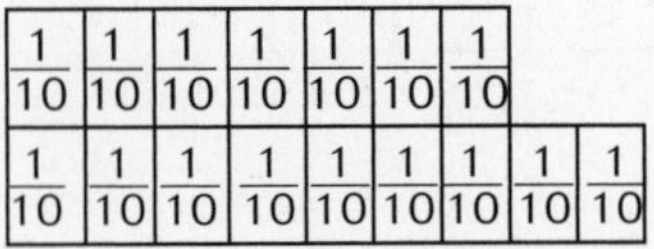

13. $\frac{2}{8}$ ◯ $\frac{1}{4}$

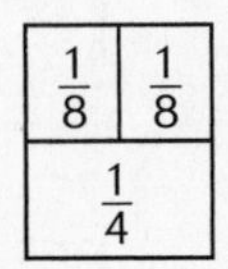

14. $\frac{8}{12}$ ◯ $\frac{5}{6}$

$\frac{1}{12}$ $\frac{1}{12}$ $\frac{1}{12}$ $\frac{1}{12}$ $\frac{1}{12}$ $\frac{1}{12}$ $\frac{1}{12}$ $\frac{1}{12}$

$\frac{1}{6}$ $\frac{1}{6}$ $\frac{1}{6}$ $\frac{1}{6}$ $\frac{1}{6}$

15. $\frac{6}{8}$ ◯ $\frac{6}{10}$

$\frac{1}{8}$ $\frac{1}{8}$ $\frac{1}{8}$ $\frac{1}{8}$ $\frac{1}{8}$ $\frac{1}{8}$

$\frac{1}{10}$ $\frac{1}{10}$ $\frac{1}{10}$ $\frac{1}{10}$ $\frac{1}{10}$ $\frac{1}{10}$

16. $\frac{3}{6}$ ◯ $\frac{6}{12}$

$\frac{1}{6}$ $\frac{1}{6}$ $\frac{1}{6}$

$\frac{1}{12}$ $\frac{1}{12}$ $\frac{1}{12}$ $\frac{1}{12}$ $\frac{1}{12}$ $\frac{1}{12}$

17. $\frac{3}{5}$ ◯ $\frac{7}{12}$

$\frac{1}{5}$ $\frac{1}{5}$ $\frac{1}{5}$

$\frac{1}{12}$ $\frac{1}{12}$ $\frac{1}{12}$ $\frac{1}{12}$ $\frac{1}{12}$ $\frac{1}{12}$ $\frac{1}{12}$

18. $\frac{1}{2}$ ◯ $\frac{3}{8}$

$\frac{1}{2}$

$\frac{1}{8}$ $\frac{1}{8}$ $\frac{1}{8}$

19. $\frac{3}{5}$ ◯ $\frac{6}{10}$

$\frac{1}{5}$ $\frac{1}{5}$ $\frac{1}{5}$

$\frac{1}{10}$ $\frac{1}{10}$ $\frac{1}{10}$ $\frac{1}{10}$ $\frac{1}{10}$ $\frac{1}{10}$

20. $\frac{1}{5}$ ◯ $\frac{1}{8}$

$\frac{1}{5}$

$\frac{1}{8}$

21. Reasoning Two students are timed on a math facts test. Nathan finished $\frac{5}{6}$ of the problems. Terrell finished $\frac{5}{8}$ of the problems. Which student finished a greater part? ____________

Name ______________________________

Adding Fractions with Like Denominators

Materials crayons or markers

Nur wove $\frac{2}{5}$ of a rug in February and $\frac{1}{5}$ of it in March. Find what part of the rug she has finished in all by answering 1 to 4.

1. Color $\frac{2}{5}$ of the rectangle on the right.

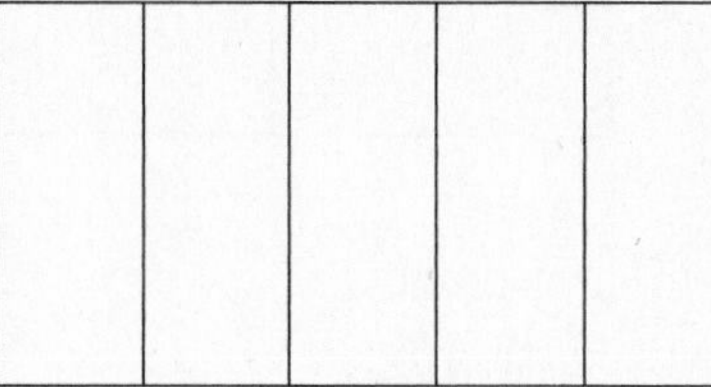

2. Color $\frac{1}{5}$ more of the rectangle on the right.

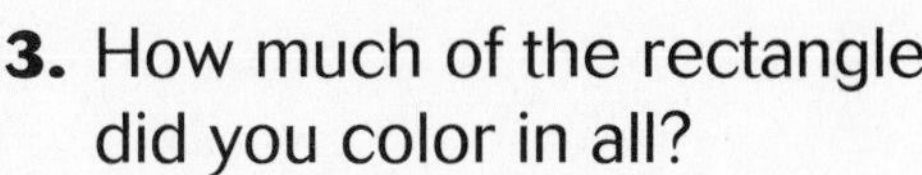

3. How much of the rectangle did you color in all?

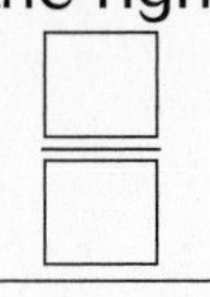

This is the sum of $\frac{2}{5}$ and $\frac{1}{5}$. So, $\frac{2}{5} + \frac{1}{5} = \frac{3}{5}$.

4. What part of her rug has Nur finished in all? ______

Jamal wove $\frac{2}{6}$ of a rug in February and $\frac{2}{6}$ in March. Find what part of the rug he has finished in all by answering 5 to 11.

5. Color $\frac{2}{6}$ of the rectangle on the right.

6. Color $\frac{2}{6}$ more of the rectangle on the right.

7. How much of the rectangle did you color in all? $\frac{\square}{\square}$

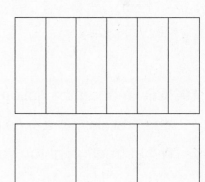

8. What is $\frac{2}{6} + \frac{2}{6}$? ______

9. What is a fraction equivalent to $\frac{4}{6}$, but with smaller numbers? Color the second rectangle to find out. $\frac{4}{6} = \frac{\square}{\square}$

10. So, $\frac{2}{6} + \frac{2}{6} = \frac{4}{6} = \frac{\square}{\square}$.

11. What part of his rug has Jamal finished in all? ______

Name ______________________________

Adding Fractions with Like Denominators (continued)

12. Reasoning Explain how to add $\frac{1}{9} + \frac{4}{9}$.

Add.

13. $\frac{1}{3}$ | $\frac{1}{3}$

$\frac{1}{3} + \frac{1}{3} =$ ______

14. $\frac{1}{5}$ | $\frac{3}{5}$

$\frac{1}{5} + \frac{3}{5} =$ ______

15. $\frac{1}{4}$ | $\frac{2}{4}$

$\frac{1}{4} + \frac{2}{4} =$ ______

16. 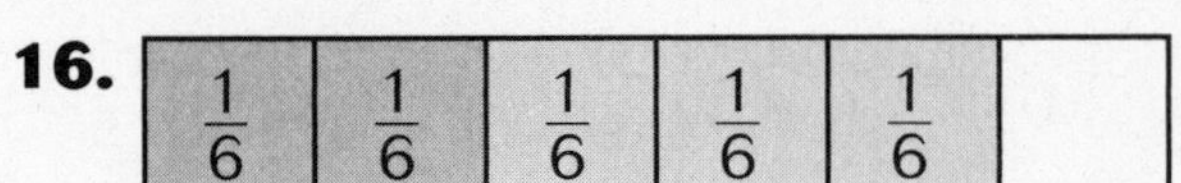

$\frac{2}{6} + \frac{3}{6} =$ ______

17. $\frac{2}{8} + \frac{5}{8} =$ ______

18. $\frac{3}{10} + \frac{2}{10} =$ ______ $=$ ______

19. Calvin bought a gallon of yogurt. He ate $\frac{1}{6}$ gallon the first day, and $\frac{2}{6}$ gallon the second day. What fraction of the yogurt did he eat? ______

20. Three-fifths of Mr. James' class are wearing blue jeans and white shirts. One-fifth of the class are wearing blue jeans and red shirts. One-fifth of the class are wearing brown pants and white shirts. What fraction of Mr. James' class are wearing white shirts? ______

21. Reasoning What fraction would you add to $\frac{1}{3}$ to get $\frac{3}{3}$? ______

Name ______________________________

Subtracting Fractions with Like Denominators

Materials crayons or markers

Tammy loves tuna bake. When she came home from school, she found $\frac{6}{8}$ of a tuna bake on the stove. She ate $\frac{1}{8}$ of it. Find how much of the tuna bake was left by answering 1 to 5.

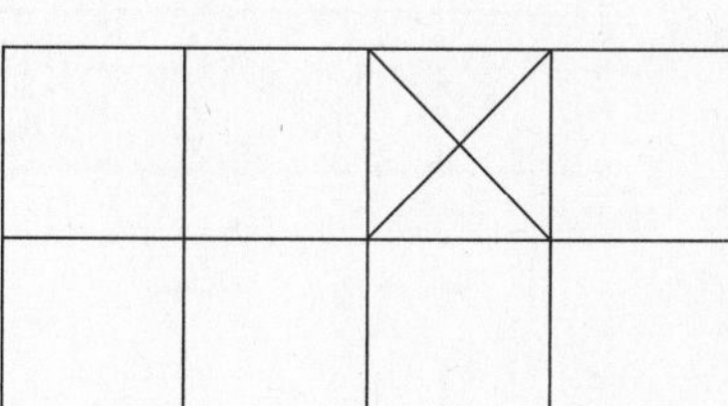

1. Color $\frac{6}{8}$ of the rectangle on the right.

2. Cross out $\frac{1}{8}$ of the part you colored.

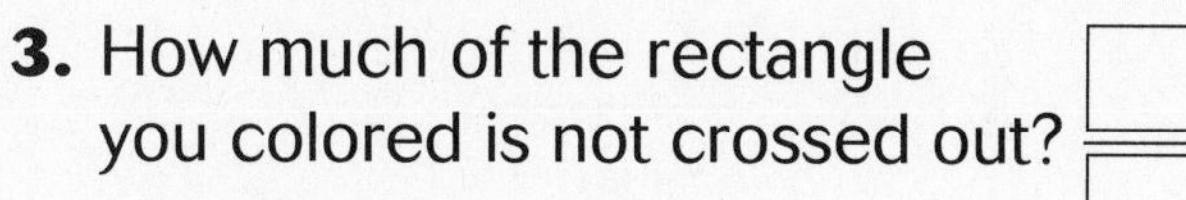

3. How much of the rectangle you colored is not crossed out? $\frac{\square}{\square}$

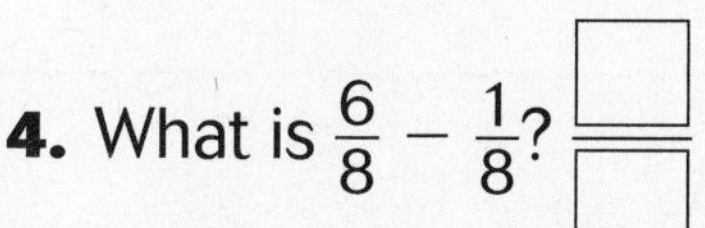

4. What is $\frac{6}{8} - \frac{1}{8}$? $\frac{\square}{\square}$

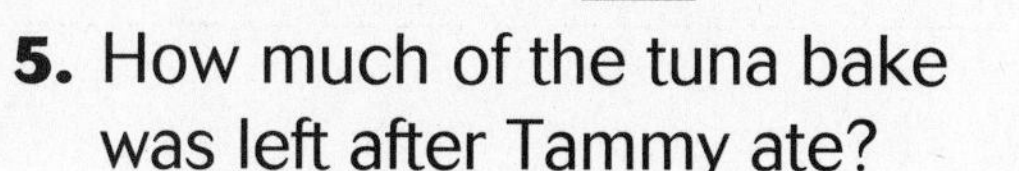

5. How much of the tuna bake was left after Tammy ate? ______

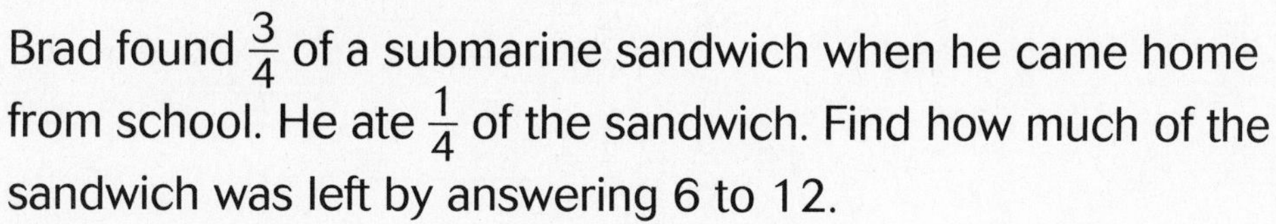

Brad found $\frac{3}{4}$ of a submarine sandwich when he came home from school. He ate $\frac{1}{4}$ of the sandwich. Find how much of the sandwich was left by answering 6 to 12.

6. Color $\frac{3}{4}$ of the rectangle on the right.

7. Cross out $\frac{1}{4}$ of the part you colored.

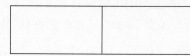

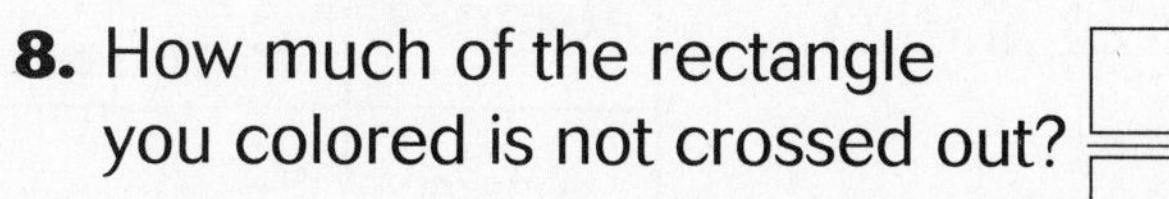

8. How much of the rectangle you colored is not crossed out? $\frac{\square}{\square}$

9. What is $\frac{3}{4} - \frac{1}{4}$? $\frac{\square}{\square}$

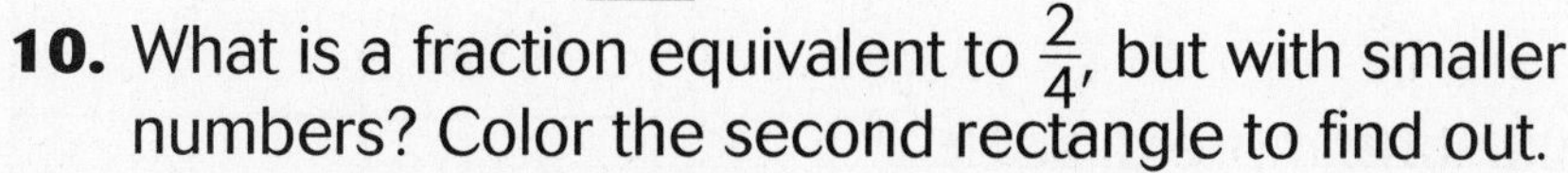

10. What is a fraction equivalent to $\frac{2}{4}$, but with smaller numbers? Color the second rectangle to find out. $\frac{2}{4} = \frac{\square}{\square}$

11. So, $\frac{3}{4} - \frac{1}{4} = \frac{2}{4} = \frac{\square}{\square}$.

12. How much of the sandwich was left after Brad ate? ______

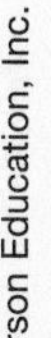

Name ______________________________

Subtracting Fractions with Like Denominators (continued)

13. Reasoning Explain how to subtract $\frac{5}{10} - \frac{2}{10}$.

Subtract.

14.

$\frac{1}{6}$	$\frac{1}{6}$	$\frac{1}{6}$	$\frac{1}{6}$	$\frac{1}{6}$	

$\frac{5}{6} - \frac{3}{6} =$ ______

15.

$\frac{1}{5}$	$\frac{1}{5}$	$\frac{1}{5}$		

$\frac{3}{5} - \frac{1}{5} =$ ______

16.

$\frac{1}{4}$	$\frac{1}{4}$	$\frac{1}{4}$	

$\frac{3}{4} - \frac{1}{4} =$ ______

17.

$\frac{1}{5}$	$\frac{1}{5}$	$\frac{1}{5}$	$\frac{1}{5}$	

$\frac{4}{5} - \frac{2}{5} =$ ______

18. $\frac{4}{7} - \frac{3}{7} =$ ______

19. $\frac{5}{9} - \frac{4}{9} =$ ______

20. $\frac{7}{8} - \frac{1}{8} =$ ______ $=$ ______

21. $\frac{4}{6} - \frac{1}{6} =$ ______ $=$ ______

The table shows the distances run by members of a track team. Use the table for Exercises 22 and 23.

Runner	Distance in miles
Rosie	$\frac{7}{8}$
Tricia	$\frac{4}{8}$
Amy	$\frac{5}{8}$
Caro	$\frac{6}{8}$

22. How much farther did Rosie run than Tricia? ______________

23. How much farther did Caro run than Tricia? ______________

24. Reasoning Why would it be more difficult to subtract $\frac{2}{3} - \frac{1}{6}$ than $\frac{2}{3} - \frac{1}{3}$?

Name ____

Money

Materials: Crayons or markers

1. Have children find the pennies on the page and circle them with red. Ask: ***How much is a penny worth?*** Write 1¢ on the board or overhead.
2. Have children find the nickels on the page and circle them with blue. Ask: ***How much is a nickel worth?*** Write 5¢ on the board or overhead.
3. Have children find the dimes on the page and circle them with orange. Ask: ***How much is a dime worth?*** Write 10¢ on the board or overhead.
4. Have children circle the quarter in yellow and the dollar bill in purple.

Name ______________________________

Money (continued)

Match.

1.   5¢

2.  10¢

3.  2¢

4.  1¢

5.  

Reasoning Count on. Write how much in all.

6.       

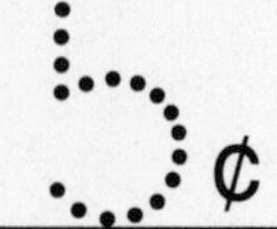 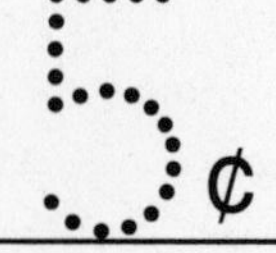  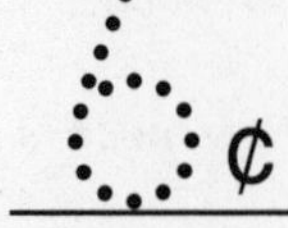   

5 ¢ | 6 ¢ | ___ ¢ | ___ ¢ | ___ ¢ | ___ ¢ in all

Name ______________________________

Pennies and Nickels

1.    

5¢ 10¢ 15¢ 20¢ 20¢ in all

2.    

___¢ ___¢ ___¢ ___¢ ___¢ ___¢ in all

3. 

Materials: 5 nickels and 5 pennies per child

1. Have children place a nickel on top of each nickel in item 1. Ask: ***How much is a nickel worth?*** Have children write 5 next to the cent sign.
2. Have children skip count by 5s and write the numbers. Ask: ***How much are 4 nickels worth in all?*** Have children write 20.
3. Have children place nickels and pennies on top of each coin in item 2. Have them count by 5s and then count on and write the numbers. Have them write how much in all.
4. Have children use coins to show how much the car costs. Have them circle the coins needed to buy the car.

Name ______________________________

Pennies and Nickels (continued)

Count on. Write how much in all.

4.     

5¢ 10¢ ___¢ ___¢ ___¢ ___¢ in all

5.     

___¢ ___¢ ___¢ ___¢ ___¢ ___¢ in all

Circle the coins that match each price.

6. 

7. 

Name ______________________

Dimes

1.

10¢ 20¢ ___¢ ___¢ ___¢ ___¢ in all

2.

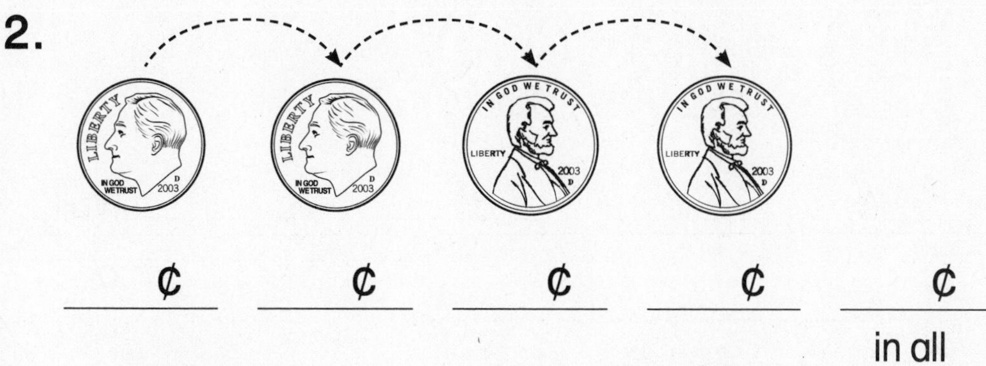

___¢ ___¢ ___¢ ___¢ ___¢ in all

3.

Materials: 5 dimes and 5 pennies per child

1. Have children place a dime on top of each dime and a penny on top of each penny, in item 1. Ask: ***How much is a dime worth?*** Have children write 10 next to the cent sign.
2. Have children skip count, count on, and write the numbers. Ask: ***How much are the coins worth in all?*** Have children write 32.
3. Repeat for item 2.
4. Have children use coins to show how much the dinosaur costs. Have them circle the coins needed to buy the dinosaur.

Name ______________________

Dimes (continued)

Count on. Then write how much money in all.

4.

10¢ 20¢ ____¢ ____¢ ____¢ in all

5.

____¢ ____¢ ____¢ ____¢ ____¢ in all

6.

____¢ ____¢ ____¢ ____¢ ____¢ in all

Circle the coins to match the price.

7.

Name ______________________________

Counting Pennies, Nickels, and Dimes

1.   

10¢ 20¢ 25¢ 26¢ 26¢ in all

2.     

____¢ ____¢ ____¢ ____¢ ____¢ ____¢ in all

3.     

____¢ ____¢ ____¢ ____¢ ____¢ ____¢ in all

Materials: 5 dimes, 5 nickels, and 5 pennies per child or pair

1. Have children place matching coins on top of each coin in item 1. Have them skip count, count on, and write the numbers. Ask: ***How much are the coins worth in all?*** Have children write 26.
2. Repeat for the other two items.

Name ______________________________

Counting Pennies, Nickels, and Dimes (continued)

Write each amount.

4.

13 ¢

5.

¢

6.

¢

7.

¢

8. **Reasoning** You have this amount.

Do you have enough money to buy the orange?

Circle **Yes** or **No.**

Yes No

Name ____________________

Quarters

1.  or 

quarter

25¢

2.    

25¢ 30¢ ___¢ ___¢ ___¢ in all

3.    

___¢ ___¢ ___¢ ___¢ ___¢ in all

Materials: 1 quarter, 2 dimes, 2 nickels, and 2 pennies per child

1. Have children point to the quarter. Ask: ***How much is a quarter worth?*** Have children write 25. Then have them circle coins that equal 25 cents.
2 Have children place matching coins on top of each coin in item 2. Have them count and write the numbers. Ask: ***How much are the coins worth in all?*** Have children write 50.
3. Repeat for the other item.

Name ______________________________

Quarters (continued)

Circle the coins that equal 25¢.

4.

5.

Circle the coins to match each price.

6.

7.

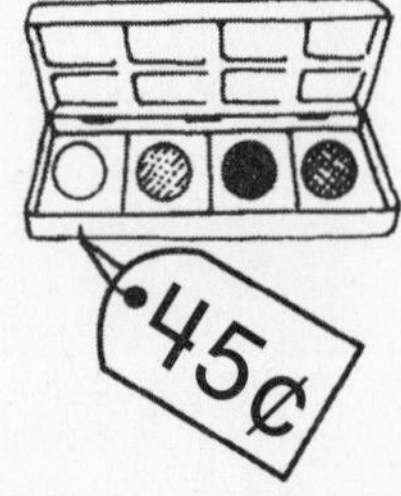

8. **Reasoning** You have 4 coins. They equal a quarter. Circle the coins you have.

Name ______________________________

Half-Dollars

1.

50¢

or

A half-dollar is worth 50¢.

____¢ ____¢ ____¢ ____¢ ____¢ ____¢ ____¢ in all

2.

50¢ ____¢ ____¢ ____¢ ____¢ ____¢ in all

3. Reasoning

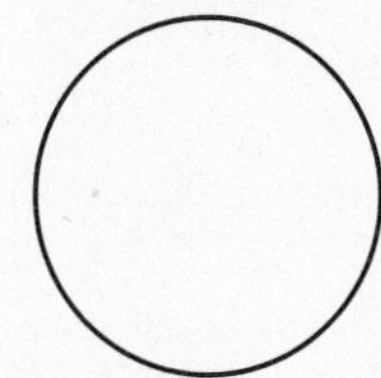

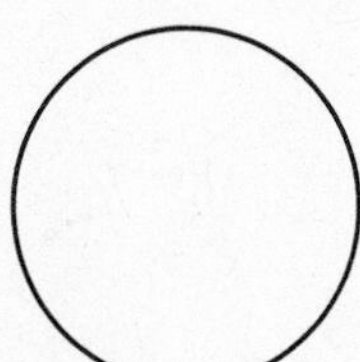

Materials: 2 quarters, 5 dimes, 5 nickels per child or pair

1. Have children use the coins to match the ones in the first group and arrange the coins in order from least to greatest. Then, have them count on to count the coins. Ask: ***How much in all?*** Explain that the coins are worth 50 cents, the same as a half-dollar.
2. Have children count on to find how much in all, starting with the half-dollar. Ask a child to explain how he or she counted.
3. Have children use the coins to find two coins with the same value as a half-dollar. Have them write the values of the coins in the circles.

Name ______________________

Half-Dollars (continued)

Write how much money in all.
Circle the group that is worth one half-dollar.

4.

_____ ¢

5.

_____ ¢

Count on to find how much in all.

6.

_____ ¢ _____ ¢ _____ ¢ _____ ¢ in all

7.

_____ ¢ _____ ¢ _____ ¢ _____ ¢ _____ ¢ _____ ¢ in all

Name ______________________________

Counting Sets of Coins

1.   

25¢ 50¢ 75¢ 80¢ 80¢ Total

2. 

25¢ ___¢ ___¢ ___¢ ___¢ ___¢ ___¢ Total

3. 

___¢ ___¢ ___¢ ___¢ ___¢ ___¢ ___¢ Total

Materials: 3 quarters, 3 dimes, 2 nickels, 2 pennies per child or pair

1. Have children count on and write the numbers. Have them write the total value.
2. Have children use the coins to match the ones in the picture. Have them arrange the coins from greatest to least. Then, have them count on, write the numbers, and write the total value.
3. Do the last problem, similarly.

Name ______________________________

Counting Sets of Coins (continued)

Do you have enough money to buy each item?
Count the money.
Circle **yes** or **no.**

4.

_____ ¢ Yes No

5.

_____ ¢ Yes No

6.

_____ ¢ Yes No

7.

_____ ¢ Yes No

Name ______________________

Comparing Sets of Coins

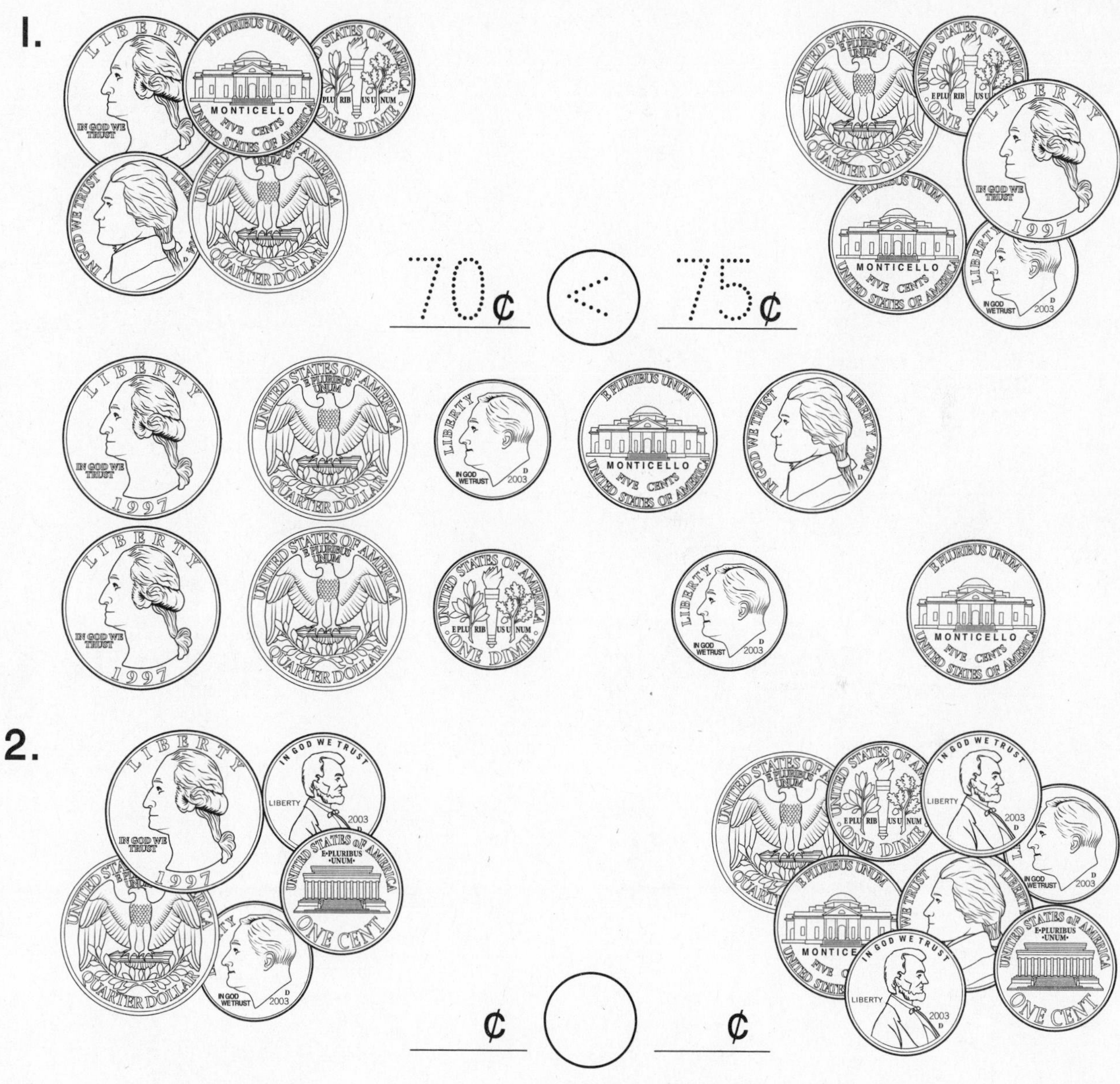

Materials: 3 quarters, 5 dimes, 3 nickels, and 3 pennies per child or pair.

1. Have children use the coins to match the ones in the first group. Have them arrange the coins, count on, and write the total value.
2. Have children line up the two groups of coins as shown. Have them cross out the first quarter in each group because they have the same value. Have them continue to cross out coins with the same value, 2 quarters, 2 dimes, and then 2 nickels and the dime. Since the second group of coins has a nickel left, it is greater than the first set. That means and the first set is less than the second. Have children write <.
3. Point out that 70 cents is less than 75 cents, since 70 is less than 75.
4. Repeat for the second group of coins. Tell children to not use coins from their first group.
5. Have children find the value of each set of coins in item 2 and compare.

Name ______________________________

Comparing Sets of Coins (continued)

Write the total amounts and compare them.
Write <, >, or =.

3.

48¢ 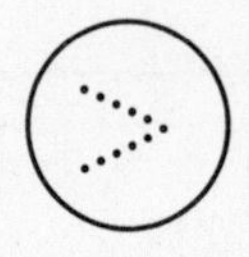 43¢

4.

_____ ¢ 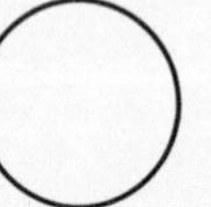 _____ ¢

_____ ¢ 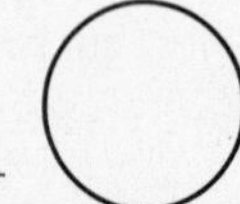 _____ ¢

Name ______________________________

Ways to Show the Same Amount

1.    

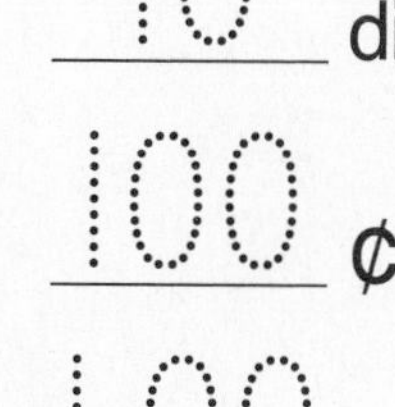

10 dimes

100 ¢

$1.00

2. 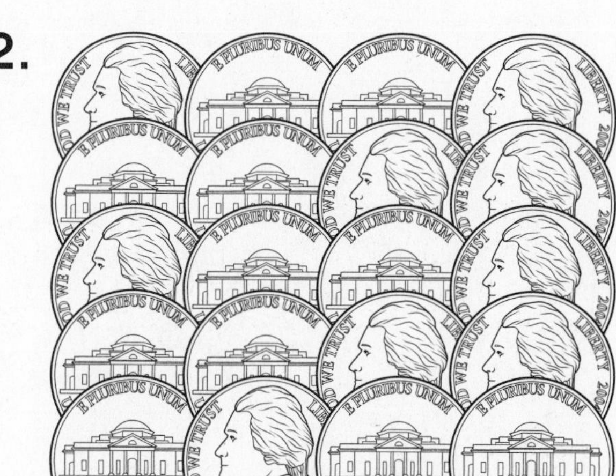

______ nickels

______ ¢

$___.___

3. 

______ quarters

______ ¢

$___.___

1. Ask: ***How many dimes?*** Have children write 10. Ask: ***What is the value of 10 dimes?*** Have children write 100 next to the cent sign.
2. Say: ***Ten dimes or 100 cents equal a dollar. You can use a dollar sign and a decimal point to write a dollar.*** Write $1.00 on the board or overhead. Have children write $1.00.
3. Do 20 nickels and 4 quarters similarly.

Name ______________________

Ways to Show the Same Amount (continued)

Write each amount in cents.
Then write the amount in dollars.

4. 

100 ¢

$1.00

5. 

_____ ¢

$ ___.___

6. 

_____ ¢

$ ___.___

7. 

_____ ¢

$ ___.___

Name ______________________

Dollars

1.

37 ¢

2.

______ ¢

$ ___ . ___

3.

______ ¢

$ ___ . ___

1. Have children find the value of the set of coins and write 37.
2. Ask: ***How much is a dollar worth?*** 100 cents ***So, how much is a dollar and 37 cents worth?*** Have children write 137 next to the cent sign.
3. Say: ***You can use a dollar sign and a decimal point to write dollars and cents.*** Write 137¢ = $1.37 on the board or overhead. Say: ***137 cents equals one dollar and 37 cents.*** Have children write $1.37.
4. Have children find and write the value of the other group of bills and coins.

Name ____________________

Dollars (continued)

Write each amount in cents. Then write the amount in dollars.

4.

145 ¢

$ 1.45

5.

_____ ¢

$ ___ . ___

6.

_____ ¢

$ ___ . ___

7. **Reasoning** You have this amount.
Do you have enough money?

Yes No

Name ______________________________

Fractions and Decimals

Materials crayons or markers

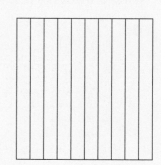

1. Color 7 of the equal parts in the square at the right.

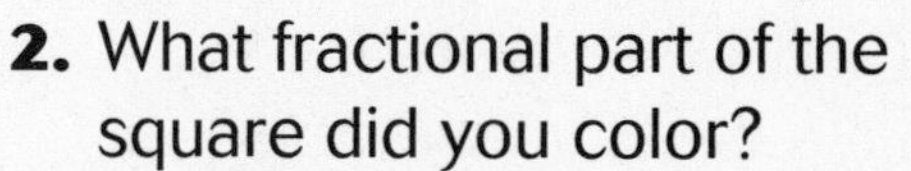

2. What fractional part of the square did you color? ________

The fraction $\frac{7}{10}$ can be written as a decimal.

3. How many tenths did you color? ______

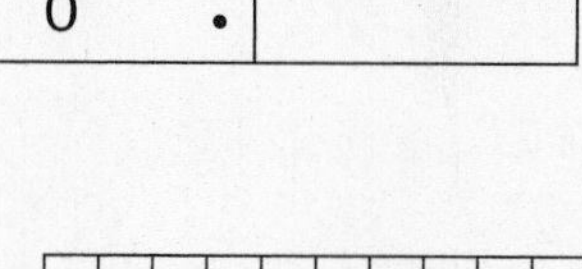

Ones	Tenths
0 .	

4. Write a 7 in the tenths place of the place-value chart at the right.

0.7 is read, "seven tenths." $\frac{7}{10} = 0.7$

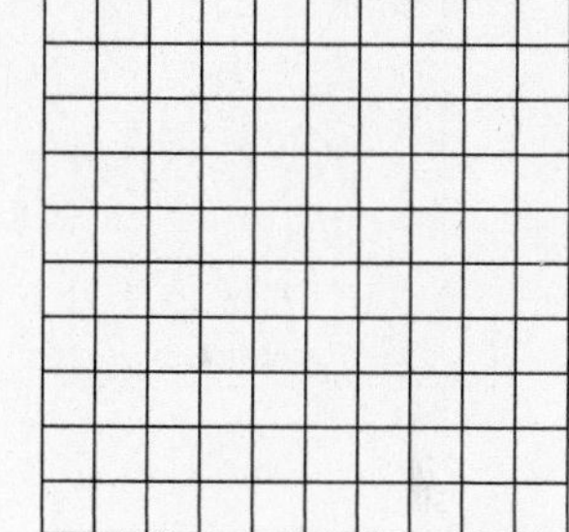

5. Color 31 of the equal parts in the square at the right.

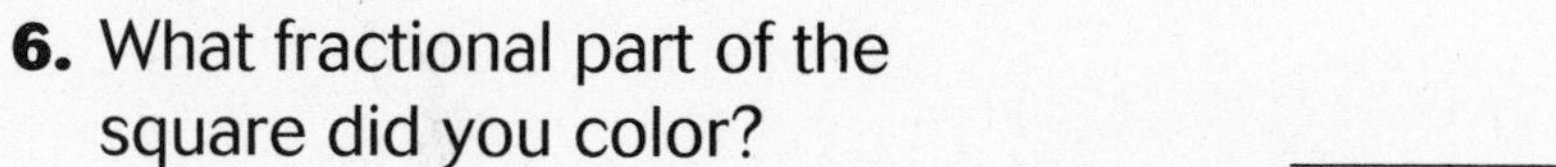

6. What fractional part of the square did you color? ________

The fraction $\frac{31}{100}$ can be written as a decimal.

7. How many hundredths did you color? ______

8. Write a 3 in the tenths place and a 1 in the hundredths place of the place-value chart at the right.

Ones	Tenths	Hundredths
0 .		

0.31 is read, "thirty-one hundredths." $\frac{31}{100} = 0.31$

9. Use the place-value chart at the right to write a decimal equal to $\frac{6}{100}$.

Ones	Tenths	Hundredths
0 .		

$\frac{6}{100} =$ ______

Name ____________________

Fractions and Decimals (continued)

Write a fraction and a decimal for each shaded part.

10. 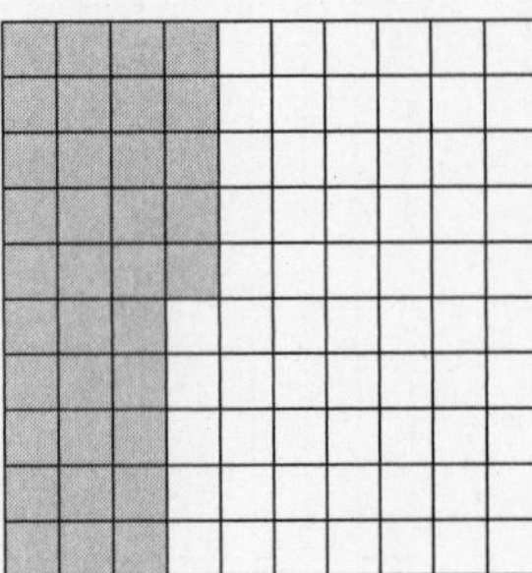

____

11. 

____

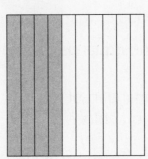

12. 

____

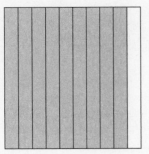

13. 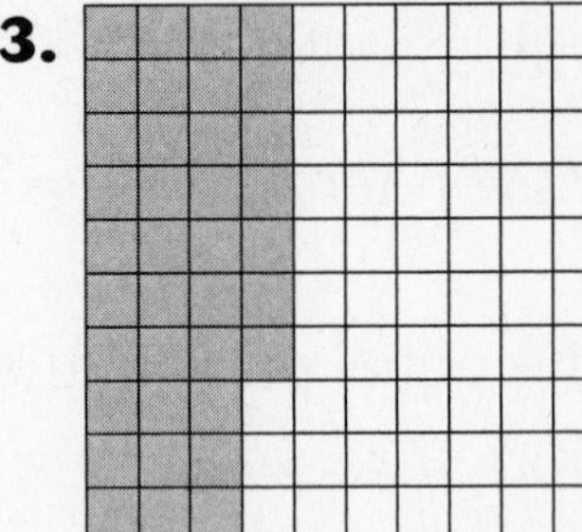

____

14. 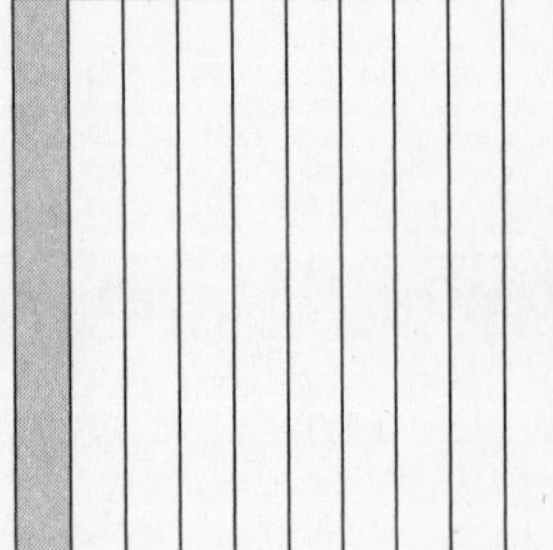

____

15. 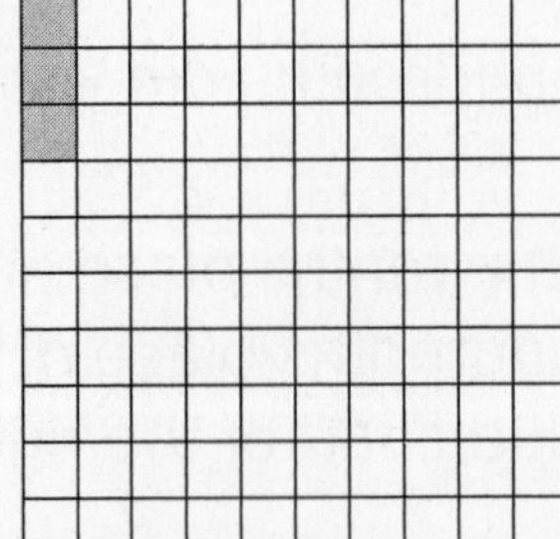

____

16. Reasoning A pan of lasagna was cut into 10 equal sections. A family ate 8 of the sections. Write a fraction and a decimal to represent the amount of lasagna the family ate. ____________________

Name ______________________________

Counting Money

Gary has a $1 bill, a quarter, 2 dimes, a nickel, and a penny.

When you count money, start with the bill or coin of greatest value. Then count on to find the total.

1. Count Gary's money.

$1.00 ________ $1.35 ________ ________ ________

2. How much money does Gary have? ________

3. Write $1.51 in words. one dollar and ____________ cents

4. Ty has a $1 bill, a half-dollar, 2 quarters, and 3 dimes. Count Ty's money.

$1.00 ________ ________ ________ $2.10 ________ ________

5. How much money does Ty have? ________

6. Who had more money, Gary or Ty? ________

Name ______________________________

Counting Money (continued)

Write the total value in dollars and cents.

7.

______

8. 1 five-dollar bill, 3 quarters, 1 nickel, 2 pennies

______

9. 1 one-dollar bill, 1 half-dollar, 4 nickels, 8 pennies

______

10. 1 one-dollar bill, 2 quarters, 4 dimes, 3 nickels, 1 penny

______

11. 1 five-dollar bill, 1 one-dollar bill, 1 quarter, 4 dimes, 3 nickels

______

Compare the amounts. Write <, >, or =.

12. \$1.17 ◯ 4 quarters, 2 dimes

13. \$0.49 ◯ 4 dimes, 1 nickel

14. 2 quarters, 6 dimes ◯ \$1.10

15. 3 half-dollars, 3 nickels ◯ \$1.70

16. Reasoning Anita and Ted both have \$1.49, but each have different coins. What coins could each have?

Name ______________________________

Making Change

Ivan bought a plastic dinosaur for $3.68. He paid with a $5 bill. Answer 1 to 10 to find how much change Ivan received.

To make change, start with coins that will make it easier to skip count. Count up to the amount you paid.

1. Start with $3.68. Count on with pennies until you get to an amount that ends in 0 or 5.

   $3.68, $3.69, ________

2. How many pennies did you count? ________
3. How much are 2 pennies worth? $0.________ ________
4. Count on from $3.70 with dimes.

   $3.70, ________, ________, ________

5. How many dimes did you count? ________
6. How much is 3 dimes and 2 pennies worth? $0.________ ________
7. Count on from $4.00 with one-dollar bills until you get to the $5.00 Ivan paid.

   $4.00, ________

8. How many dollar bills did you count? ________
9. How much is 1 dollar bill, 3 dimes and 2 pennies worth? $________. ________ ________

Name ___________________________________

Making Change (continued)

10. How much change did Ivan receive? ________

List the coins and bills you would use to make change.
Then write the change in dollars and cents.

11. Cost: $1.40
Amount paid: $2.00

____

____

12. Cost: $3.17
Amount paid: $4.00

____

____

13. Cost: $0.76
Amount paid: $5.00

____

____

14. Cost: $1.33
Amount paid: $5.00

____

____

____

15. Reasoning Beverly bought a gallon of juice for $2.69.
She used three $1 bills. Give two ways to show the change.
Circle the one that uses the fewest coins.

Name ______________________________

Using Money to Understand Decimals

1. How many dimes are equal to one dollar? ________

2. What fraction of a dollar is each dime? ________

3. What decimal shows what part of a dollar each dime is? ______

4. How many pennies are equal to one dollar? ________

5. What fraction of a dollar is each penny? ________

6. What decimal shows what part of a dollar each penny is? ________

7. Show $1.32 in the place-value chart at the right.

dollars (ones		dimes (tenths)	pennies (hundredths)
	.		

8. $1.32 = _____ dollar + 3 dimes

+ _____ pennies

1.32 = _____ one + _____ tenths + 2 hundredths

9. $1.32 = _____ dollar + 32 pennies

1.32 = _____ one + _____ hundredths

Reading decimals and money are very similar.
$1.32 is read "one dollar and thirty-two cents."
1.32 is read "one and thirty-two hundredths."

10. Show two dollars and sixty four cents in the chart at the right.

dollars (ones		dimes (tenths)	pennies (hundredths)
	.		

11. Write two and sixty-four hundredths with a decimal point. ________

Name ______________________________

Using Money to Understand Decimals (continued)

Write the values for the money amounts and the decimal numbers.

12. \$4.62 = _____ dollars + _____ dimes + _____ pennies

4.62 = _____ ones + _____ tenths + _____ hundredths

13. \$7.31 = _____ dollars + _____ dimes + _____ penny

7.31 = _____ ones + _____ tenths + _____ hundredth

14. \$1.04 = _____ dollar + _____ dimes + _____ pennies

1.04 = _____ one + _____ tenths + _____ hundredths

15. \$2.87 = _____ dollars + _____ pennies

2.87 = _____ ones + _____ hundredths

16. \$9.16 = _____ dollars + _____ pennies

9.16 = _____ ones + _____ hundredths

17. \$7.39 = _____ dollars + _____ pennies

7.39 = _____ ones + _____ hundredths

18. Write three and ninety-one hundredths with a decimal point. __________

19. Write seven and twenty-six hundredths with a decimal point. __________

20. Lisabeth wants to buy school supplies for \$5.25. How can she pay for them using only dollars, dimes, and pennies?

____

21. Reasoning Explain why the 2 in \$6.27 represents tenths of a dollar.

Name ______________________________

Patterns

1.

2.

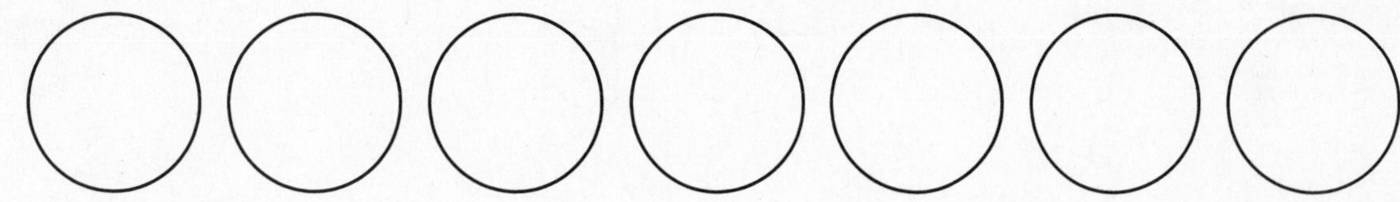

3.

4.

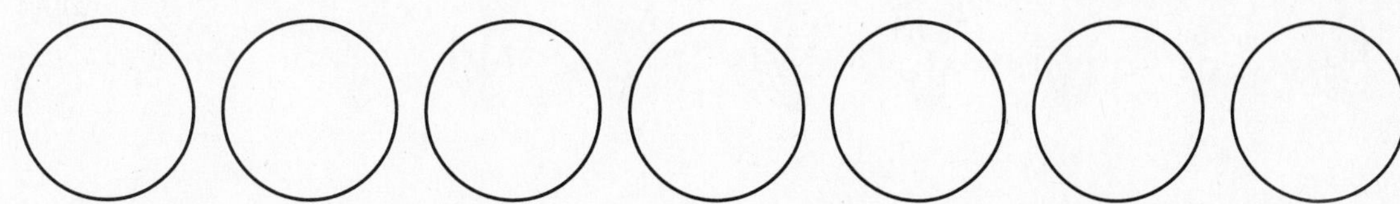

Materials: Crayons or markers

1. Have a child describe the pattern. The child could say cat, dog, dog, cat, dog, dog. Ask: ***What comes next?*** Have children draw a line from the last dog to the cat.
2. Ask: ***What comes next in this similar sound pattern: meow, bark, bark, meow, bark, bark?*** Children should say meow.
3. Have children color the first circle red, the second circle blue, the third circle blue, and the fourth circle red. Ask: ***If this color pattern is similar to the cats and dogs pattern, what color comes next?*** Have children color the next circle blue. Have children finish the pattern.
4. Repeat with the next pattern. Use sounds like slosh, snap, swish. Then have children color the circles red, blue, yellow, and red. Have them finish the pattern.

Name ______________________________

Patterns (continued)

Draw a line to the picture that comes next in the pattern. Then color the circles to match the pattern.

5.

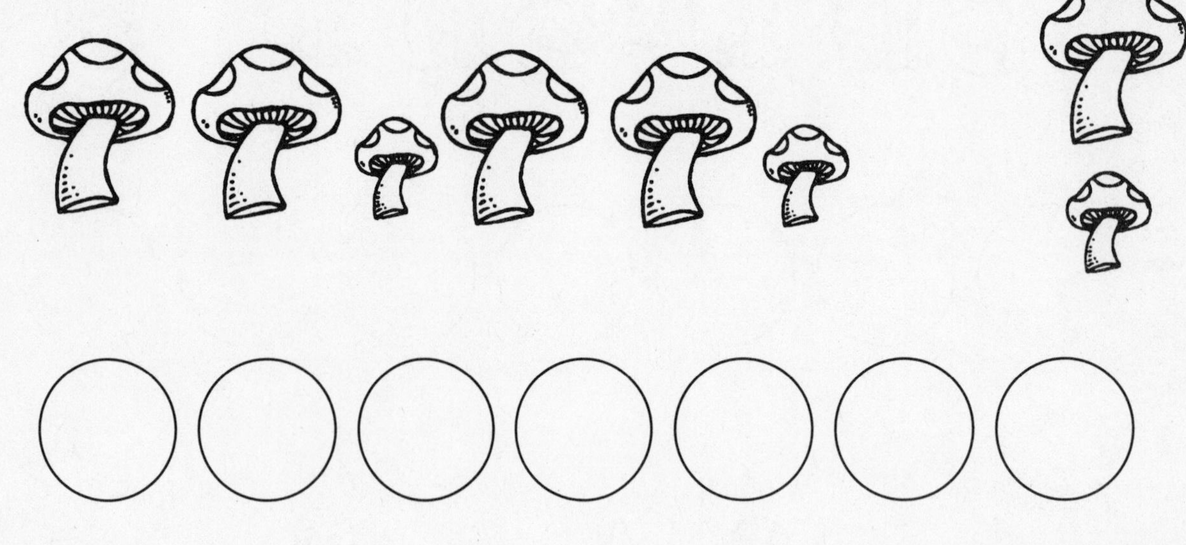

6.

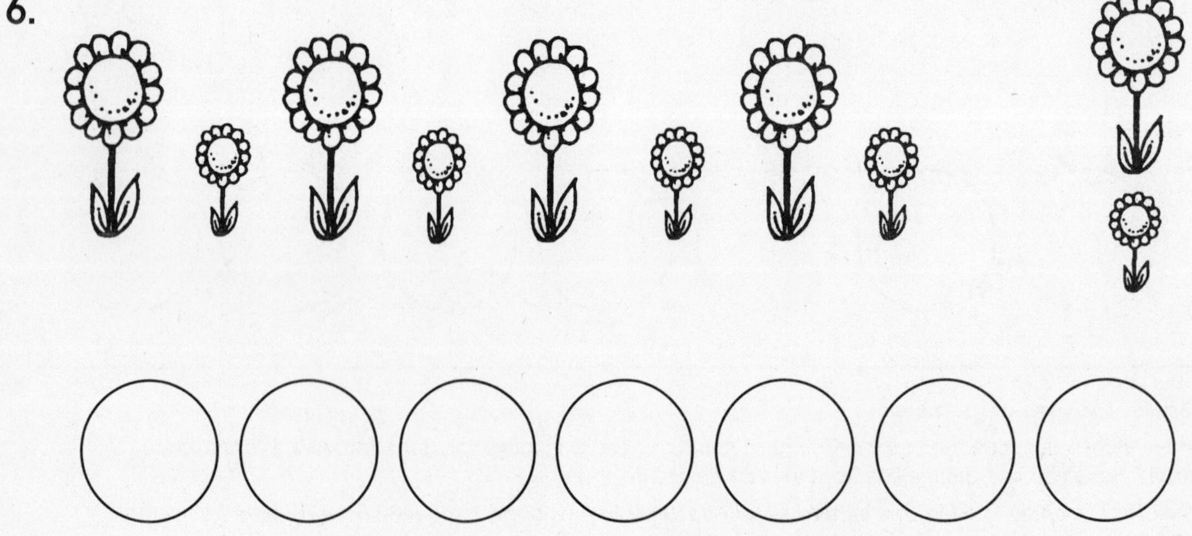

Name ______________________________

Describing Patterns

1.

2.

3.

Materials: Crayons or markers, 10 snap cubes per child, 4 of one color, 4 of another color, and 2 of a third color

1. Ask a child to describe the pattern in the acorns. The pattern is big, little, little, big, little, little.
2. Have children make a train of 3 snap cubes where the first is one color and the next two are another color. Have them make two more trains like this, using the same colors, so they have 3 in all. Have them put the three trains together. Ask: ***Does the pattern of the snap cubes match the pattern of the acorns?*** Yes.
3. Have children color the snap cubes to match the train they created. Ask: ***What part of the snap cube pattern repeats?*** Have children circle the part that repeats. Then have them circle the part of the acorn pattern that repeats.
4. Have children do the same for the other two patterns. Encourage them to make trains of snap cubes with the repeating part before putting the trains together.

Name ______________________________

Describing Patterns (continued)

Circle the part that repeats.

4.

5.

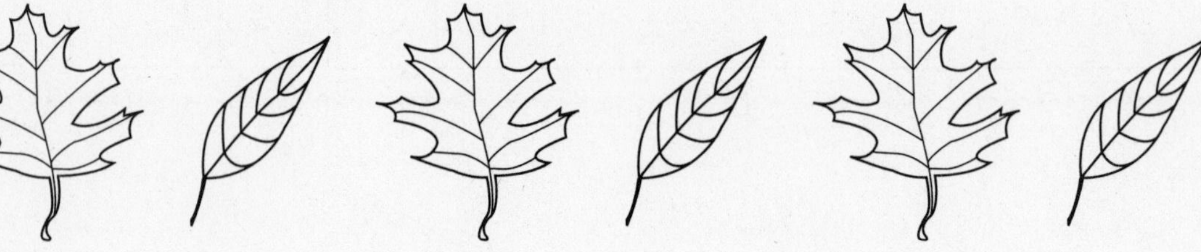

6.

7. Reasoning

Name ______________________________

Using Patterns to Predict

1.

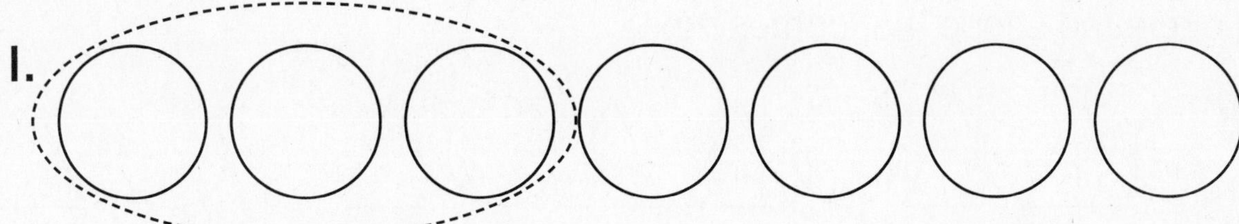

2.

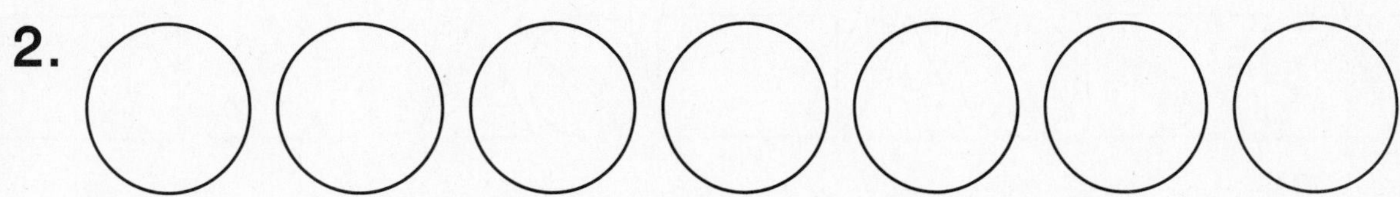

3.

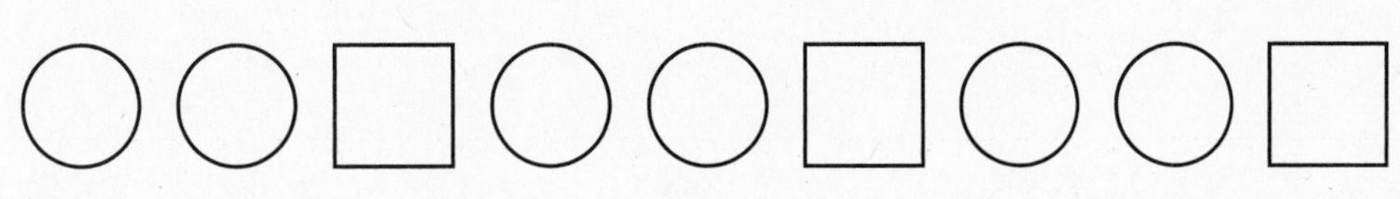

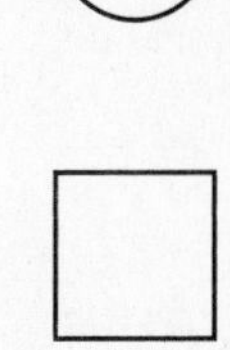

4.

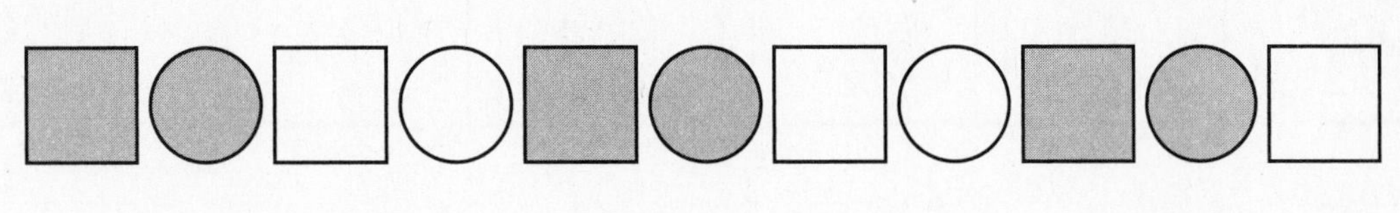

Materials: Crayons or markers

1. Have children color the first circle red, the next two blue, the fourth one red, and then the next two blue. Ask: ***What part of the pattern repeats?*** Have children ring the first 3 circles. Ask: ***If the pattern continued, what color would be next?*** Have children color the last circle red.
2. In item 2 have children color the circles red, blue, yellow, red, blue, yellow. Have them ring the part that repeats and color the last circle to show what comes next.
3. In item 3 have children ring the part of the circle and square pattern that repeats and then ring what comes next.
4. Do the last pattern similarly.

Using Patterns to Predict (continued)

Circle the part that repeats.
Then circle the shape that comes next.

5.  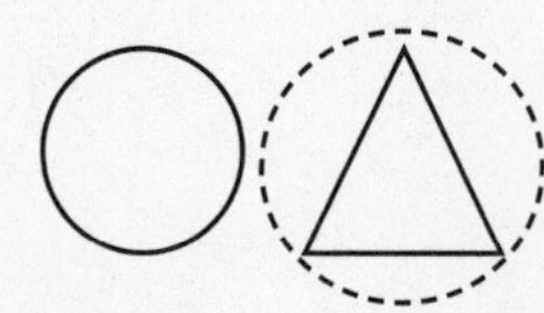

6. 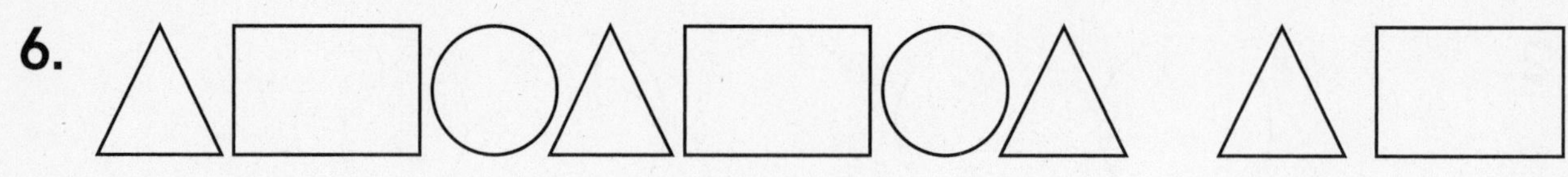

7. 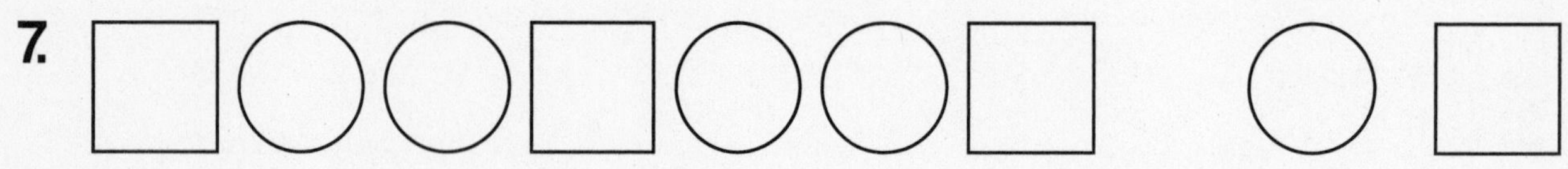

8.  

9. 

10. 

11. **Reasoning** Draw what comes next in the pattern.

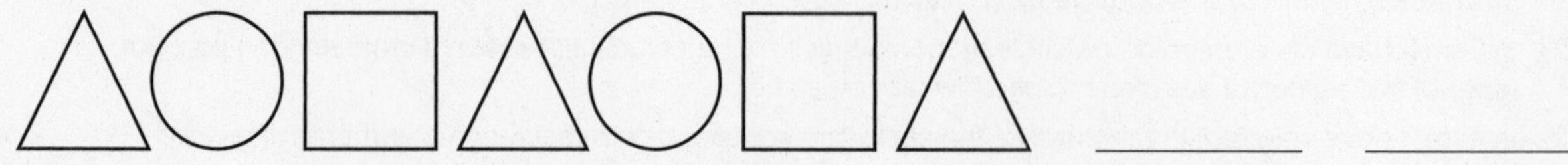 ________ ________

Name ______________________________

Extending Shape Patterns

Next

1. 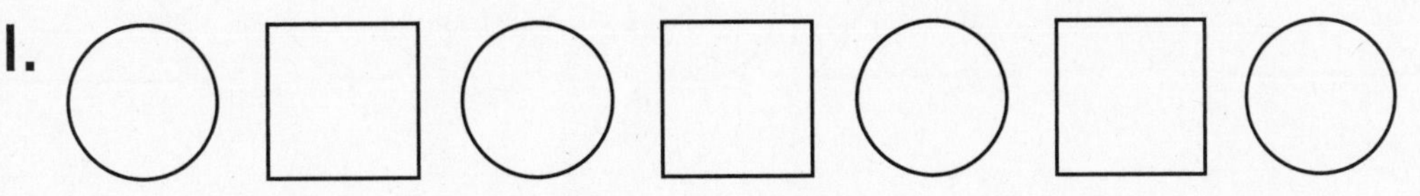 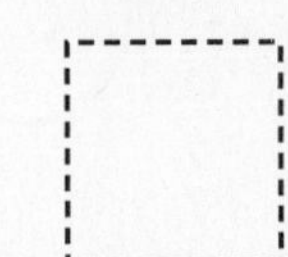

2. 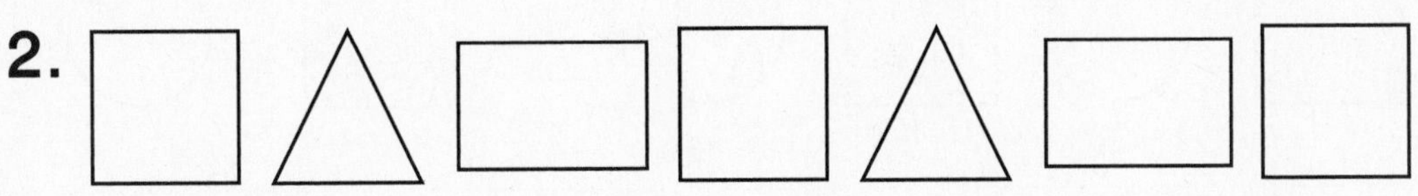

3. 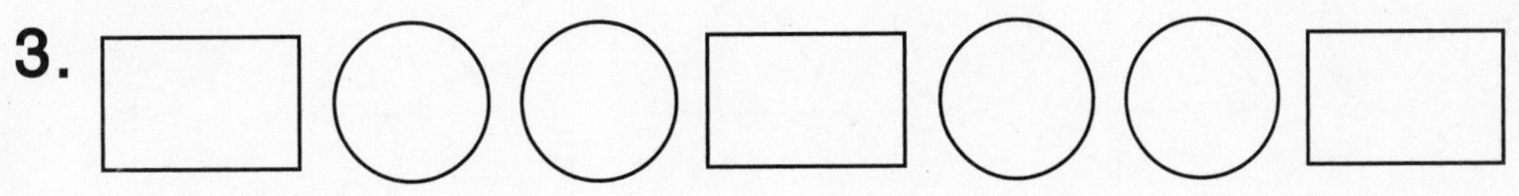

4. 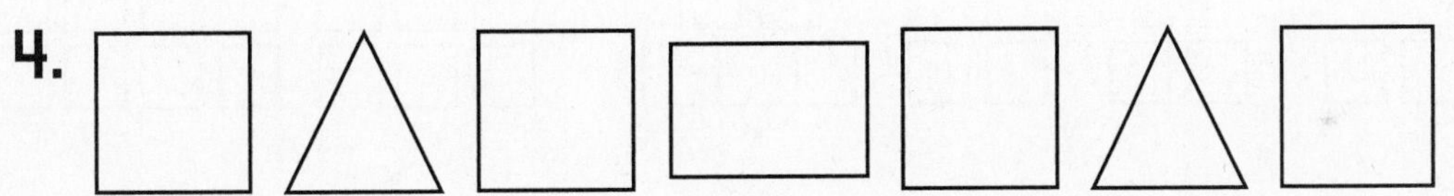

5.

Materials: Crayons or markers

1. Have children color the circles red and the squares yellow. Ask a child to describe the color pattern. The child should say red, yellow, red, yellow, red, yellow, red.
2. Ask another child to describe the shape pattern. The child should say circle, square, circle, square, circle, square, circle. Ask: ***What shape comes next?*** Have children draw a square under Next. If children have trouble deciding which shape comes next, ask which color would come next. If children say yellow, ask which shapes were yellow.
3. For each item have children color each shape a different color and use the color pattern to decide which shape comes next, if necessary. Have them draw the shape that comes next for each pattern.
4. Have children draw their own shape pattern on the rug.

Name ______________________

Extending Shape Patterns (continued)

Circle the shape that comes next.

6. 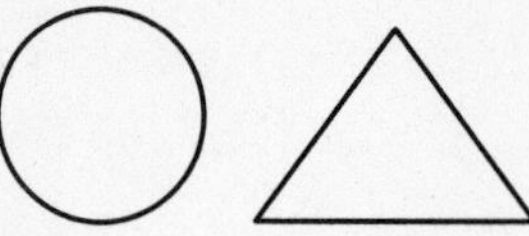 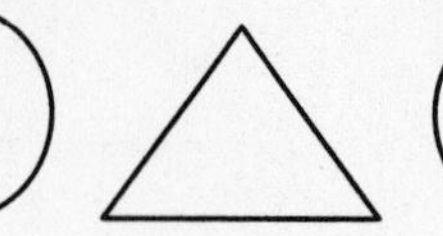 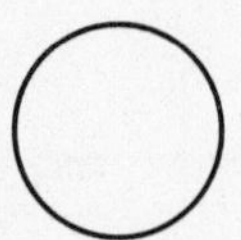 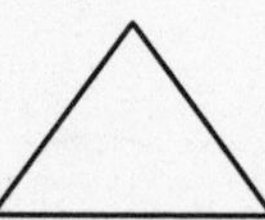

7.   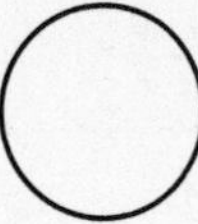  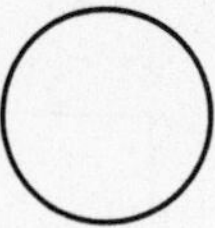  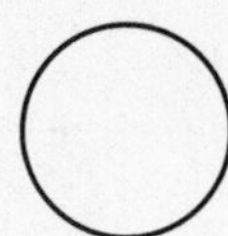

8. 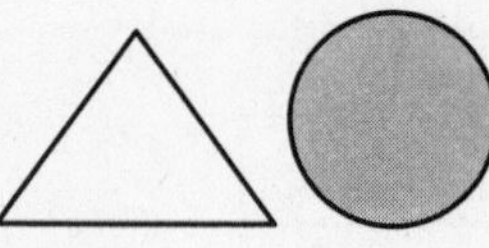 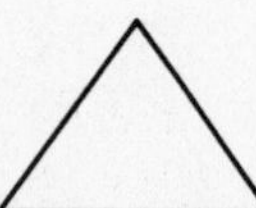 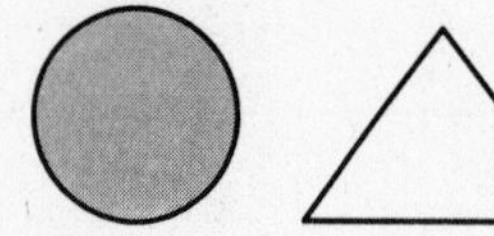 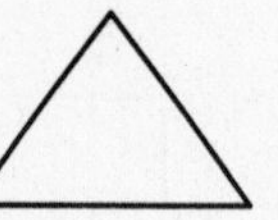 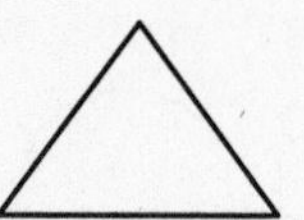 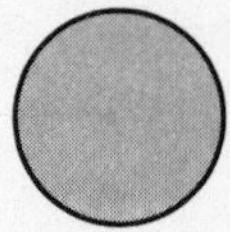

9.   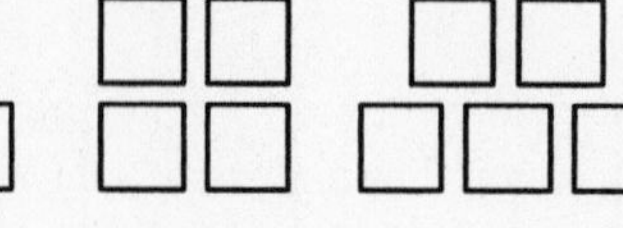 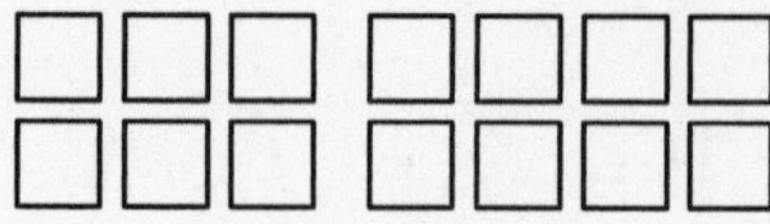

Reasoning Draw the missing shapes.

10.  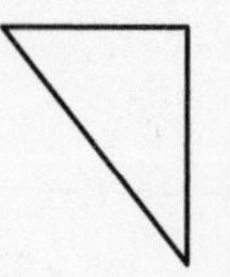 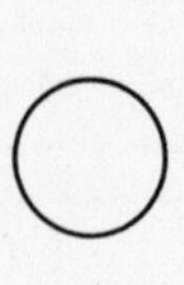 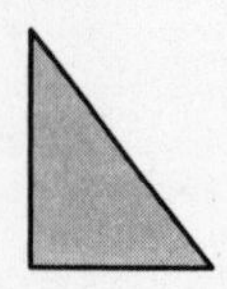 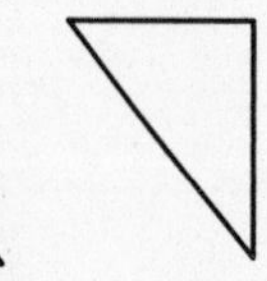 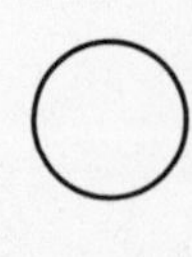 ______ 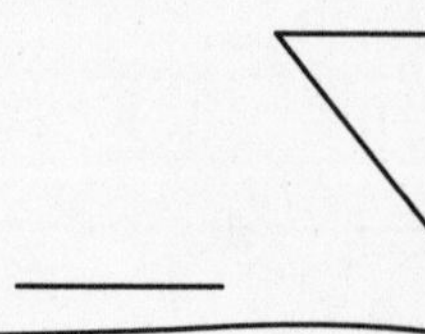

11. 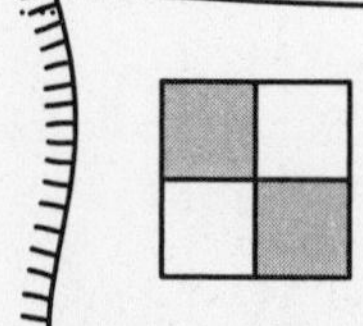 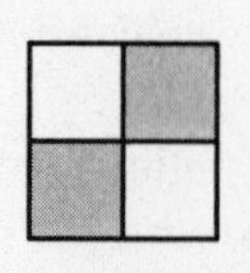 ______  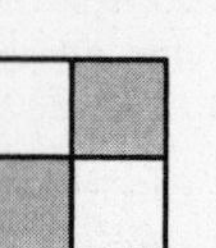 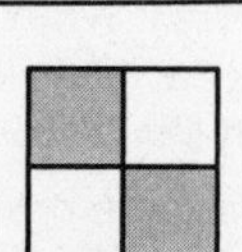 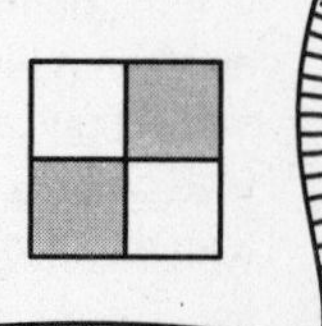

Name ______________________________

Translating Patterns

1.

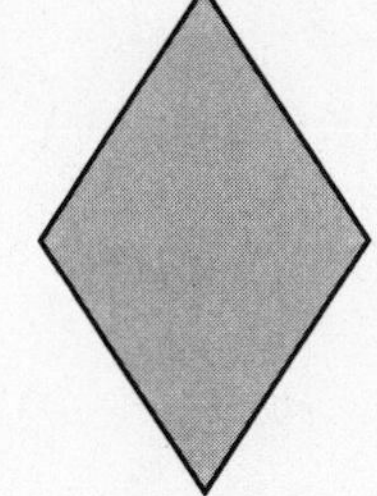
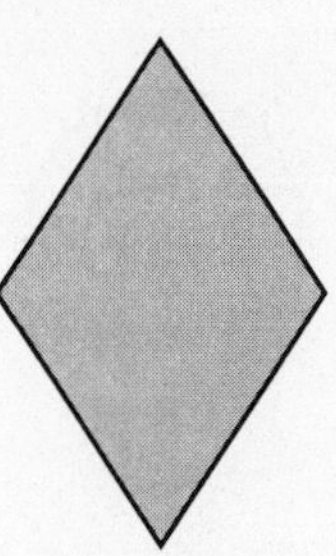
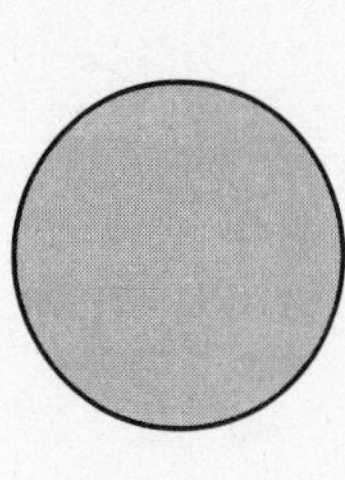
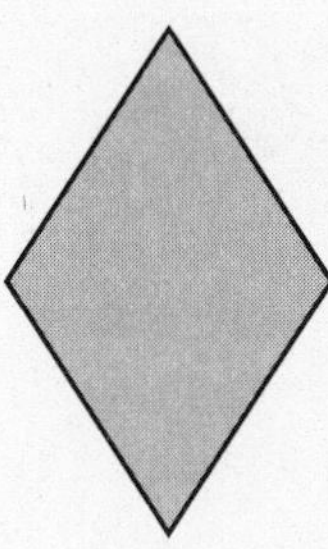

_______ _______ _______ _______ _______

2. A B B A B

3. A B A C A

Materials: Pattern blocks or cut out shapes, 4 of one shape, 4 of another shape, and 2 of a third shape per child or pair.

1. Have children describe the pattern and name the part that repeats. Have them write an A below each diamond and a B below each circle. Ask: ***Do the letters have the same pattern as the shapes?*** Help children see that the way the patterns repeat are essentially the same.
2. Have children use the pattern blocks or cut out shapes to create a pattern like the pattern of letters. Have them trace the shapes to show the pattern.
3. Do the other problem similarly. Make sure children use 3 shapes when there are 3 letters.

Name ______________________________

Translating Patterns (continued)

Make the same pattern using A, B, and C.

4.

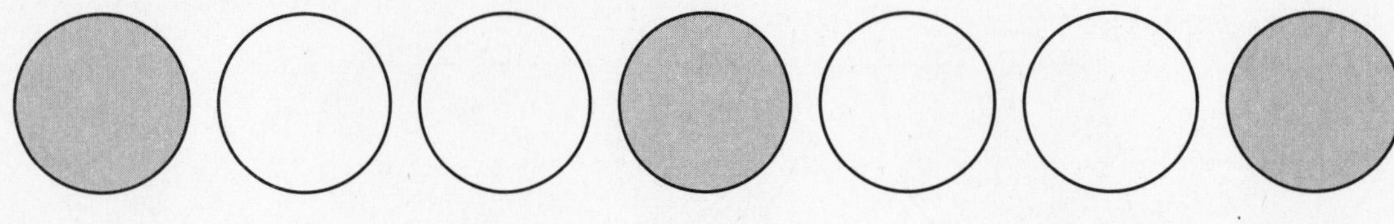

____ ____ ____ ____ ____ ____ ____

5.

____ ____ ____ ____ ____ ____ ____

Color to match the pattern.

6. A A B A A B A

7. A B B B A B B

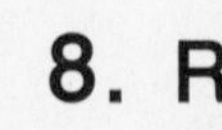

8. **Reasoning** Make your own shape pattern. Write a letter pattern to match it.

Name ______________________________

Find a Rule

1.

Teddy Bears	Bears and Dolls
2	5
3	6
5	8
6	
8	
9	

Rule: +3

2.

Tacos	Tacos Left
3	1
4	2
6	4
9	
12	
14	

Rule: ______

Materials: Two-color counters, 20 per child or pair

1. Have children show 2 counters for the teddy bears. Have them add or subtract counters until they get to 5. Ask: ***Did you add or subtract?*** Add ***How much did you add or subtract?*** 3
2. Have children show 3 red counters for the teddy bears in the second row. Have them add 3 yellow counters. Ask: ***Does the same rule, add 3, work to get 6 from 3?***
3. Have children see if the rule works to get 8 from 5. Then have them write the rule.
4. Have children use the rule to complete the table.
5. Have children show 3 counters for the tacos. Have them add or subtract counters until they get to 1. Ask if they added or subtracted and how much.
6. Have children see if the rule works for the next two rows. Then have them write the rule and use it to complete the table.

Name ____________________

Find a Rule (continued)

Write a rule and complete each table.

3.

In	Out
6	11
7	12
9	14
10	
12	
15	

Rule: +5

4.

In	Out
9	1
10	2
12	4
14	
15	
17	

Rule: ______

5.

In	Out
6	2
8	4
9	5
10	
12	
14	

Rule: ______

6.

In	Out
2	12
4	14
4	15
6	
8	
10	

Rule: ______

Name ______________________________

Repeating Patterns

Materials pattern blocks or shapes cut out of colored paper (10 orange squares, 10 green triangles, 10 red trapezoids) for each pair of students; 24 index cards (eight labeled 2, eight labeled 3, and eight labeled 4) for each pair of students

Look at the pattern of shapes.

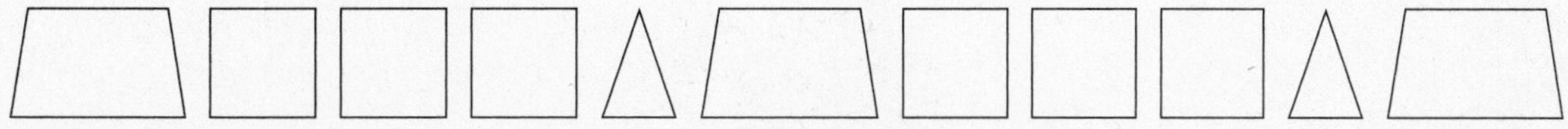

1. Work with your partner to show the pattern. What is the next shape? ____________

2. Continue the pattern. What is the 14th shape? ____________

3. What is the 16th shape? ____________

4. Work with your partner and use the shapes to make a new pattern. Draw the pattern below. Draw the next four shapes.

Look at the pattern of numbers.

3	3	2	4	3	3	2	4	3

5. Work with your partner to show the pattern. What is the next number? ____________

6. Continue the pattern. What is the 12th number? ____________

7. What is the 15th number? ____________

8. Work with your partner and use the numbers to make a new pattern. Write the pattern below. Write the next four numbers.

Name ______________________________

Repeating Patterns (continued)

Draw the next three shapes to continue each pattern.

9.  _____ _____ _____

10.  _____ _____ _____

11. ☺ ⇧ ☺ ⇩ ☺ ⇧ ☺ ⇩ ☺ ⇧ _____ _____ _____

Write the next three numbers to continue each pattern.

12. 1, 4, 6, 7, 1, 4, 6, 7, 1, 4, _____, _____, _____

13. 8, 8, 9, 8, 8, 9, 8, 8, 9, 8, _____, _____, _____

14. 3, 2, 0, 0, 3, 2, 0, 0, 3, 2, 0, _____, _____, _____

15. 4, 4, 6, 6, 8, 8, 4, 4, 6, 6, 8, 8, 4, _____, _____, _____

16. Create a pattern using all the shapes shown below.

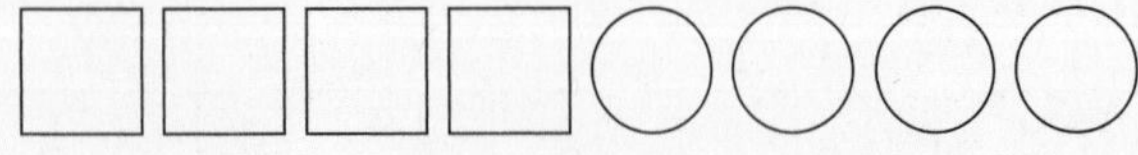

_____ _____ _____ _____ _____ _____ _____ _____

17. Create a pattern using all the letters shown below.

T T T L L W W L W

Name ______________________________

Number Patterns

Find the next three numbers in the pattern 1, 3, 5, 7, 9, by answering 1 to 5.

1. Plot 1, 3, 5, 7, and 9 on the number line. Then continue to draw arrows from 3 to 5, from 5 to 7, and from 7 to 9.

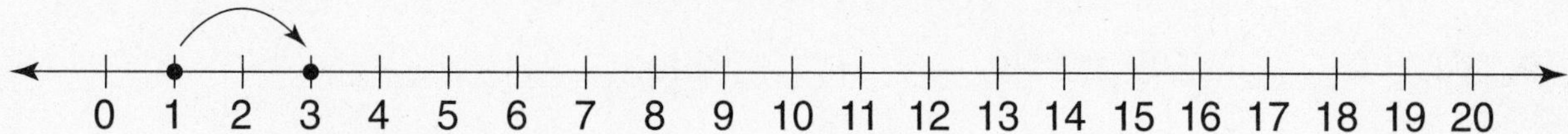

2. How many spaces are between each number plotted on the number line? ______________

3. Do you add or subtract the number of spaces to get to the next number? ______________

4. What is the rule for this pattern? ______________

5. What are the next three numbers in the pattern 1, 3, 5, 7, 9? ______, ______, ______

6. Draw arrows on the number line to find the next two numbers in the following pattern.

26, 22, 18, 14, ______, ______

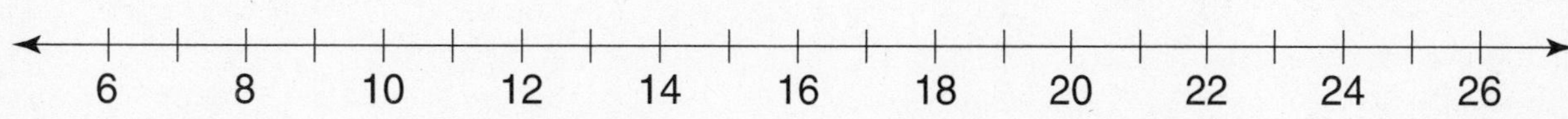

7. What is the rule for this pattern? ______________

Name ______________________________

Number Patterns (continued)

Find the missing numbers, and write the rule for the pattern.

8. 32, 34, 36, 38, _____, _____, _____ Rule: ______________

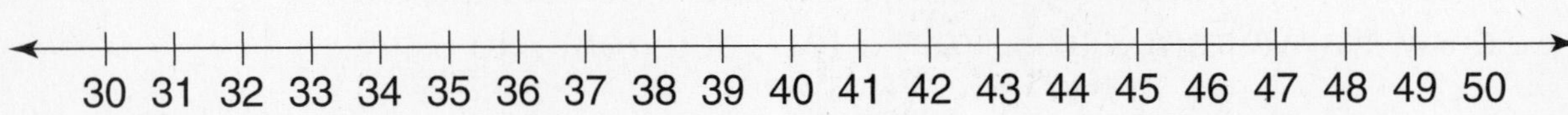

9. 34, 31, _____, 25, 22, _____, _____ Rule: ______________

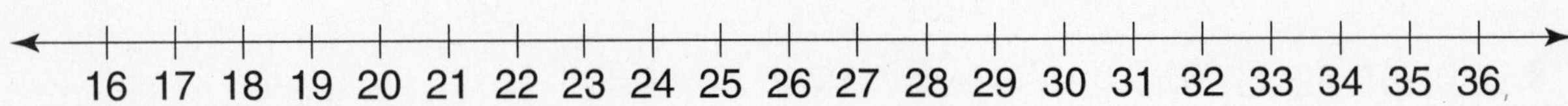

Complete the pattern. Write the rule.

10. 3, 6, 9, 12, _____, _____, _____ Rule: ______________

11. 100, 90, 80, 70, _____, _____, _____ Rule: ______________

12. 4, 9, _____, 19, 24, _____, _____ Rule: ______________

13. 36, _____, _____, 18, 12, 6, _____ Rule: ______________

14. 24, 34, 44, 54, _____, _____, _____ Rule: ______________

15. Reasoning How can you tell an addition pattern from a subtraction pattern?

16. The rule for a pattern is *Add 10*. The pattern starts at 55. Write the next three numbers. ______________

17. Create a rule for a pattern. Then write the first five numbers of the pattern. ______________

Name ______________________________

Input/Output Tables

1. There are 5 pennies in a nickel. Draw two sets of 5 pennies next to the row with 2 nickels, in the table below.

Nickels	Pennies
1	5
2	
3	
4	
5	
7	
8	

2. How many pennies equal 2 nickels? Write your answer in the table.

3. Complete the table. Draw pennies, if necessary.

4. What is the rule for the table? ______________

5. Reasoning How can you find the number of pennies in 9 nickels?

6. How many pennies are in 9 nickels? ______________

7. How many pennies are in 10 nickels? ______________

Name ___________________________

Input/Output Tables (continued)

Complete the table. Write the rule.

8.

Number of Ants	Number of Legs
1	6
2	12
3	
4	24
5	30

Rule: ________________

9.

Regular Price	Sale Price
$5	$3
$7	$5
$8	$6
$12	$10
	$15

Rule: ________________

10.

My Age	My Brother's Age
9	12
	13
12	15
15	
20	23

Rule: ________________

11.

Number of Packages	Number of Pencils
1	8
3	24
	40
6	
8	64

Rule: ________________

12.

Loaves of Bread	2	4	5		10
Number of Eggs Used	8		20	28	40

Rule: ________________

13.

Total Weight of Suitcase and Contents in Pounds	5	7	9		14
Content of Suitcase in Pounds	3		7	9	12

Rule: ________________

Name ______________________________

Geometric Growth Patterns

Franco is making quilted wall hangings. He puts 5 squares in each row.

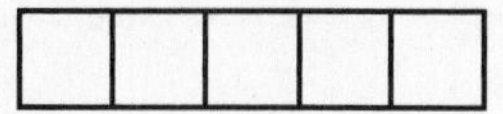

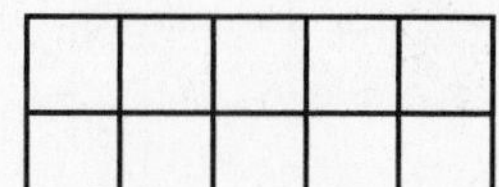

1 row 2 rows 3 rows

1. How many squares are in 2 rows? _____
Write the number in the table below.

Number of Rows	1	2	3	4	5
Number of Squares	5				

2. How many squares are in 3 rows? _____
Write the number in the table above.

3. Draw a wall hanging with 4 rows in the grid on the right.

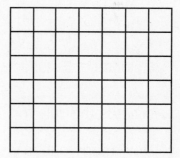

4. How many squares are in 4 rows? _____
Write the number in the table above.

5. How many squares are in 5 rows? _____
Write the number in the table above.

6. What is the rule for the table?

____

7. Reasoning How could you find the number of squares Franco needs for 7 rows?

____

8. How many squares will be in 7 rows? _____

Name ______________________________

Geometric Growth Patterns (continued)

Complete the table, and find the rule.

9. Each patch contains nine small squares.

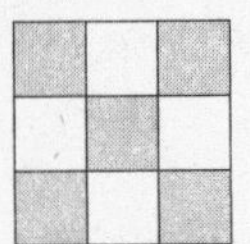
1 patch

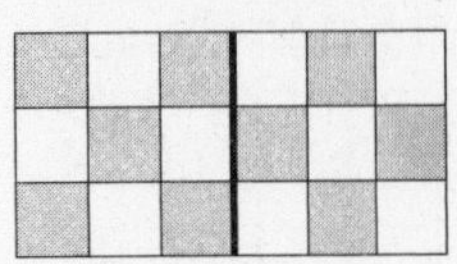
2 patches

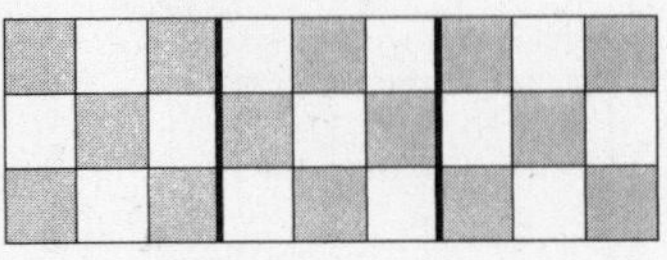
3 patches

Number of Patches	1	2	3	4	5
Number of Small Squares	9				

10. What is the rule for the table? ________________

11. How many small squares would 8 patches have? ______

12. Jocelyn is making towers out of cubes.

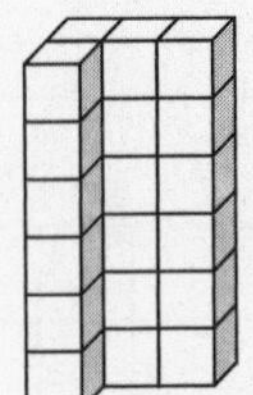
6 stories

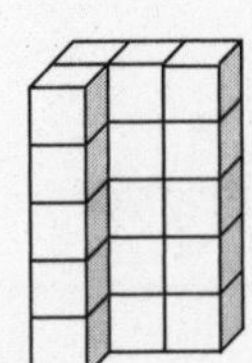
5 stories

4 stories

Number of Stories	6	5	4	3	2
Number of Cubes	24	20	16		

13. What is the rule for the table? ________________

14. How many cubes would a 10-story tower have? ______

15. Create your own geometric pattern below and complete the table.

Number of					
Number of					

Name ______________________________

Translating Words to Expressions

Materials counters, 12 per student

Show each word phrase with counters. Draw a picture of your counters. Then, write a number expression for each word phrase.

	Word Phrase	Picture of your Counters	Number Expression
1.	15 pennies separated into 3 equal groups	O O O O O O O O O O O O O O O	$15 \div 3$
2.	the total of 8 pennies and 4 pennies		
3.	4 times as many as 3 pennies		
4.	give away 6 of 10 pennies		
5.	6 divided into groups with 2 in each		

Name ______________________________

Translating Words to Expressions (continued)

Write a number expression for each word phrase.

6. twice as many as 8 yards

____

7. 16 rings shared equally by 4 boys

____

8. 21 separated into 7 equal groups

____

9. the total of 14 boys and 15 girls

____

10. 16 fewer than 20

____

11. 3 times as far as 8 miles

____

12. 4 hours shorter than 6 hours

____

13. the total of 6, 3, and 8

____

14. 8 toys put into 2 equal groups

____

15. 6 more than 7 apples

____

16. 5 fewer than 12 eggs

____

17. 3 times as many as 9 carrots

____

18. Reasoning Can you have 7 fewer than 5 dogs?

19. Reasoning Socorra reads the phrase *18 decreased by 9* and writes the expression 9 − 18. Do you agree with Socorra's expression? Explain.

Name ______________________________

Counting by Hundreds

1. 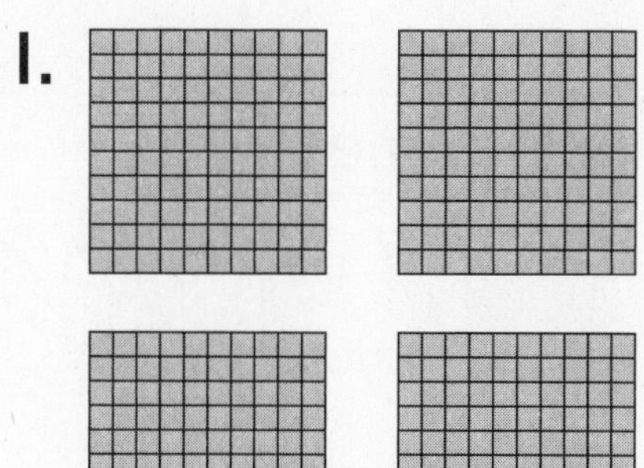

hundreds	tens	ones
4	0	0

400

2. 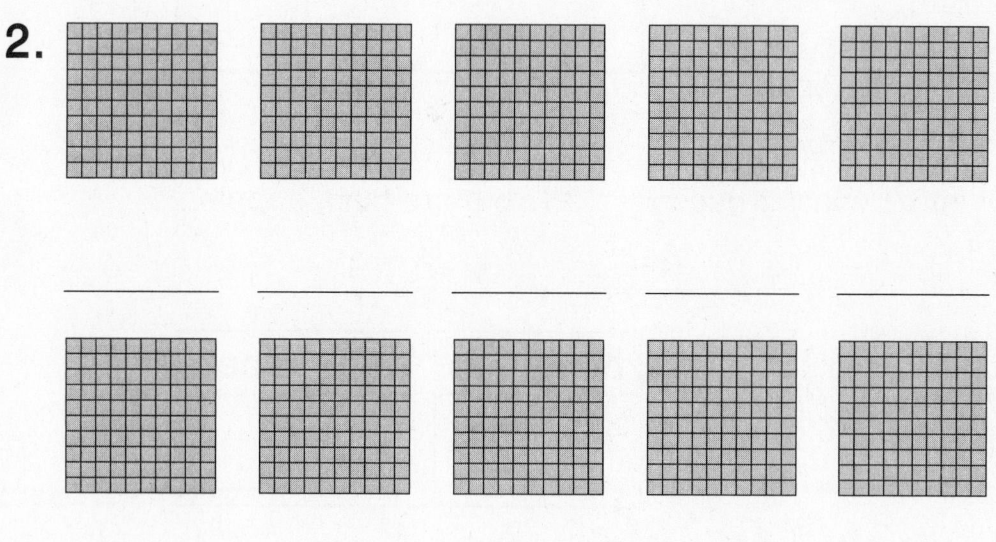

1. Ask: ***How many hundreds?*** Have children write 4 in the hundreds column of the place value chart. ***How many tens are left?*** Have children write 0 in the tens column of the place value chart. ***How many ones are left?*** Have children write 0 in the ones column of the place value chart. Say: ***This is 400.*** Write 400 on the board. Have children write 400.
2. For item 2 count the groups of 100 out loud, altogether as a class.
3. Have children say the numbers again, to themselves, and write the numbers.

Name ______________________

Counting by Hundreds (continued)

Count by hundreds. Write the numbers.

3. 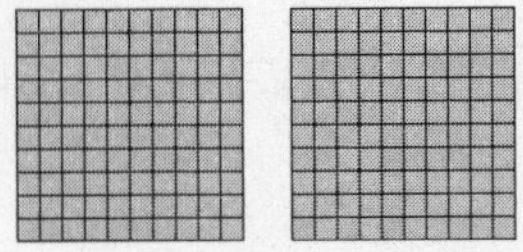

hundreds	tens	ones
2	0	0

200

4. 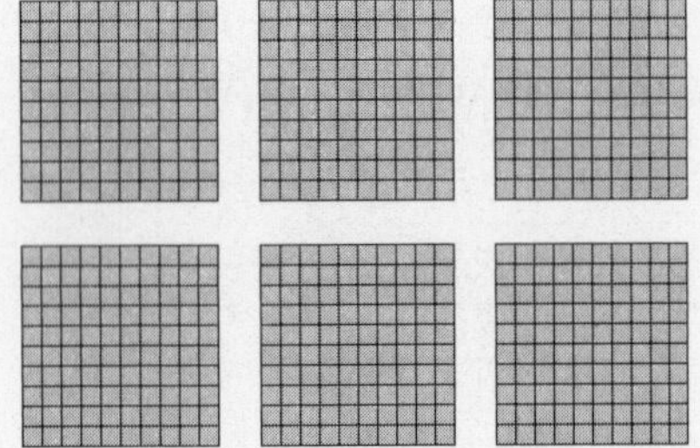

hundreds	tens	ones

______

5. 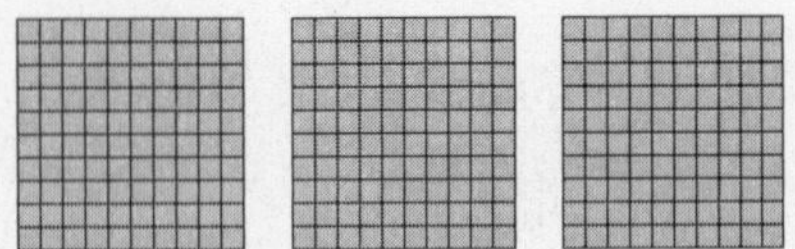

hundreds	tens	ones

______

6. 

hundreds	tens	ones

______

Name ______________________________

Building Numbers to 999

I.

hundreds	tens	ones
3	5	4

354

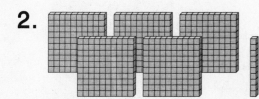

300 + 50 + 4 = 354

2.

hundreds	tens	ones

______

______ + ______ + ______ = ______

Materials: Place-value blocks, 5 hundreds, 5 tens, and 8 ones per pair or group

1. Have students show 3 hundreds, 5 tens, and 4 ones.
2. Ask: ***How many hundreds?*** Have children write 3 in the hundreds column of the place value chart. ***How many tens are left?*** Have children write 5 in the tens column of the place value chart. ***How many ones are left?*** Have children write 4 in the ones column of the place value chart. Say: ***This is 354.*** Write 354 on the board. Have students write 354.
3. Ask: ***How much is 3 hundreds?*** Have children write 300 in the first blank of the expanded form. ***How much is 5 tens?*** Have children write 50 in the second blank of the expanded form. ***How much is 4 ones?*** Have children write 4 in the third blank of the expanded form. Say: ***300 + 50 + 5 = 354***. Have students write 354.
4. Do item 2 similarly.

Name ____________________

Building Numbers to 999 (continued)

Write how many hundreds, tens, and ones.
Write the number. Read it.

3.       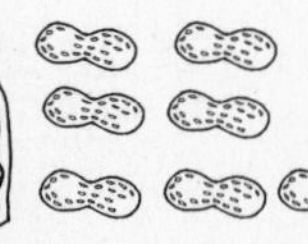

4 hundreds ______ tens ______ ones 437

400 + ______ + ______ = ______

4.         

______ hundreds ______ tens ______ ones ______

______ + ______ + ______ = ______

5. **Reasoning** Miguel has 3 bags with 100 peanuts in each bag. He also has 7 loose peanuts. How many peanuts does he have? ______ peanuts

6. Complete: 700 + 30 + 5 = ______

Name ______________________

Reading and Writing Numbers to 999

1. three hundred sixty-one

300 + 60 + __1__

= __361__

2. four hundred fifty-eight

400 + ______ + ______

= ______

Number Words		
Ones	**Teens**	**Tens**
1 one	11 eleven	10 ten
2 two	12 twelve	20 twenty
3 three	13 thirteen	30 thirty
4 four	14 fourteen	40 forty
5 five	15 fifteen	50 fifty
6 six	16 sixteen	60 sixty
7 seven	17 seventeen	70 seventy
8 eight	18 eighteen	80 eighty
9 nine	19 nineteen	90 ninety

3. 236 = 200 + __30__ + __6__

__two__ hundred __thirty-six__

4. 549 = 500 + ______ + ______

______ hundred ______________

1. Ask: ***The number three hundred sixty-one can be written as 300 plus 60 plus what?*** Have the students write the 1 in the blank.
2. Say: ***What does 300 plus 60 plus 1 equal?*** Write 361 on the board. Have students write 361.
3. Have children do item 2 similarly.
4. Write 236 on the board or overhead. Have children write the number in expanded form. Avoid saying two hundred thirty-six.
5. Ask a child how to say the number written on the board or overhead. Say: ***To write 236, write the number of hundreds and the word hundred. Then write the 36 as you did for two-digit numbers. Thirty hyphen six.*** Have children write two in the blank before hundred and thirty-six in the blank after.
6. Have children do item 4 similarly.

Name ______________________________

Reading and Writing Numbers to 999 (continued)

Write each number in expanded and standard form.

5. four hundred twelve

400 + 10 + 2

= 412

6. eight hundred seventy

______ + ______ + ______

= ______

7. three hundred fifty-one

______ + ______ + ______

= ______

8. nine hundred four

______ + ______ + ______

= ______

Write the number in expanded form and in words.

9. 238 = ______ + ______ + ______

____

10. 667 = ______ + ______ + ______

____

11. 540 = ______ + ______ + ______

____

12. 415 = ______ + ______ + ______

____

Name ____________________

Changing Numbers by Hundreds and Tens

1. 357

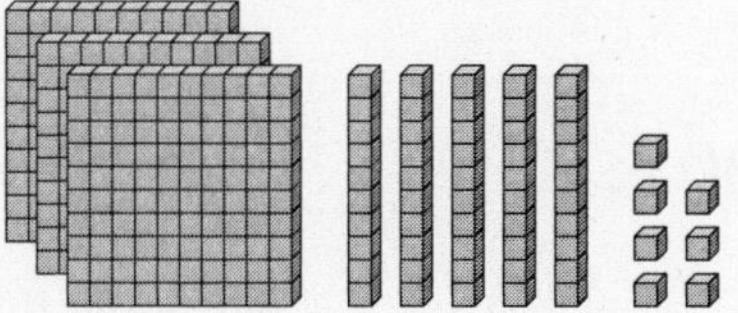

357 + 10 = 367   357 − 10 = 347

357 + 100 = ______   357 − 100 = ______

2. 468

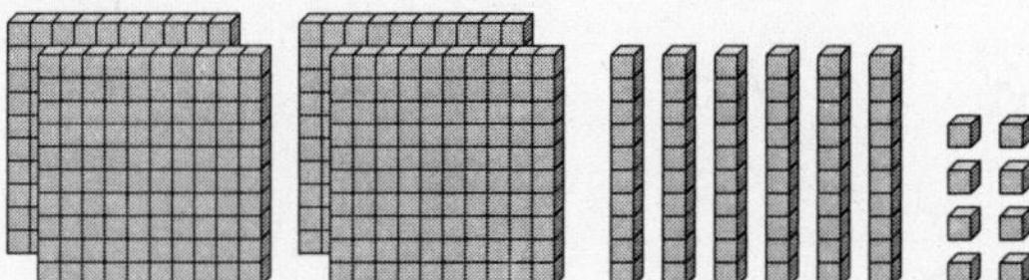

468 + 20 = ______   468 − 20 = ______

468 + 200 = ______   468 − 200 = ______

Materials: Place-value blocks, 6 hundreds, 6 tens, and 8 ones per pair or group

1. Have one child show 357 with the place-value blocks. Have another child in each pair or group add one more ten rod. Ask: ***How much is 357 and 10 more?*** Have children write 367.
2. Have children take away the ten rod so each pair or group has 357 again. If children are in groups, have a third child add a hundred flat. Ask: ***How much is 357 and 100 more?*** Have children write 457.
3. Repeat, having children take away 1 ten rod and then 1 hundred flat to represent 10 less and 100 less.
4. For item 2 have one child show 468 with the place-value blocks. Have another child in each pair or group add two more ten rods. Ask: ***How much is 468 and 20 more?*** Have children write 488.
5. Have children take away the ten rods so each pair or group has 468 again. If children are in groups, have a third child add two hundred flats. Ask: ***How much is 468 and 200 more?*** Have children write 668.
6. Repeat, having children take away 2 ten rods and then 2 hundred flats to represent 20 less and 200 less.

Name ______________________

Changing Numbers by Hundreds and Tens (continued)

Use models, drawings, or mental math to solve the problem.

3. 632 − 10 = ________

632 − 100 = ________

4. 555 + 20 = ________

555 + 200 = ________

5. 438 − 20 = ________

438 − 200 = ________

6. 353 + 30 = ________

353 + 300 = ________

7. **Reasoning** Max has 157 sports cards. Paulo has 10 more cards than Max. How many cards does Paulo have? ________ cards

8. Use place-value blocks to find what number is 200 more than 422. ________

Name ______________________________

Patterns with Numbers on Hundreds Charts

210	220	230	240	250	260	270	280	290	300
310	320	330	340	350	360	370	380	390	400
410	420	430	440	450	460	470	480	490	500
510	520	530	540	550	560	570	580	590	600

1. 430 + 10 = ________

2. 430 − 10 = ________

3. 430 + 100 = ________

4. 430 − 100 = ________

5. 220 + 10 = ________

6. 480 + 100 = ________

7. 370 − 10 = ________

8. 550 − 100 = ________

9.

47	48	
57		59
	68	

10.

470		490
	580	
	680	690

1. Have children find 430 on the chart. For item 1 Say: ***To find the number that is 10 more than 430, move 1 space right.*** Ask: ***What number is 10 more than 430?*** Have children write 440. For item 2 Say: ***To find the number that is 10 less than 430, move 1 space left from 430.*** Ask: ***What number is 10 less than 430?*** Have children write 420.
2. For items 3 and 4 Say: ***To find the number that is 100 more than 430, move 1 row down from 430.*** Ask: ***What number is 100 more than 430?*** Have children write 530. Say: ***To find the number that is 100 less than 430, move 1 row up from, 430*** Ask: ***What number is 100 less than 430?*** Have children write 330.
3. Have children do items 5 to 8 similarly.
4. Have children complete the chart in item 9. Say: ***In the chart in item 9, numbers change by one as you move left and right. How do the numbers change as you move left and right in the chart in item 10?*** By 10s ***In the chart in item 9, numbers change by ten as you move up and down rows. How do the numbers change as you move up and down rows in the chart in item 10?*** By 100s
5. Have children use the chart in item 9 to help them complete the chart in item 10.

Name ______________________________

Patterns with Numbers on Hundreds Charts (continued)

Use the hundreds chart to complete.

410	420	430	440	450	460	470	480	490	500
510	520	530	540	550	560	570	580	590	600
610	620	630	640	650	660	670	680	690	700
710	720	730	740	750	760	770	780	790	800
810	820	830	840	850	860	870	880	890	900

11. 690 + 10 = ________

12. 530 + 100 = ________

13. 850 − 10 = ________

14. 720 − 100 = ________

15. 740 + 100 = ________

16. 870 − 10 = ________

Find the missing numbers.

17.

65		
	76	77
85		87

18.

650		670
	760	
	860	870

19.

	22	23
	32	
41	42	

20.

210		230
		330
	420	430

Name ______________________________

Comparing Numbers to 999

I.

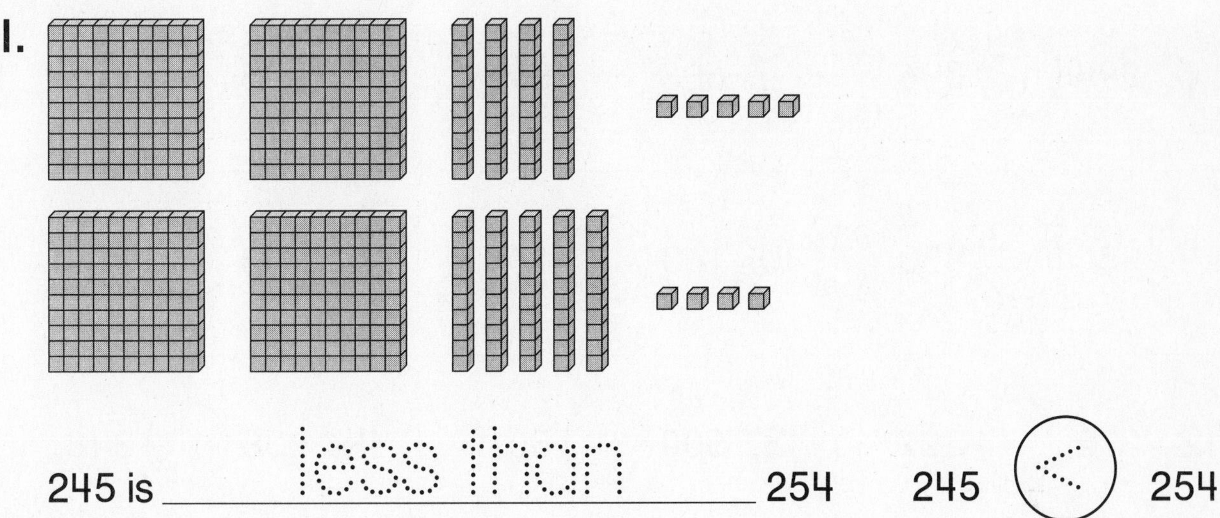

245 is less than 254   245 (<) 254

Circle <, >, or =.

2. 287 < > = 426

3. 157 < > = 154

4. 306 < > = 306

5. 140 < > = 104

Materials: Place-Value blocks, 6 hundreds, 10 tens, and 15 ones per pair or group.

1. Have children show 245 and 254 with place-value blocks.
2. Say: ***To compare three-digit numbers, first compare the hundreds.*** Ask: ***Are the hundreds the same or different?*** After children say *the same,* say: ***Since the numbers are the same, compare the tens.*** Ask: ***Are the tens the same or different?*** After children say *different,* ask: ***How does the 4 in 245 compare to the 5 in 254?*** After children say *the 4 is less than the 5,* say: ***Since 40 is less than 50, 245 is less than 254.*** Write 245 is less than 254 on the board or overhead. Have children write less than.
3. Review the <, >, and = symbols. Ask: ***Which symbol can we use to show 245 is less than 254?*** Write 245 < 254 on the board or overhead and have children write < on their paper.
4. Have children do the other problems similarly, circling the correct symbol.

Name ______________________________

Comparing Numbers to 999 (continued)

Compare. Write <, >, or =.

6. 294 ◯ 346	7. 603 ◯ 598	8. 803 ◯ 903
9. 450 ◯ 450	10. 163 ◯ 173	11. 295 ◯ 259
12. 372 ◯ 327	13. 500 ◯ 501	14. 438 ◯ 348
15. 704 ◯ 740	16. 912 ◯ 911	17. 443 ◯ 443
18. 621 ◯ 612	19. 801 ◯ 801	20. 172 ◯ 182
21. 278 ◯ 287	22. 350 ◯ 349	23. 986 ◯ 968

Reasoning Use the clues to find each number.

24. It is greater than 836.
It is less than 841.
It has a 9 in the ones place.

The number is ________.

25. It is greater than 297.
It is less than 302.
It has a 1 in the ones place.

The number is ________.

Name ______________________________

Before, After, and Between

211	212	213	214	215	216	217	218	219	210
221	222	223	224	225	226	227	228	229	230
231	232	233	234	235	236	237	238	239	240
241	242	243	244	245	246	247	248	249	250

1. 227 is one before 228. 227 is one after 226.

2. 227 is between 226 and 228.

3. 227 is ten before 237. 227 is ten after 217.

4. 239 is one before ________. 239 is one after ________.

5. 239 is between ________ and ________.

6. 239 is ten before ________. 239 is ten after ________.

---

1. Say: ***Put your finger on 227. Two hundred twenty-seven is one before what number?*** Have children write 228.
2. Say: ***Put your finger on 227. Two hundred twenty-seven is one after what number?*** Have children write 226.
3. Say: ***If 227 is one before 228 and one after 226, then 227 is between which two numbers?*** Have children write 226 and 228.
4. Say: ***Put your finger on 227. Two hundred twenty-seven is ten before what number?*** Have children write 237.
5. Say: ***Put your finger on 227. Two hundred twenty-seven is ten after what number?*** Have children write 217.
6. Do the other problem similarly.

Name ______________________________

Before, After, and Between (continued)

Write the number that comes **after.**

7. 208, 209   516, ______   823, ______

8. 548, ______   163, ______   849, ______

9. 275, ______   789, ______   376, ______

Write the number that comes **before.**

10. 325, 326   ______, 151   ______, 643

11. ______, 185   ______, 440   ______, 988

12. ______, 712   ______, 506   ______, 810

Write the number that comes **between.**

13. 704, 705, 706   415, ______, 417

14. 521, ______, 523   649, ______, 651

15. 174, ______, 176   806, ______, 808

Math Diagnosis and Intervention System
Intervention Lesson **A86**

Name ______________________

Ordering Numbers to 999

1.

132	223	124

124 < 132 < 223
least   greatest

2. 213 | 141 | 236   _____ > _____ > _____
least   greatest

3. 436 | 487 | 243   _____ > _____ > _____
least   greatest

4. 431 | 283 | 281   _____ > _____ > _____
least   greatest

Materials: Place value blocks, 10 hundreds, 8 tens, 10 ones per pair or group

1. Have children show 132, 223, and 124 with blocks.
2. Ask: ***Which number has the greatest number of hundreds?*** 223 Say: ***If one number has more hundreds than all the others, it is the greatest.*** Have children write 223 on the line with greatest.
3. Ask: ***Does one number have the fewest number of hundreds?*** No, 132 and 124 have the same number of hundreds. Say: ***When two or more numbers have the same number of hundreds, compare the tens. Which number has fewer tens, 132 or 124?*** 124 Say: ***So, 124 is the least.*** Have children write 124 on the line with least.
4. Ask: ***Which number is between 124 and 223?*** Have children write 132.
5. Say: ***So the numbers in order from least to greatest are: 124, 132, 223.***
6. Have children order the other sets of numbers, using place value blocks, if they wish.

Name ______________________________

Ordering Numbers to 999 (continued)

Write the numbers in order from **least** to **greatest.**

5. 188 128 243 — 128 > 188 > 243 (least … greatest)

6. 465 323 512 — ______ > ______ > ______ (least … greatest)

7. 342 215 251 — ______ > ______ > ______ (least … greatest)

8. 767 876 676 — ______ > ______ > ______ (least … greatest)

9. 809 783 784 — ______ > ______ > ______ (least … greatest)

10. 645 154 646 — ______ > ______ > ______ (least … greatest)

11. **Reasoning** The Lions have 117 points, the Cougars have 112 points, and the Tigers have 121 points. Which team has the least number of points? ______________

Name ______________________________

Numbers to 999 on the Number Line

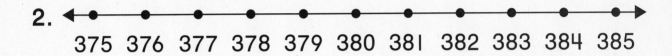

1. 426 427 428 429 430 431 432 433 434 435 436

2. 375 376 377 378 379 380 381 382 383 384 385

3. 611 612 613 614 615 616 617 618 619 620 621

4.
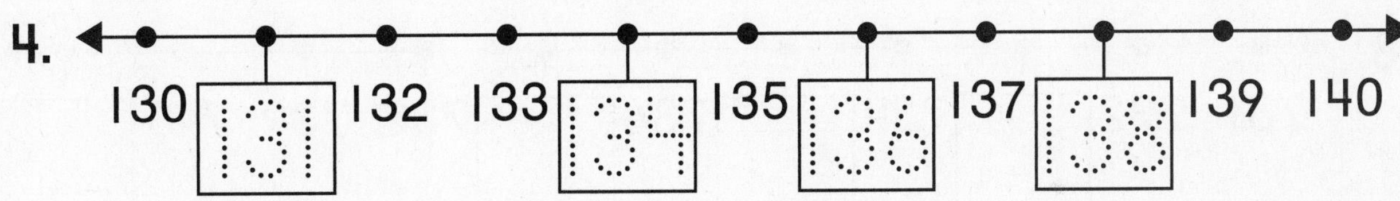

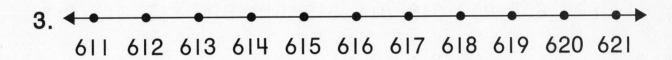

5.
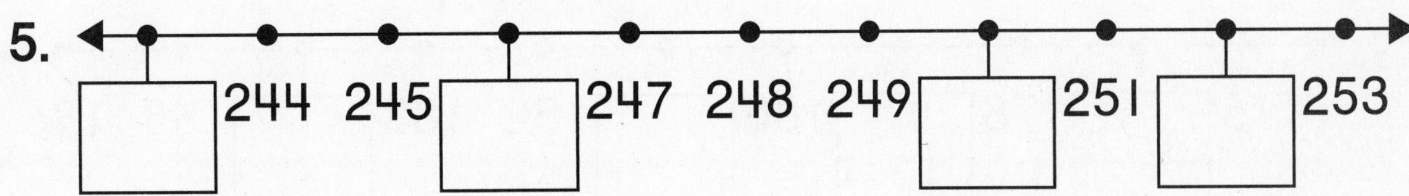

1. Say: ***Every number has its own place on the number line. The numbers go in order from least to greatest.***
2. Say: ***Find 428 on the number line. Circle the number and its point***. Ask: ***What number is before 428?*** 427 ***After?*** 429 Say: ***Circle 431 and its point.*** Ask: ***Is 428 greater than or less than 431?*** Less than
3. For item 2 have children circle 379 and its point and then 384 and its point.
4. For item 3 say: ***Circle a number that is greater than 613 on the number line***. Say: ***Circle a number that is less than 613***.
5. For item 4 say: ***What number comes after 130?*** Have children write 131 in the box.
6. Say: ***What number comes between 133 and 135?*** Have children write 134 in the second box.
7. Have children complete the number lines for items 4 and 5. Ask questions like those above for children who have difficulty.

Name ______________________

Numbers to 999 on the Number Line (continued)

Circle the numbers on the number line.

6. 524 and 531

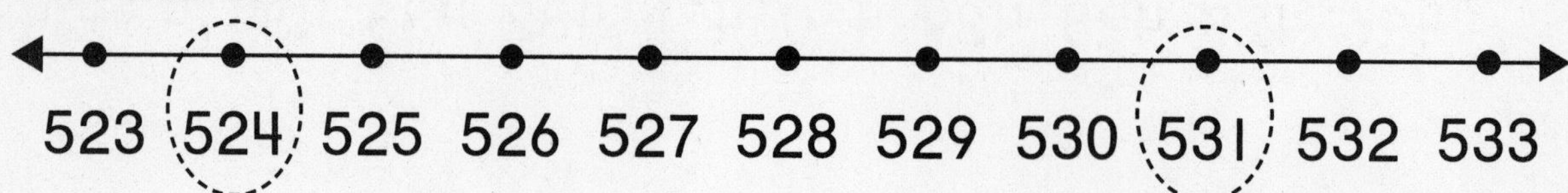

7. 810 and 813

Write the missing numbers.

8.

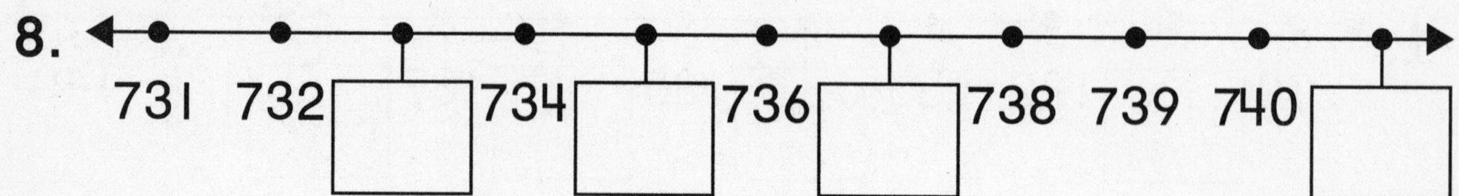

9.

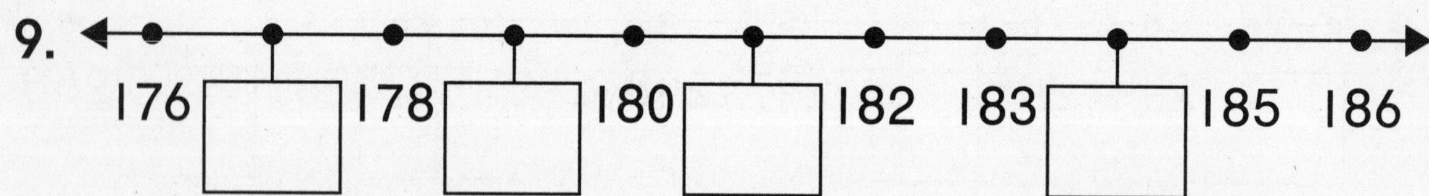

10.

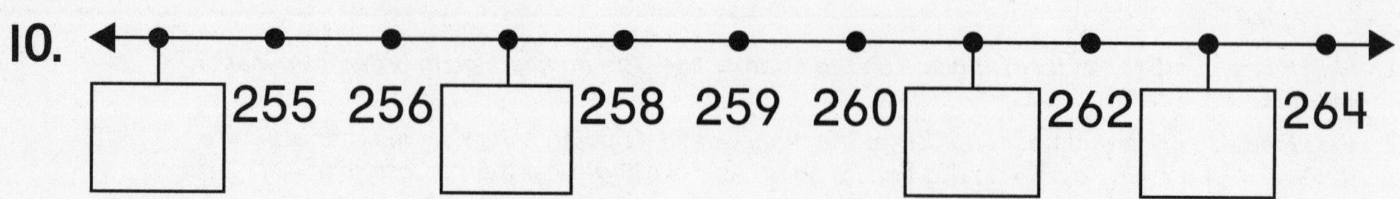

11.

Name ______________________________

Skip Counting on the Number Line

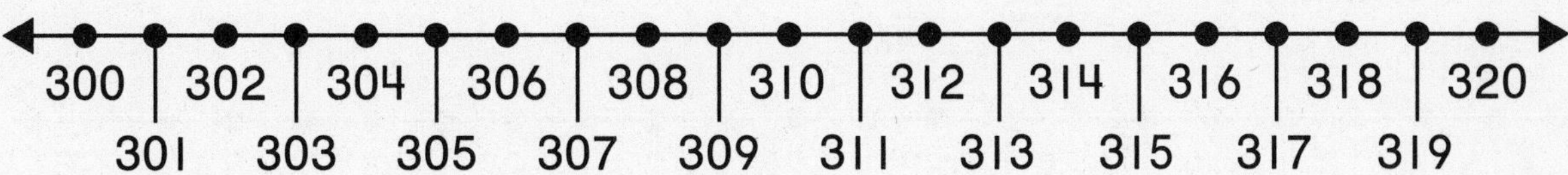

1. 300, 302, 304, 306, 308, ______
2. 300, 305, 310, ______, ______, ______
3. 300, 304, 308, ______, ______, ______
4. 300, 303, 306, ______, ______, ______

5.
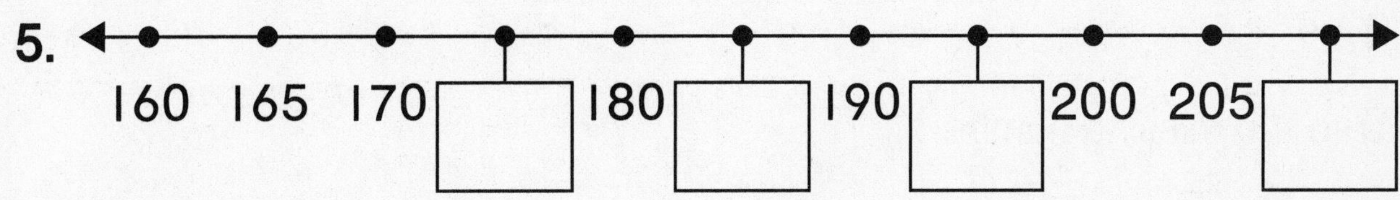

6.
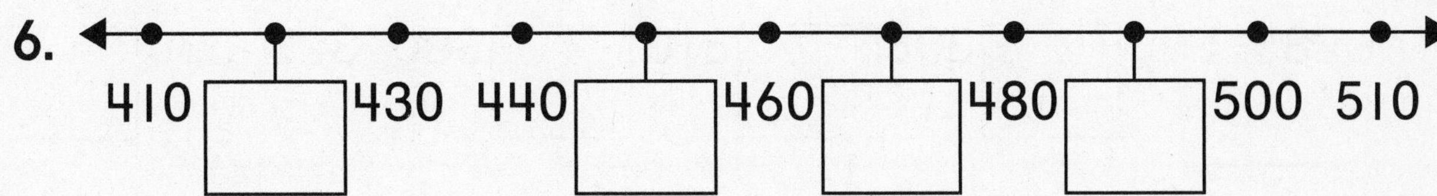

7.
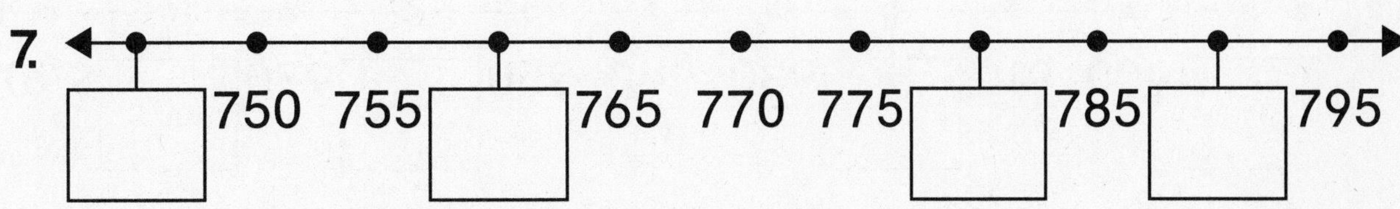

1. For item 1 have children use the number line to skip count by 2s and write the numbers.
2. Repeat for items 2–4 having children skip count by 5s, then 4s, then 3s.
3. For item 5 have children skip count by 5s and write the missing numbers. If necessary, ask questions like: ***When skip counting by 5s, what number comes after 170? What number comes between 180 and 190?***
4. Have children complete all the number lines. Ask questions like those above for children who have difficulty.

Name ____________________

Skip Counting on the Number Line (continued)

Use the number line to skip count.
Write the numbers.

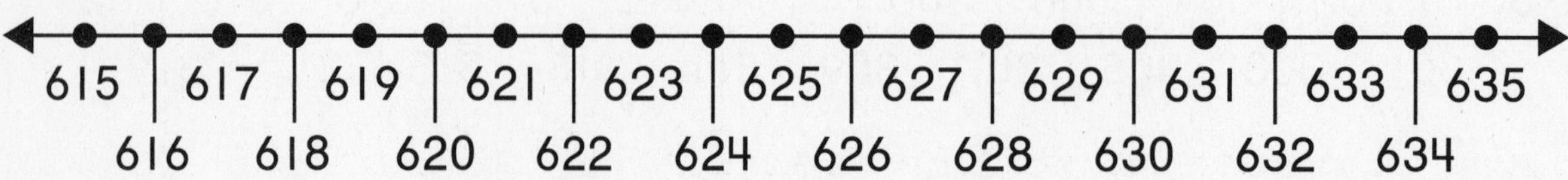

8. 615, 620, 625, 630, 635, 640

9. 616, 618, 620, ______, ______, ______

10. 616, 620, 624, ______, ______, ______

11. 615, 618, 621, ______, ______, ______

Write the missing numbers.

12.

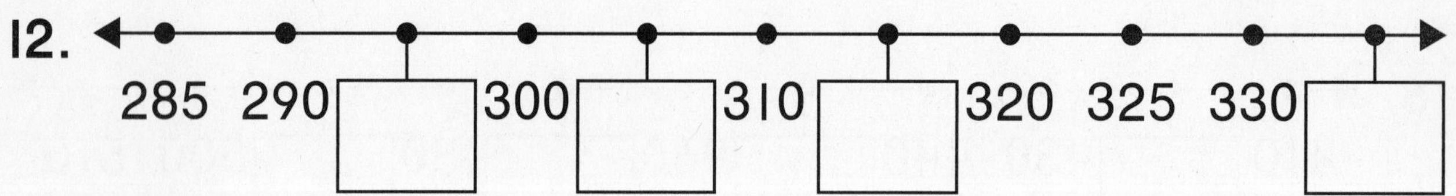

13.

14.

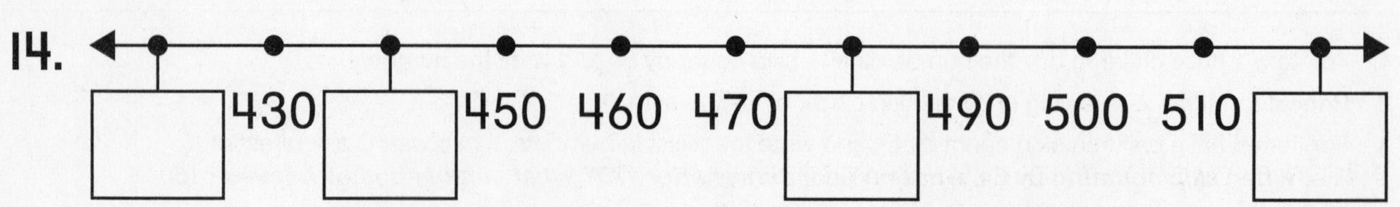

Name ____

Ways to Show Numbers

Materials 124 craft sticks and 13 rubber bands, per pair, or place-value blocks, 124 ones, 12 tens, and 1 hundred block per pair

There are various ways to show 124. Answer 1 to 9 to learn how.

If using craft sticks: use rubber bands to put the craft sticks in as many groups of 10 as possible. If using place-value blocks: trade groups of 10 ones for tens with place-value blocks.

1. How many groups of ten are there? _____

2. How many ones are left? _____

Wrap 10 groups of ten craft sticks to make a hundred or trade 10 tens place-value blocks for a hundred block.

3. How many hundreds are there? _____

4. How many tens are left? _____

5. How many ones are left? _____

6. How many in all? _____

The number 124 is written in standard form.

7. 124 = _____ hundred _____ tens _____ ones or _____ tens _____ ones

8. In expanded form, 124 is written 100 + _____ + _____.

9. In words, 124 is written __________ hundred twenty-__________.

There are various ways to write 238. Answer 10 to 12.

10. 238 = _____ hundreds _____ tens _____ ones or _____ tens _____ ones

11. In expanded form, 238 is written _____ + _____ + _____.

12. In words, 238 is written ____.

Name ______________________________

Ways to Show Numbers (continued)

Write each number in standard form.

13. ________

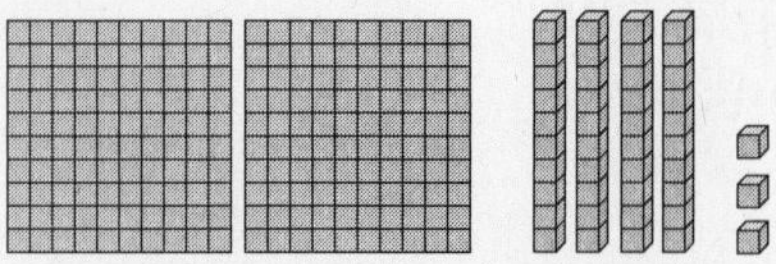

14. ________

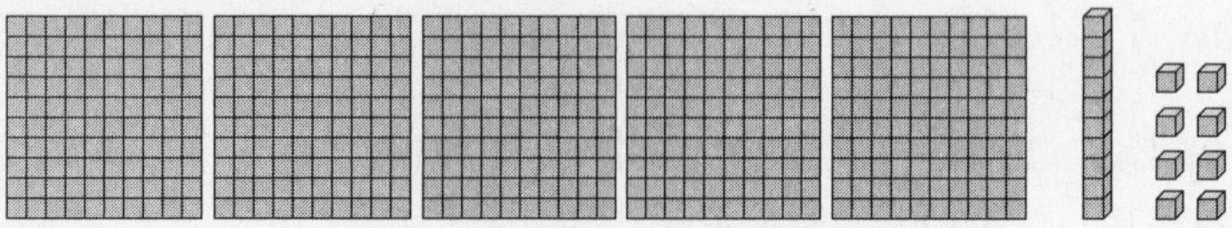

Write each number in expanded form.

15. 462 ______________ **16.** 853 ______________

17. 321 ______________ **18.** 760 ______________

Write each number as groups of tens and ones only.
You may use place-value blocks to help.

19. 427 ______________ **20.** 933 ______________

21. 106 ______________ **22.** 514 ______________

Write each number in standard form.

23. six hundred twenty-two ______ **24.** eight hundred ten ______

Write each number in words.

25. 210 ______________________________

26. 782 ______________________________

27. 105 ______________________________

28. 316 ______________________________

Name ______________________________

Rounding to the Nearest Ten and Hundred

Materials 8 inches of yarn per pair

To round 77 to the nearest ten, answer 1 to 6.

1. Plot 73 on the number line below.

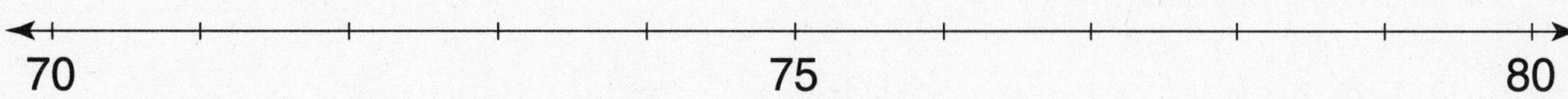

2. Use the yarn to help you decide whether 73 is closer to 70 or 80. Which is it closer to? ______

3. So, what is 73 rounded to the nearest ten? ______

4. Plot 77 on the number line above.

5. Use the yarn to help you decide whether 77 is closer to 70 or 80. Which is it closer to? ______

6. So, what is 77 rounded to the nearest ten? ______

To round 336 to the nearest hundred, answer 7 to 12.

7. Plot 380 on the number line below.

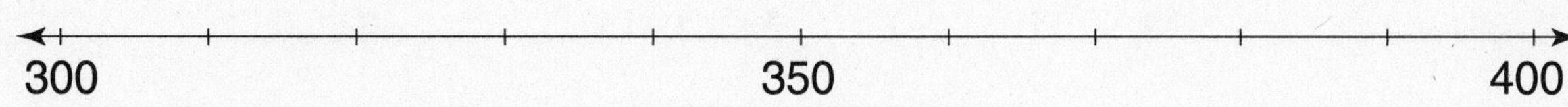

8. Use the yarn to help you decide whether 380 is closer to 300 or 400. Which is it closer to? ______

9. So, what is 380 rounded to the nearest hundred? ______

10. Plot 336 on the number line above.

11. Use the yarn to help you decide whether 336 is closer to 300 or 400. Which is it closer to? ______

12. So, what is 336 rounded to the nearest hundred? ______

Name ______________________

Rounding to the Nearest Ten and Hundred (continued)

Round 459 to the nearest hundred by answering 13 to 17.

13. What digit is in the hundreds place in 459? ________

14. What digit is to the right of the 4? ________

15. Is the digit to the right of 4 less than 5, or is it 5 or greater? ________

If the digit to the right of the number is 5 or more, the number rounds up. If the digit is less than 5, the number rounds down.

16. Do you need to round 459 up or down? ________

17. Change the 4 to the next higher digit and change the 5 and 9 to 0s. So, what is 459 rounded to the nearest hundred? ________

Round to the nearest ten.

18. 54 ______ **19.** 37 ______ **20.** 81 ______ **21.** 65 ______

Round to the nearest hundred.

22. 609 ______ **23.** 351 ______ **24.** 491 ______ **25.** 850 ______

26. A rancher has 43 cattle in his herd. To the nearest ten, how many cattle are in the rancher's herd? ________

27. A new computer costs $876. To the nearest hundred, how many dollars does the computer cost? ________

28. Reasoning Round 549 to the nearest hundred and round 551 to the nearest hundred. Do you get the same answers? Explain.

Name ______________________________

Reading and Writing 4-Digit Numbers

1. Write 2,537 in the place-value chart below.

thousands	hundreds	tens	ones

2. What place is the 2 in? ____________ So its value is 2,000.

3. What place is the 5 in? ____________ So what is its value? __________

4. What place is the 3 in?____________ So what is its value? __________

5. What place is the 7 in? ____________ So what is its value?__________

6. In expanded form, 2,537 equals 3,000 + __________ + __________+ 7.

7. Write 2,537 in words.

__________ thousand, __________ hundred thirty-__________

8. Write 6,084 in the place value chart below.

thousands	hundreds	tens	ones

9. What place is the 6 in? ____________ So what is its value? __________

10. What place is the 0 in? ____________ So it has no value.

11. What place is the 8 in? ____________ So what is its value? __________

12. What place is the 4 in? ____________ So what is its value? __________

13. In expanded form, 6,084 equals __________ + __________ + __________.

14. Write 6,084 in words.

__________ thousand, ______________

Name ______________________

Reading and Writing 4-Digit Numbers (continued)

Write each number in standard form.

15. 1,000 + 500 + 20 + 7 ____________

16. nine thousand, four hundred ____________

17. 8,000 + 100 + 30 ____________

18. five thousand, six hundred one ____________

19. 4,000 + 500 + 2 ____________

20. six thousand, eight hundred ninety ____________

Write each number in expanded form.

21. 3,716 ____________

22. 2,091 ____________

Write the value of the underlined digit.

23. 1,8<u>6</u>3 ____________

24. <u>9</u>,504 ____________

25. 5,12<u>9</u> ____________

26. <u>1</u>83 ____________

27. Write 3,995 in words.

____

28. Write 4,716 in words.

____

29. Use the digits 1, 5, 7, and 3. Write the greatest possible four-digit number using each of the digits only once. ____________

30. Reasoning What number would make the number sentence 5,000 + 800 + ■ + 6 = 5,826 true? ____________

Name ______________________________

Numbers Halfway Between and Rounding

Answer 1 and 2 to find the number that is halfway between 200 and 300.

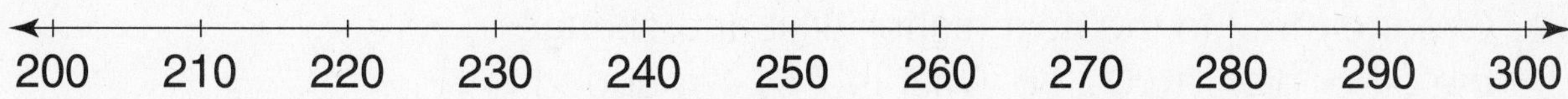

1. Use your pencil to draw a hop from 200 to 210, and then backwards from 300 to 290. Repeat one hop on each side until the hops meet at a point. Draw a dot where they meet. This is the number that is halfway between 200 and 300.

2. What number is halfway between 200 and 300? ______________

Round 6,375 to the nearest hundred by answering 3 to 7.

3. What number is halfway between 6,300 and 6,400? ______________

4. Is 6,375 greater than or less than the halfway number? ______________

5. Plot 6,375 on the number line below.

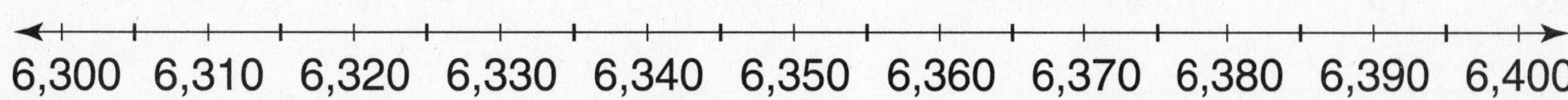

6. Is 6,375 closer to 6,300 or 6,400? ______________

7. So, what is 6,375 rounded to the nearest hundred? ______________

Round 7,824 to the nearest thousand without using a number line. Answer 8 to 12.

8. What digit is in the thousands place in 7,824? ______________

9. What digit is to the right of the 7? ______________

10. Is the digit to the right of 7 less than 5 or is it 5 or greater? ______________

Name ______________________

Numbers Halfway Between and Rounding (continued)

If the digit to the right of the number is 5 or more, the number rounds up. If the digit is less than 5, the number rounds down.

11. When you round 7,824 to the nearest thousand, do you need to round the 7 up or down? ____________

12. Change the 7 to the next higher digit and change the other digits to 0s. So, what is 7,824 rounded to the nearest thousand? ____________

Find the number halfway between each pair of numbers.

13. 70 and 80 ____________

14. 500 and 600 ____________

15. 2,000 and 3,000 ____________

Round each number to the nearest ten.

16. 4,769 ____________

17. 8,274 ____________

18. 6,616 ____________

19. 995 ____________

Round each number to the nearest hundred.

20. 3,248 ____________

21. 9,929 ____________

22. 1,372 ____________

23. 2,050 ____________

Round each number to the nearest thousand.

24. 5,604 ____________

25. 7,487 ____________

26. 2,868 ____________

27. 6,452 ____________

28. Reasoning If 4,500 is halfway between 4,000 and 5,000, why does 4,509 round up to 5,000 when rounding to the nearest thousand?

Name ______________________________

Comparing and Ordering Numbers

Seth's class collected 1,382 cans during the food drive. Yolanda's class collected 1,357 cans of food. Determine whose class collected more by answering 1 to 6.

1. Write 1,382 and 1,357 in the place value chart.

thousands	hundreds	tens	ones

2. Use <, >, or = to compare the thousands. 1,000 ______ 1,000

3. Since the thousands are equal, compare the hundreds. 300 ______ 300

4. Since the hundreds are equal, compare the tens. 80 ______ 50

5. Since 80 > 50, Which value is greater, 1,382 or 1,357? ____________

6. Whose class collected more cans of food? ____________

Zoe scored 3,496 points, Mario scored 2,908 points, and Kim scored 3,520 points. Determine who scored the most points by answering 7 to 12.

7. Write 3,496, 2,908, and 3,520 in the place value chart.

thousands	hundreds	tens	ones

8. Compare the thousands. Since 2,000 < 3,000, what is the least number? ____________

Name ____________________

Comparing and Ordering Numbers (continued)

9. Use the chart you completed in 7 to compare the hundreds of the other two numbers. 400 ______ 500

10. Since $400 < 500$, then is 3,496 greater than or less than 3,520? ____________

11. What are the numbers in order from least to greatest?

____________, ____________, ____________

12. Who scored the most points? ____________

Compare. Write >, <, or =.

13. 514 ◯ 512 **14.** 394 ◯ 349 **15.** 809 ◯ 809

16. 1,078 ◯ 178 **17.** 236 ◯ 2,036 **18.** 7,530 ◯ 7,240

19. 9,089 ◯ 9,098 **20.** 4,517 ◯ 5,417 **21.** 3,728 ◯ 3,727

Write the numbers in order from **least** to **greatest.**

22. 428 418 422

____

23. 1,234 134 123

____

24. 5,619 5,691 569

____

25. 1,010 1,001 1,100

____

26. Reasoning What is the smallest digit that makes $1{,}328 > 1{,}■28$ true?

27. Daniella has 1,241 trading cards. Mark has 1,099 trading cards. Who has more cards? ____________

28. Maria scored 3,950 points playing a video game. Leigh scored 3,590 points. Kathy scored 3,905. Order their scores from least to greatest.

Name ______________________________

Place-Value Patterns

Materials 4 pieces of centimeter grid paper, crayons, markers, or colored pencils

Show 1,200 with grid paper by answering 1 to 8.

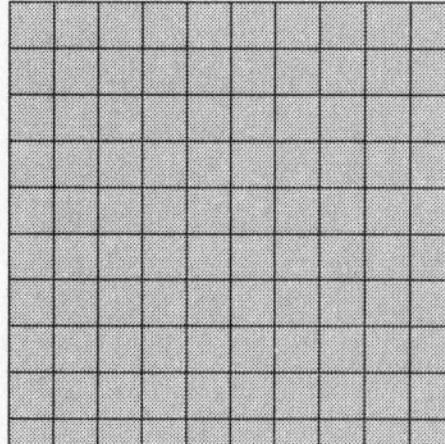

1. In the upper left corner of your grid paper, color a 10 by 10 square like the one on the right.

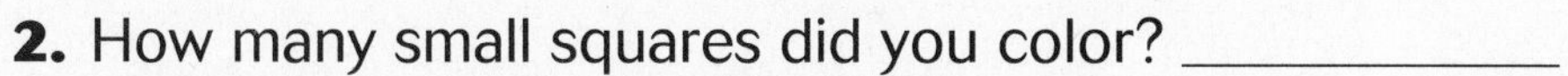

2. How many small squares did you color? __________

3. Since 1,000 = 10 hundreds, show the 1,000 in 1,200 by coloring nine more 10 by 10 squares on your grid paper, to make 10 in all.

4. Show the 200 in 1,200 by coloring two more 10 by 10 squares on your grid paper.

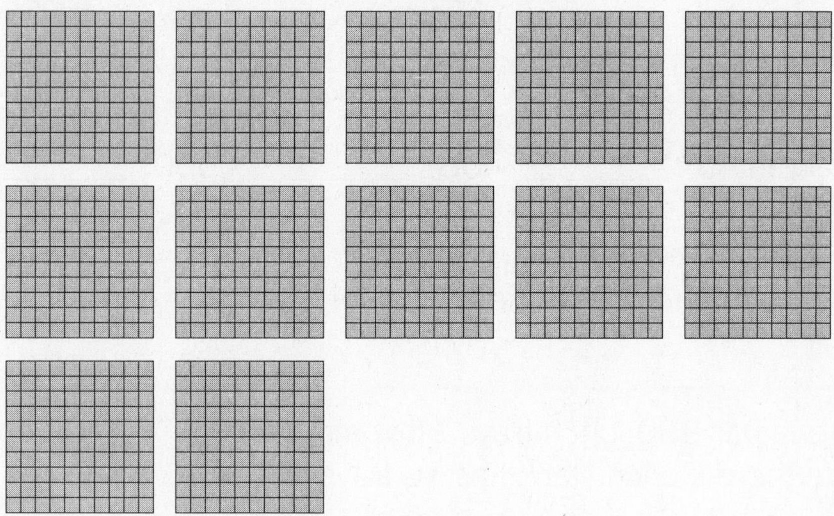

5. All the 10 by 10 squares together show 1,200. How many 10 by 10 squares do you have? __________

6. 1,200 = __________ hundreds

7. How many tens are in each 10 by 10 square? __________

8. So, 1,200 = __________ tens and 1,200 = __________ ones.

Name ______________________________

Place-Value Patterns (continued)

Fill in the blanks to name each number in two different ways.

9. 200

________ hundreds

________ tens

10. 840

________ tens

________ ones

11. 1,600

________ hundreds

________ tens

12. 3,200

________ hundreds

________ tens

13. 700

________ hundreds

________ tens

14. 820

________ tens

________ ones

15. 1,300

________ hundreds

________ tens

16. 570

________ tens

________ ones

17. 1,400

________ hundreds

________ tens

18. How many tens are in 40? ________ 400? ________ 4,000? ________

19. The state fair ordered 2,200 new cages for the rabbit barn. How many stacks would there be if there were 100 cages in each stack? ________

20. The school cafeteria has 900 lunch trays. How many stacks of trays are there if each stack has 10 trays in it? ________

21. **Reasoning** What is the next number in this pattern?

2,377 2,477 2,577 ________

Explain how you know.